MW00613761

LINEAR IC/OP AMP HANDBOOK

2ND EDITION

BY JOSEPH J. CARR

TAB
TAB BOOKS Inc.
BLUE RIDGE SUMMIT, PA 17214

SECOND EDITION

FIRST PRINTING

Printed in the United States of America

Library of Congress Cataloging in Publication Data

Carr, Joseph J.
Linear IC/op amp handbook.

Includes index.
1. Operational amplifiers. 2. Integrated circuits.
I. Title.
TK7871.58.06C367 1983 621.3815'35 82-19422
ISBN 0-8306-0150-3
ISBN 0-8306-1550-4 (pbk.)

Appendix C specification data sheets are provided courtesy of Burr-Brown Research Corporation.

Contents

Acknowledgments

I extend my gratitude to certain people and firms who assisted in the preparation of this book. Motorola, Burr-Brown, Fairchild, National Semiconductor, Signetics, and Analog Devices supplied applications literature that proved extremely valuable.

A particular note of thanks is in order for my wife Bonnie, for toleration of the activities needed to finish the book: my commandeering of the dining room table as an impromptu office and my typing at all hours of the day and night. Special thanks go to Prof. Marvin F. Eisenberg of the George Washington University School of Engineering and Applied Science (Department of Electrical Engineering & Computer Science) for his critical reading of the manuscript. His comments, criticisms, and suggestions have been integrated into this work—making for a much better book.

Introduction

Operational amplifiers were originally used to perform mathematical *operations* on electrical analogs of either physical phenomena or nondimensional quantities such as numbers. In those early days, a typical operational amplifier was constructed of vacuum tubes, which made a subassembly that was quite bulky, consumed large amounts of power, operated at a high temperature, had an almost daily maintenance problem, and was quite unstable due to dc drift. The modern operational amplifier, on the other hand, is an integrated circuit (IC) and will run rings around all but the very best vacuum-tube models. It is not unusual to find two op amps in a single 8-pin dual in-line package (DIP) or "similar to TO-5" package. Certain single op amps offer such high specs compared to early types that one is tempted to wonder about those early antecedents and whether they even worked at all!

Op-amp applications are limited only by the imagination and technical acumen of the designer. Our little IC operational amplifiers can perform the traditional operations of addition, subtraction, multiplication, and division as well or better than vacuum-tube designs, and yet are free of many of the defects that plagued the tube types. Other math functions that can be performed by the IC amps are several of the trigonometric functions, squaring, finding the square root of numbers, converting to the logarithm or antilog, and the calculus functions of integration and differentiation.

It is, though, the noncomputer applications which tend to excite the imagination. This applies to both standard analog and digital electronics. For example, op amps can be connected in circuits to act as a voltage comparator, zero-crossing detector, ac and dc signal amplifiers, audio amplifiers, video amplifiers, and null detectors for bridge circuits. They can be used to generate such signals as sine waves, square waves, or triangle waves. All of this is found in a device that can cost only pennies for first-quality units and uses a design equation as simple as Ohm's law.

The chapters that follow explain how the op amp works and how certain circuits associated with op amps work. This should give you the insight needed to design your own op-amp circuits. You will be introduced to a new IC, a quasi op amp, called the *current difference* amplifier (CDA) or *Norton* amplifier. You also will find information on the *operational transconductance* amplifier (OTA).

Chapter 1

Inverting Followers

What is an operational amplifier? Unfortunately, that is one of those questions with too many possible answers! There are, for instance, "ideal" op amps discussed mostly in textbooks and engineering journals, and then there are real-world op amps (the kind you can actually buy) that aren't quite as good as the ideal. In this latter group, we find high-cost precision types which offer wide bandwidths and near perfect characteristics alongside "sloppier" but very low-cost "economy" models. For our more immediate purposes we will discuss only the ideal, mostly because it simplifies matters to a point where we need not worry about certain observed inconsistencies. In due course (Chapter 4) we tackle op-amp problems and their solutions.

THE OP AMP AT WORK

One of the things which helps account for the utter simplicity of op-amp circuitry is the fact that we are allowed to treat the device as a simple gain block, in which the output voltage (E_{OUT}) is a function of the input voltage (E_{IN}) and a gain factor (A_V). The ideal operational amplifier has the following properties:

- Infinite input impedance.
- Infinite open-loop (no feedback) gain, A_{VOL}.
- Zero ohms output impedance.

A gain block with these properties will deliver an output voltage such that:

$$E_{OUT} = A_V E_{IN} \tag{1-1}$$

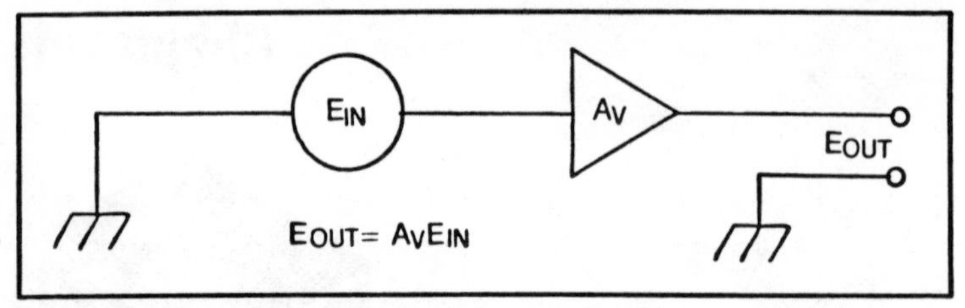

Fig. 1-1. Elementary operational amplifier model.

From the first of our criteria it can be seen that the input terminal neither accepts nor delivers any current flow, since $Z = E/I$ (and in this case the Z term is infinite!). Of course, the real kind-you-can-buy op amps don't meet this ideal, but the imperfect approximations are near enough to be most exciting! For practical purposes, read *infinite* as "very, very high" and *zero* as "very, very, low."

The op amp of Fig. 1-1 is a little too simplified for wide-ranging application. The standard procedure is to build op amps with two inputs which have equal, but opposite effects on the output (see Fig. 1-2). One of the inputs will cause an output voltage which is of the same polarity as the input; this is called the "noninverting input." The other input causes an output of a polarity opposite to that of the input. This alternate input is called the "inverting input." Industry-wide standard convention designates the inverting input with a minus symbol (−) and the noninverting input with a plus symbol (+).

One of the first and most inescapable implications of the standard dual-input scheme is that the output voltage must be proportional to the *difference* between the two input voltages. Since the inputs cause equal but *opposite* effects on the output:

$$E_{\mathrm{OUT(+)}} = A_{\mathrm{V}} E_2 \quad (1\text{-}2)$$

$$E_{\mathrm{OUT(-)}} = A_{\mathrm{V}} E_1 \quad (1\text{-}3)$$

$$I_{\mathrm{F}} E_1 = E_2$$

$$E_{\mathrm{OUT(+)}} + E_{\mathrm{OUT(-)}} = 0 \quad (1\text{-}4)$$

Whenever the two input voltages are not equal, an output voltage proportional to their difference will be generated:

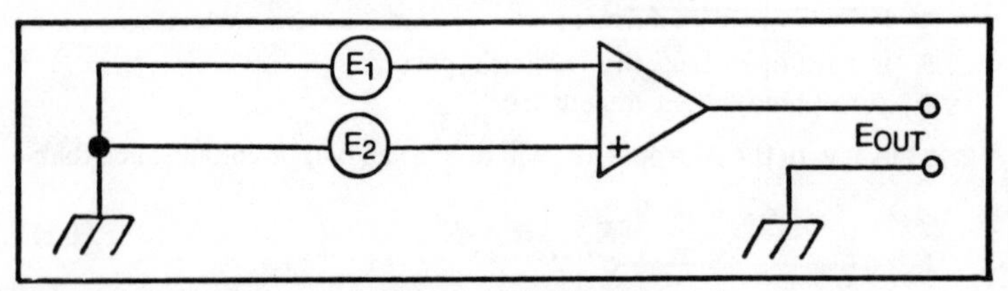

Fig. 1-2. Basic differential input operational amplifier.

$$E_{OUT} = A_V (E_1 - E_2) \quad (1\text{-}5)$$

This relationship is partially responsible for some of the varied applications of the operational amplifier. Although we will shortly discuss circuits in which both inputs are used, for the time being we will assume that the noninverting input is grounded, making $E_2 = 0$.

POWER SUPPLY CONSIDERATIONS

The operational amplifier must be capable of providing output voltages which can be either positive or negative, depending upon the polarity of the input signal. This requirement imposes the necessity of using two power supplies; one is positive with respect to ground while the other is negative. A typical arrangement is shown in Fig. 1-3. As is usual in op-amp circuits, these supplies have equal magnitude, but are of opposite polarities.

Ideally, these power sources should be well regulated. This is especially true where the supply is operated from the ac power mains, or from an alternator-charged storage battery (such as in a motor vehicle electrical system). One feature of regulated supplies is that the ac supply ripple component is reduced by the regulation process.

It would be convenient to always have dual-polarity power supplies available in equipment or circuits using operational amplifiers. Unfortunately, this is not always possible. In an automobile, for example, the designer is strapped to the use of a single 12—14V supply. In other instances, the designer might want to use a single op amp in a hybrid circuit with other semiconductor devices (such as transistors). The transistors may require only a single-polarity supply. If the op amp is a minority feature of the overall design, it might prove uneconomical to provide a second dc source of opposite polarity. There are, however, certain circuitry tactics for using the operational amplifier in single-polarity configurations.

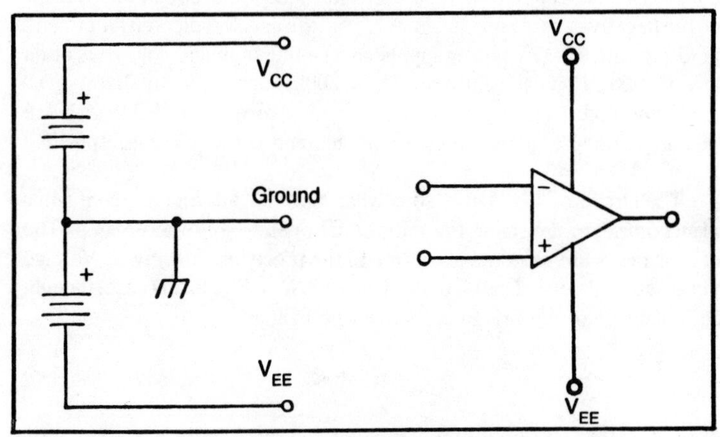

Fig. 1-3. Power connections and typical power supply configuration.

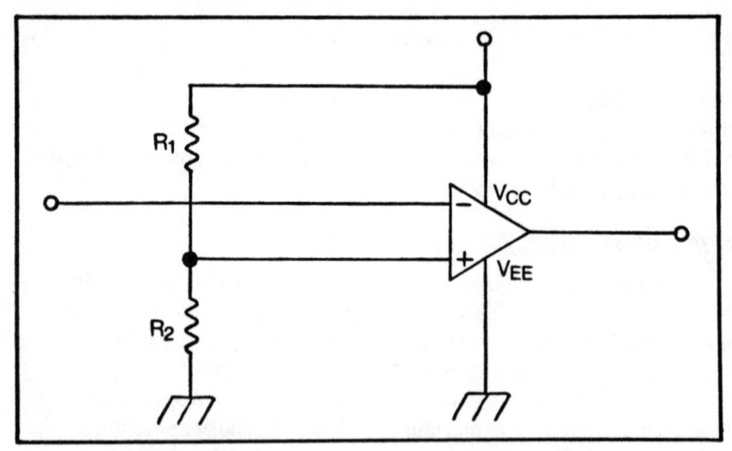

Fig. 1-4. Circuit which allows the use of a single power supply requires a voltage divider to shift the operating point.

Figure 1-4 shows one method which, although limited in application, is an economical approach. In this circuit the minus supply terminal (V_{EE}) of the operational amplifier is grounded, while the positive is connected to V_{CC} in the usual manner. The noninverting + input is connected to a junction on a voltage-divider network; a step which effectively raises the operating point. The ratio between resistors R_1 and R_2 is selected so that the + input is at a certain minimum dc level chosen either by examination of the op amp's internal circuitry or from the data sheet. In case such information is listed, make sure that the chosen dc level is some value greater than the difference between maximum negative supply voltage and the maximum allowable negative input voltage. If not given (or not calculable from what is given), examine the internal schematic of the device. To be safe, allow 0.9V dc for each base-collector and base-emitter junction between the + input and the negative supply terminals. A 1:3 ratio is usually selected for circuits operating with 9—15V power supplies since the minimum voltage is often close to +3V. Popular values are $R_1 = 2000\Omega$ and $R_2 = 1000\Omega$.

Zener diodes are employed in the circuit shown in Fig. 1-5 to stabilize the positive and negative supply voltages and clamp them to specified values.

The circuit at Fig. 1-6 is somewhat more useful. Since it contains a balanced bridge, it retains the differential operation of the op amp. The resistor ratios are selected according to the procedure just given. Voltage gain is set, by the usual method, from the ratio R_F/R_{IN}. In this case, though, the resistance of the bridge arms must be included.

$$R_{IN} = R_S + R_B \tag{1-6}$$

where R_S is the impedance of the driving source (hopefully, but not always,

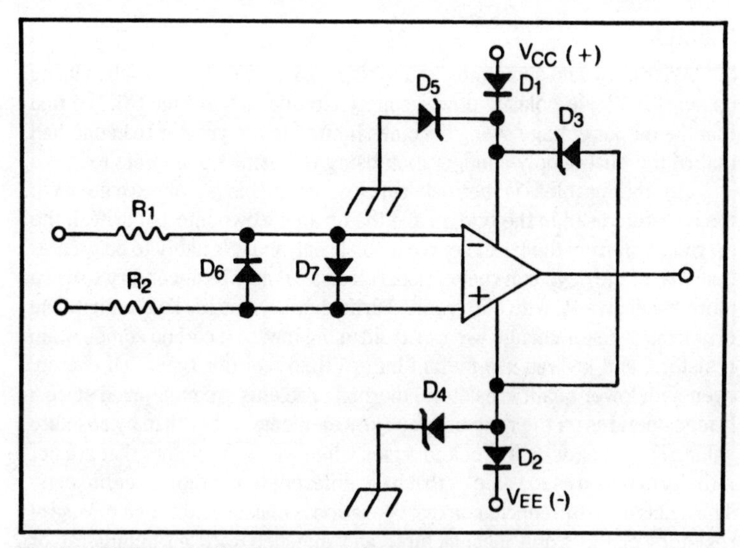

Fig. 1-5. Diode protection to prevent damage to op amp.

low) and R_B is the Thevenin equivalent of one bridge arm. For most practical applications, this will be approximately equal to the parallel combination of the two resistors in one arm—i.e., $(R_3 R_4)/(R_3+R_4)$. If the dc level is to be the "standard" 1:3 V_{CC} then the value of R_B can be taken as 0.67 times the value of the lower resistor in the pair.

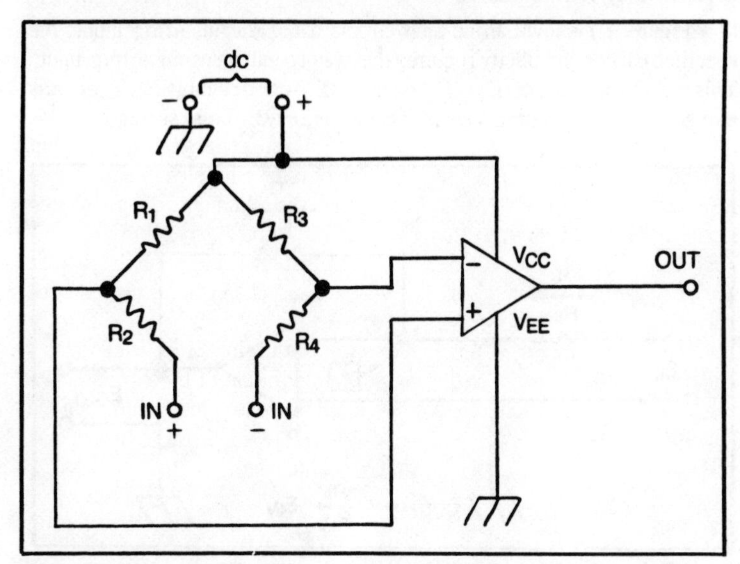

Fig. 1-6. Bridge network preserves amplifier's differential input when using a single supply.

PROBLEMS

We rarely gain something for nothing, and such is the case when using op amps in single-polarity power-supply circuits—as in Fig. 1-6. We find that the output voltage swing becomes limited to not greater than one-half that of the dual-supply configuration using the same op-amp device.

Another problem is thermal drift. Primarily, this is from two sources: the resistors used in the bridge, and the op amp's own internal drift. If the thermal drift from the latter source is too great, and it is likely to be greater than that of the device in conventional circuits, it may be necessary to use a more expensive IC with better initial drift characteristics. To eliminate the drift from resistor change, we can avoid using low-cost carbon composition resistors, and instead use metal film or other superior types. Of course, even with lower quality resistors, thermal problems are minimized since a bridge operates on the ratio between key elements rather than by absolute value. The resistor drift problem arises when we use resistors that are not initially matched as to value or that have different temperature coefficients. This leads us to the conclusion that operation is enhanced through the use of resistors of the same manufacturer and matched with an ohmmeter or Wheatstone bridge. One reasonably decent solution is to use a resistor package. Several manufacturers offer metalized film precision resistors mounted to the same substrate (which means identical thermal environment) packaged in an 8-, 14-, or 16-pin DIP. An 8-pin DIP resistor bank contains all four resistors needed in the bridge.

INVERTING OP-AMP CIRCUITS

Figure 1-7 shows an op-amp circuit using the inverting input. As specified earlier, simplicity requires that we ground the noninverting input. This makes the value of $(E_1 - E_2)$ equal to $(E_1 - 0)$ or simply E_1. There are two resistors used in this circuit. One resistor, R_{IN}, is in series with the

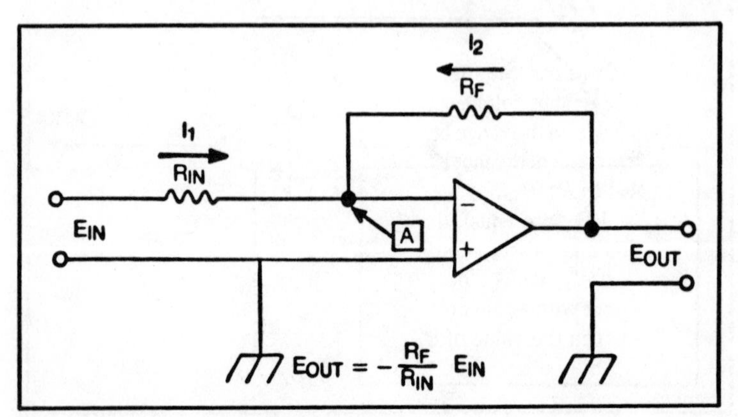

Fig. 1-7. Standard op-amp inverting follower.

input and the signal voltage source. The other is a feedback resistor connected between the output and the input. Point A in the diagram is called the *summing junction* for reasons which shall soon be apparent.

One of the more interesting characteristics of the two operational amplifier inputs is that feedback makes them "follow" each other. Since the + input is grounded, the other tends to be at ground level. Effectively, then, point A is a *virtual ground*. This makes any current flow applied through the input resistor equal to E_{IN}/R_{IN} by Ohm's law.

While not exactly unbelievable, you might still experience some chagrin at the concepts described so far: inputs that neither accept nor deliver currents yet can still affect the output and are at virtual ground!

Kirchhoff 's law states that the algebraic sum of all currents entering and leaving a point must be zero. In order to satisfy Kirchhoff 's current law, we must produce a current that is equal in magnitude, but opposite in direction of flow with respect to the summing junction and I_1. This current is applied through feedback resistor R_F. The output terminal of the op amp supplies a voltage which is of a polarity opposite the input voltage so that current I_2 is generated to cancel I_2 ($I_2 - I_1 = 0$).

Let us assume that R_F and R_{IN} are equal. We can then express our Kirchhoff 's equation as:

$$\frac{E_{OUT}}{R_F} = -\frac{E_{IN}}{R_{IN}} \tag{1-7}$$

$$E_{OUT} = -\frac{R_F E_{IN}}{R_{IN}} \tag{1-8}$$

$$E_{OUT} = -\left(\frac{R_F}{R_{IN}}\right) E_{IN} \tag{1-9}$$

From Eq. 1-9 we can see that the output voltage is affected by both the amplitude of the input voltage and the ratio of R_F to R_{IN}. Recall that for any input voltage within the range of the op amp, an output voltage is generated equal to the product of the input voltage and an amplification factor (A_V); this term is equal to R_F/R_{IN}.

If R_F and R_{IN} are equal, the gain of the inverter will be unity (one). Although this may seem potentially unstable when we consider thermal drift more closely, it does have its uses. More typical, however, is the inverting circuit with a gain greater than unity. In those cases, the value of R_F is higher than the value of R_{IN}. If an amplifier with a gain of 10 were needed:

$$A_V = 10 = R_F/R_{IN} = 10/1 \tag{1-10}$$

In other words, we need only select a value for R_F which is 10 times whatever we chose for R_{IN}. For other voltage gains:

A_V	R_{IN}/R_{IN}
100	100/1
1000	1000/1
10,000	10,000/1

Care must be exercised when trying for higher gain figures, as feedback resistances become uncomfortably high. This can lead to both instability and to the amplification of unwanted noise generated within the resistor. In due course, we offer a circuit which allows high gain to be realized using lower, more manageable resistor values.

Another reason to be concerned about high gain is that it limits us to low input levels, lest we saturate the output by exceeding the voltage limits of the power supply. A 1 mV signal into an amplifier with a gain of 10,000, for example, demands a 10V output. If the amplifier is operated from a dc supply of 10V or less, the output will clip!

ANOTHER APPROACH

There are often several methods for describing any given phenomenon. We have discussed op amps in a simplistic Kirchhoff 's law setting which, at best, "will do." Another approach is to consider the operational amplifier from a viewpoint of elementary feedback theory. Gain can be described as the ratio of output voltage to input voltage ($A = E_{OUT}/E_{IN}$). In a feedback amplifier, we actually must consider two separate gains: closed-loop (A_V) and open-loop (A_{VOL}) where the former is with feedback and the latter is without. The relationship is:

$$A_V = \frac{A_{VOL}}{1 + A_{VOL}B} \qquad (1\text{-}11)$$

where A_{VOL} is the no-feedback, open-loop gain, A_V is the closed-loop (with feedback) gain, and B is the fraction of the output signal fed back to the input (feedback factor). In our case, using simple resistive circuit elements, B would be equal to:

$$B = \frac{R_{IN}}{R_{IN} + R_F} \qquad (1\text{-}12)$$

These two equations can be combined to form:

$$A_V = \frac{A_{VOL}}{1 + A_{VOL}\left(\frac{R_{IN}}{R_{IN} + R_F}\right)} \qquad (1\text{-}13)$$

Unfortunately, this representation does not result in a gain as actually observed in real operational amplifier inverting circuits. This is explained by the fact that these are textbook equations which assume no loss for the input signal applied through an arm of the feedback network. Real networks cause attenuation of the input signal, and this requires at least one additional term in the equation to compensate. The actual input signal in the summing junction is a percentage of the input voltage applied to R_{IN}, equal to:

$$\frac{R_F}{R_{IN} + R_F} \tag{1-14}$$

This is combined with Eq. 1-13 to form Eq. 1-15:

$$A_V = \frac{A_{VOL}\left(\frac{R_F}{R_F + R_{IN}}\right)}{1 + A_{VOL}\left(\frac{R_{IN}}{R_F + R_{IN}}\right)} \tag{1-15}$$

Since the open-loop gain A_{VOL} of an operational amplifier is typically very high, we can safely state that $A_{VOL}/(1 + A_{VOL})$ is essentially equal to A_{VOL}/A_{VOL}, or unity. This reduces Eq. 1-15 to:

$$A_V = (1)\frac{\left(\frac{R_F}{R_{IN} + R_F}\right)}{\left(\frac{R_{IN}}{R_{IN} + R_F}\right)} \tag{1-16}$$

Equation 1-10 stated that A_V was equal to R_F/R_{IN}. How does this square with Eq. 1-16? If the two are equal:

$$\frac{\left(\frac{R_F}{R_F + R_{IN}}\right)}{\left(\frac{R_{IN}}{R_F + R_{IN}}\right)} = \frac{R_F}{R_{IN}} \tag{1-17}$$

Solving the equation, we invert and multiply:

$$\left(\frac{R_{IN} + R_F}{R_{IN}}\right)\left(\frac{R_F}{R_{IN} + R_F}\right) = \frac{R_F}{R_{IN}} \tag{1-18}$$

If we cancel out the $(R_{IN} + R_F)$ terms, we are left with:

$$\frac{R_F}{R_{IN}} = \frac{R_F}{R_{IN}} \tag{1-19}$$

proving that $A_V = R_F/R_{IN}$.

OVERLOAD AND RELATED FAULTS

For the most part, operational amplifiers are tough little devices capable of sustaining a host of indignities without giving out. There are, however, several classes of failure which can be bothersome. Those faults which seem to appear most often are:

- Open output terminals (due to excessive heating under short-circuit conditions).
- Open input terminals (from excessive signal voltage).
- Open power supply terminals (due to high current transients).

In many cases, an excessive current flow can be traced either to excessive voltage between ground and one power terminal or to excessive voltage between the two power terminals. Some op amps allow more voltage to be applied between ground and any one power terminal than might be apparent from an examination of the total terminal-to-terminal supply figure given in the data sheets. Typically, most low-cost op-amp chips will not suffer damage with up to ±18V applied to a single supply terminal. This does not mean, however, that we may automatically assume that it is safe to apply 2×18, or 36V between the two power terminals. Many such devices limit the dc terminal-to-terminal voltage to typically 30V. If one terminal has the maximum value allowed (i.e., 18V), the other is limited to 30–18V, or 12V. Diode D_3 in Fig. 1-5 limits the total supply voltage while D_4 and D_5 limit the levels applied to the respective supply lines.

Although we might not ordinarily expect an existing piece of working equipment to burn out an op amp due to power supply reversal, this can happen occasionally. One method of accomplishing this neat trick is to remove and then reinstall the op amp backwards! Another is for batteries to be reinstalled backwards; a thing which happens more often. Also to be considered is the experimenter or technician breadboarding a new circuit and accidentally reversing the leads from the bench power supply. Damage from these types of accidents can be prevented by use of diodes such as D_1 and D_2 in Fig. 1-5. Any diodes capable of sustaining the op-amp current drain can be used, but those rated in the 1-ampere (1A) class are usually selected.

Damage from excessive signal voltages can be prevented by either of two methods, depending upon which is most appropriate. One is to clamp the output of any preceding stage with a zener diode. In other cases, we might prefer to use clamping diodes such as D_6 and D_7 in Fig. 1-5. For circuits with low-level inputs, these can be any low-cost silicon signal diode which will set the clamp level to around 800 mV. In high-level circuits, a zener of appropriate rating will be more suitable. Resistors R_1 and R_2, if used, will limit current flow under excessive input voltage conditions, but must be included in the gain calculation as part of R_{IN}.

Certain transient conditions will quickly destroy an operational amplifier; and these conditions may be very difficult to pin down due to their rapidly disappearing nature. Many such transients will not show up under all easily predicted circumstances, or even on any regular basis. This makes for extremely difficult troubleshooting.

One source of transients is the surge existing whenever a power supply is turned on or off. This can be handled best by the use of zener diodes in the supply line or well regulated power supplies in the equipment.

A transient will also occur when a charged capacitor or other voltage source is applied to an input of an op amp at the time when the power supplies are turned off. The op amp's internal circuitry is made on a silicon substrate which will act exactly like a diode, since it is of semiconductor material. Under normal conditions, this diode is reverse biased and no current will flow across the junction. Under some circumstances, however, this junction can become abnormally forward biased, allowing a destructive flow of current. One way this happens is for an input voltage to be larger than the negative supply voltage. This can occur momentarily at power supply turnoff since these voltages tend to decay over a short period of time rather than instantaneously. The negative supply, for a brief but very destructive moment, can still furnish a current of substantial magnitude. The same diodes which protected the op amp against reversed power supplies (Fig. 1-5) will protect against a current flow due to abnormal voltages being applied to the op amp.

Also of use in this respect are junction field-effect-transistor (JFET) constant-current sources (CCS). These are made by shorting together the gate and source terminals of an appropriate JFET. The transistors can then be series-connected into the supply lines; one each for V_{CC} and V_{EE}. One CCS will serve a single op amp, or at most a small number of devices, as long as their normal current requirements do not add to a figure higher than the current supplied by the source. The CCS works by limiting the current available to the op amp to a value which cannot cause destructive overheating of the device. This is also a useful tactic for limiting damage due to a short-circuited output terminal. Some modern op-amp devices, fortunately, use internal current regulation that prevents the output current from exceeding a certain preset level, nominally 25 mA in many devices.

Back-to-back zener diodes can be placed across the output to prevent damage from inadvertant application of an excessive voltage to that terminal. The diodes should have a rating higher than any reasonably expected output voltage and lower than a damaging voltage.

Not all of these circuit techniques will be required or even desired in any one circuit application. In fact, for many circuits none of them will be required. Many op-amp circuits have been successfully used with no protection. It is the unusual circuit (the circuit operated close to maximum ratings, which must never fail, which needs protection, etc.), that may prove difficult to predict on the drawing board.

CIRCUITS WITH MORE THAN ONE INPUT

Figure 1-8 shows an operational amplifier with two input sources, labeled E_1 and E_2, connected to the same input terminal. All currents applied to the summing junction must obey Kirchhoff 's law. Since, in this example, the currents are of like polarity, they will add. Current I_1, then, must be of a polarity and magnitude to cancel out the *sum* of I_2 and I_3. In order to provide a level of current capable of doing this, the output terminal must produce a voltage proportional to the gain factor and the sum of input currents. This feature of op-amp circuitry will be dealt with further when we consider mathematic operations using operational amplifier techniques. For now, let us state that for amplifiers receiving current from multiple inputs:

$$E_{OUT} = (R_1/R_2)\,E_1 + (R_1/R_3)\,E_2 + \ldots + (R_1/R_n)\,E_n \qquad (1\text{-}20)$$

INVERTER CIRCUIT APPLICATIONS

As mentioned earlier, the only real limitation to operational amplifier applications is the ability and imagination of the designer. The op amp succeeds in taking circuit design away from the exotic circuit specialist and allows lesser stars to shine almost as brightly. For our present purposes, though, it is merely necessary to show a few of the simpler circuits so that the reader can find his own path; where it leads is up to him.

Figure 1-9 shows a simple inverting follower with a gain of 10. As usual, the gain is set by the ratio R_F/R_{IN}, which in this example are chosen to be 100K and 10K for R_F and R_{IN}, respectively. Circuits such as this are

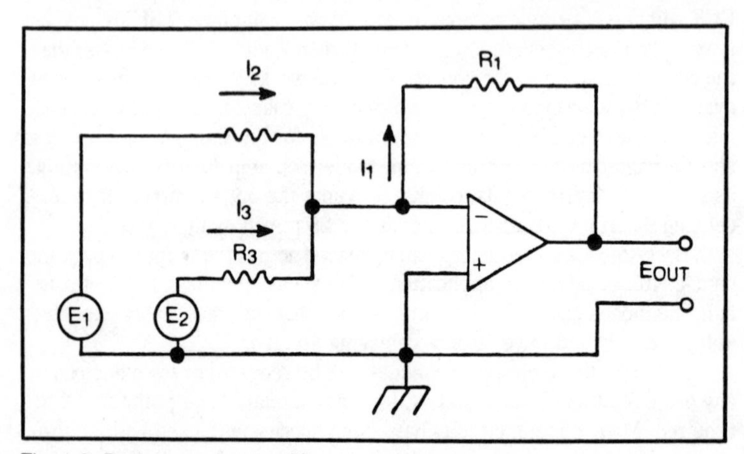

Fig. 1-8. Basic summing amplifier.

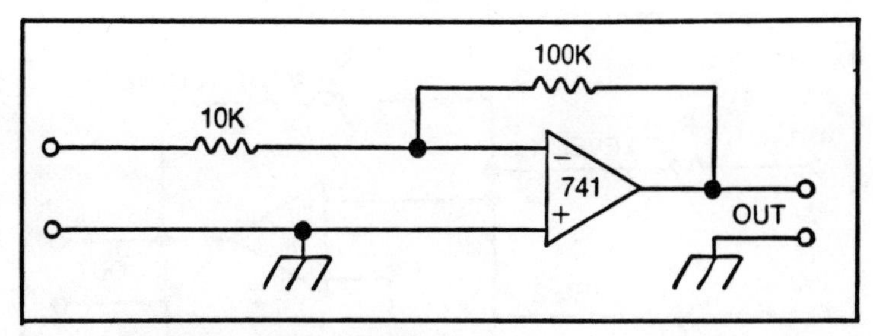

Fig. 1-9. Gain-of-ten inverting amplifier.

useful for a wide variety of purposes between dc and the bandwidth limitations of the particular op amp. Trouble develops only when you try to amplify very small signals which for certain reasons require special techniques. Besides the problems inherent in small signal processing, we also run into trouble here because of the high value resistances needed at R_F, or alternatively, the low values at R_{IN}. In such cases, both the minimum impedance load required by the source (at least 10 times its own Z_{OUT}) and the highest practical value for R_F can become important.

A useful expansion of the inverting amplifier theme is shown in Fig. 1-10. This circuit is a programmed gain amplifier. A switch is used to select appropriate feedback resistors so that gains of ×2, ×10, and ×100 are available. The switch should be a make-before-break type in order to prohibit the unstable extreme-gain condition which exists when the open-circuited feedback path tries to produce a gain of infinity.

Figure 1-11 shows an adaptation from the multiple input scheme developed earlier. This circuit can function as an audio mixer if desired. Resistors R_1 and R_2 serve as gain controls for individual channels while R_3

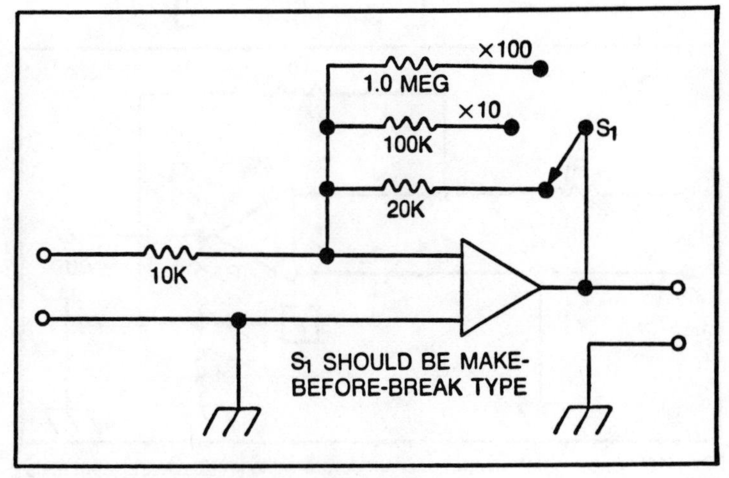

Fig. 1-10. Programmed gain inverting amplifier.

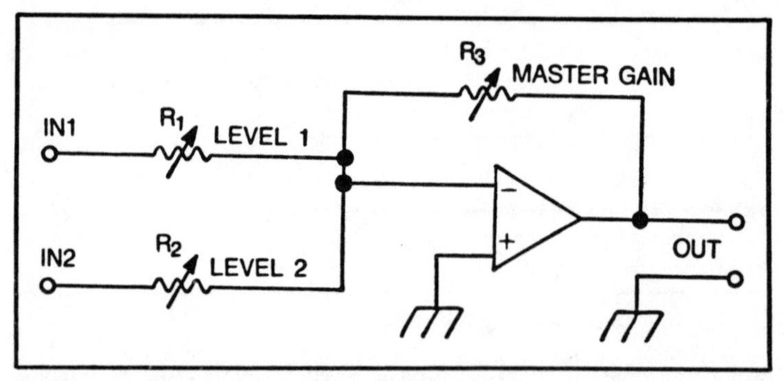

Fig. 1-11. Variable gain summing amplifier can be used as a linear mixer for audio and other signals.

serves as a master gain control for the entire amplifier circuit. It is usually deemed wise to use fixed resistors in series with potentiometers R_1 and R_2 so that unstable high-gain values (which occur when these resistors are near zero) are avoided.

The circuit shown in Fig. 1-12 offers a method for obtaining high gain without using excessive values of feedback resistors. Problems associated with this were mentioned earlier. The circuit shown here will alleviate some of the headaches associated with use of multimegohm resistors in the feedback loop. The voltage at point A in Fig. 1-12 must be equal to (R_2/R_1) E_{IN}. In order to produce this level, the output terminal of the operational amplifier must produce a voltage equal to:

$$E_{OUT} = (E_{IN}) \left[\frac{R_2 + \dfrac{R_2 R_3}{R_4} + R_3}{R_1} \right] \quad (1\text{-}21)$$

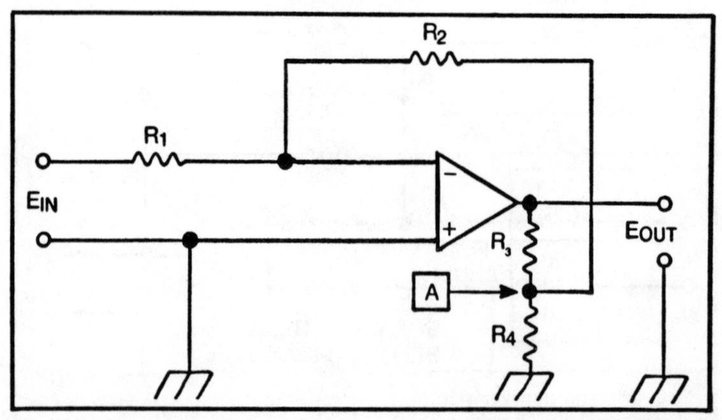

Fig. 1-12. "Super gain" inverter uses moderate value feedback and input resistors.

Figure 1-13 shows a circuit that has proven very popular. It is nothing more than our old friend, the inverting follower, with values selected for 20, 40, or 60 dB gain. Although the popular magazines have inaccurately called this an "instrumentation amplifier," that term is properly reserved for a form of differential amplifier (Chapter 3). The reason for the misnomer is that many articles have pointed out that the circuit can be used ahead of a voltmeter or other instrument which has a full-scale rating much higher than the voltage being measured. Multiplication of the input by a factor of 10 allows direct reading with only manipulation of the decimal point.

Figure 1-14 shows one form of clipper/amplifier using zener diodes as the clipping element. The amplifier will produce an output voltage equal to $E_{IN}(R_F/1000)$ so long as the output voltage is less than the reverse breakdown (zener) voltage of the diode. Actually, the correct value will be approximately 0.7V higher than the V_Z of a single diode because the alternate diode is forward biased and will have a voltage drop.

DESIGN EXAMPLES

General example 1-A:

A dc signal varies between limits of 50 and 250 mV. It is desired to amplify this signal such that it will vary from −0.75V to −3.75V. The amplification required is:

$$A_V = 3.75/0.25 = 15$$

Until we cover op-amp errors, we can only use the "rule of ten" to select a value for R_{IN}. This rule states that the impedance of a load, unless power transfer is an issue, should be 10 times the output impedance of the driving

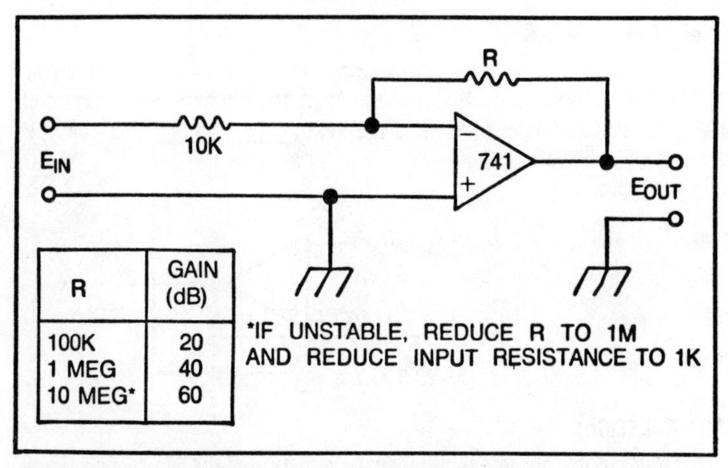

R	GAIN (dB)
100K	20
1 MEG	40
10 MEG*	60

Fig. 1-13. Inverting amplifier with component values for 20, 40, and 60 dB gain. If amplifier proves to be unstable with a 10 megohm feedback resistor, reduce it to 1 megohm and also reduce input resistor to 1K.

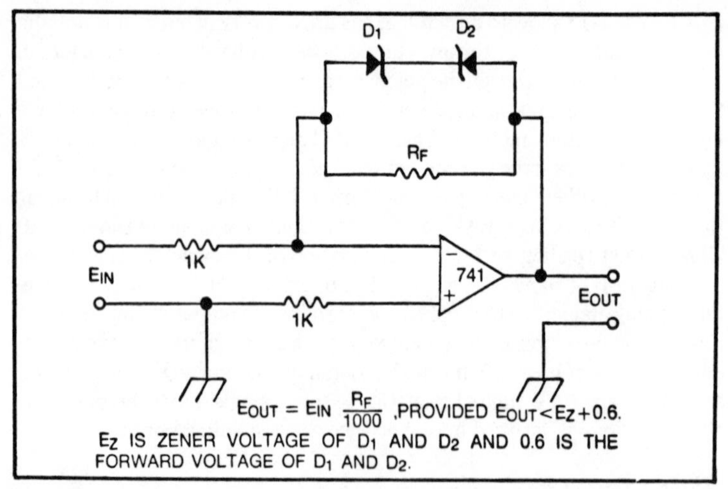

Fig. 1-14. Clipping amplifier using zener diodes to limit output voltage excursions.

source. In our case, we will assign a value of 5000Ω to the output of the stage or device driving our inverting amplifier. This means that the input resistor must be not less than 5000Ω. For ease of arithmetic, we will select a value of 10,000Ω. If R_{IN} = 10K, then

$$
\begin{aligned}
R_F &= R_{IN} A_V \\
&= (10{,}000)\ (15) \\
&= 150{,}000
\end{aligned}
$$

General example 1-B:

An amplifier has a feedback resistor of 470,000Ω. A low-frequency ac input signal is presented which varies symmetrically between 25 and 100 mV. What value of input resistor is needed to boost this signal so that the positive peak has a value of −2V?

From Eq. 1-9:

$$
\begin{aligned}
E_0 &= E_{IN}\ (R_F/R_{IN}) \\
R_{IN} &= R_F E_{IN}/E_0 \\
&= \frac{(4.7 \times 10^5)\ (1 \times 10^{-1})}{2 \times 10} \\
&= 23{,}500\Omega
\end{aligned}
$$

TEST QUESTIONS

1.1 What are three essential characteristics of the ideal operational amplifier?

1.2 The output voltage in Fig. T1-1 is:

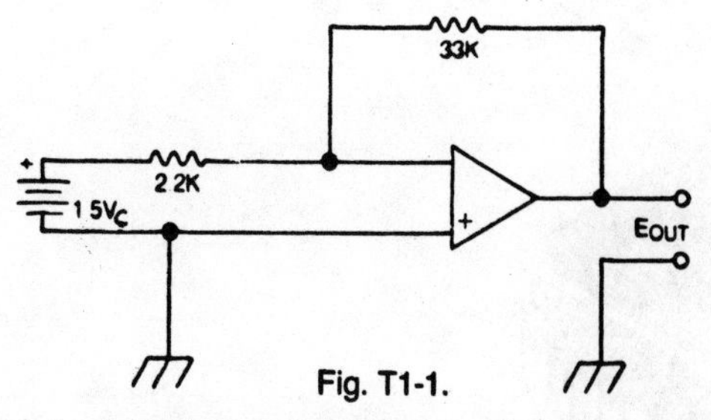

Fig. T1-1.

1.3 What is the voltage gain of the circuit in Fig. T1-2?

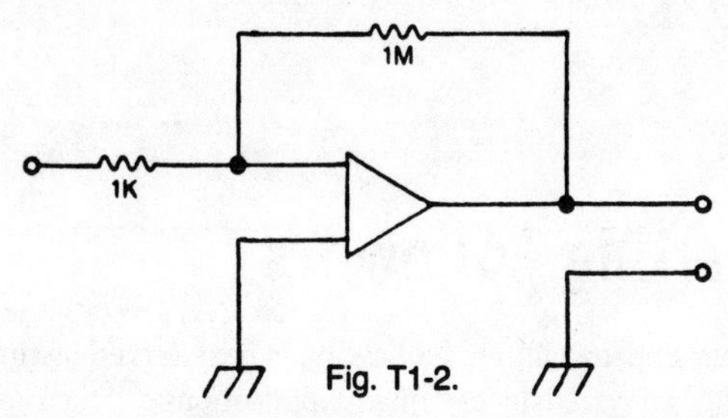

Fig. T1-2.

1.4 What is the voltage gain of the circuit in Fig. T1-3?

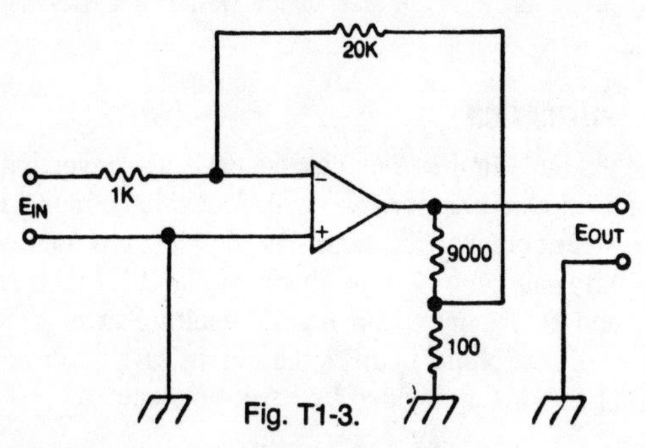

Fig. T1-3.

1.5 What is the value of E_1 in Fig. T1-4?

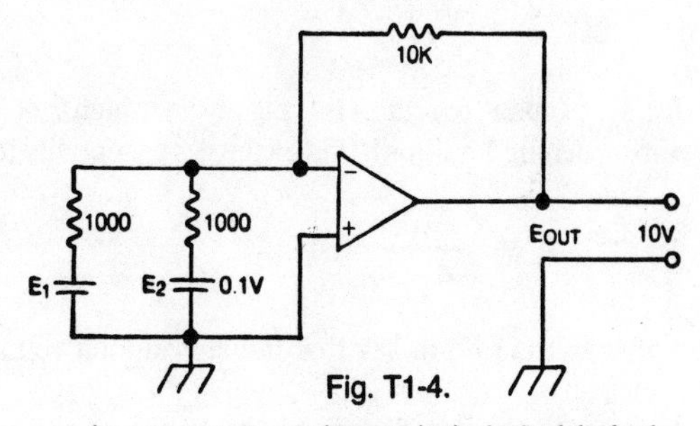

Fig. T1-4.

Answers to test questions are in the back of the book.

Chapter 2

Noninverting Followers

Not every operational amplifier application is best served by the inverting amplifier configuration. No indeed, many applications call for a *noninverting* voltage amplifier or "follower". Any situation which would benefit from extremely high-impedance amplifiers is just *made* for the noninverting follower.

UNITY GAIN AMPLIFICATION

Until now we have limited our discussion to the inverting follower amplifier circuit. In this chapter, we will deal with circuits using the remaining input—the noninverting input. The simplest type of noninverting follower is the unity gain ($A_V = 1$) type shown in Fig. 2-1. In this circuit, the output is strapped to the inverting input, resulting in a value for the feedback resistor of zero ohms. In this situation we have a gain equal to the open-loop gain of the device divided by itself-plus-one:

$$A_V = \frac{A_{VOL}}{A_{VOL} + 1} \tag{2-1}$$

Since the value for A_{VOL} (open-loop gain) is typically very high (not less than 10,000 and often approaching 1 million), this evaluates essentially to unity:

$$A_V \cong \frac{A_{VOL}}{A_{VOL}} \cong 1 \tag{2-2}$$

For practical purposes, it is safe to say that the closed-loop voltage does equal unity!

In the first chapter, we also described the action of the inverting

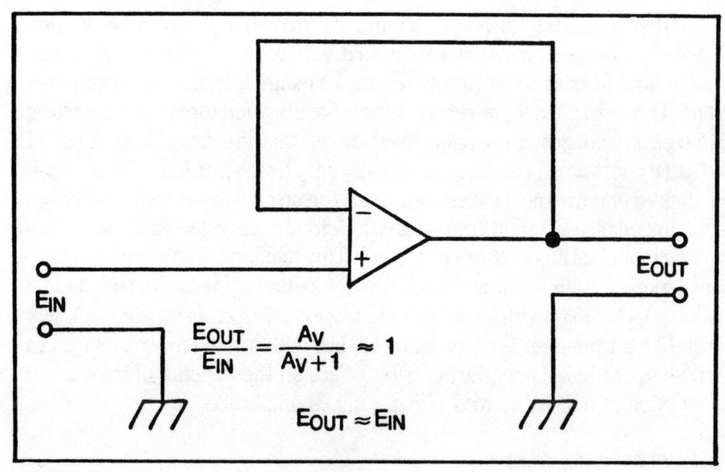

Fig. 2-1. Noninverting unity gain follower.

amplifier from the viewpoint of feedback equations. Applying this same general form to the unity gain follower, we find, again, some justification for certain simplifications. Recall the general equation:

$$A_V = \frac{A_{VOL}}{1 + A_{VOL}B} \tag{2-3}$$

where B represents that fraction of the output signal feedback to an input as defined by the ratio:

$$B = \frac{R_{IN}}{R_{IN} + R_F} \tag{2-4}$$

In the case of the unity gain follower, B is equal to unity since *all* of the output signal appears at the inverting input and the terms R_{IN} and R_F do not exist. Since B is equal to one, it has no effect on Eq. 2-1. It is therefore safe to state, from either point of view, that:

$$E_{OUT} = A_V E_{IN} \tag{2-5}$$
$$E_{OUT} = (1) E_{IN} \tag{2-6}$$
$$E_{OUT} = E_{IN} \tag{2-7}$$

While it might *seem* to be a somewhat useless exercise to produce an amplifier with a gain of unity, there are actually quite a few applications for such a circuit. In fact, there are at least two different classes of application. The first of these is as a buffer amplifier to isolate one circuit from the loading effects of a following stage. Certain circuits, such as a high-stability oscillator, should "look into" the highest possible impedance. The noninverting follower offers the highest input impedance of the op-amp configurations.

Other circuits, however, should be driven by a relatively low-impedance source or a source with a relatively constant output impedance. Power amplifiers of some categories are an example of this latter requirement. This leads us to the second general application for the noninverting follower: impedance conversion. You'll recall that the output impedance of the usual operational amplifier is typically very low, being less than a couple of hundred ohms in most cases. However, the op amp has an extremely high input impedance as seen from a driving circuit, provided that the noninverting input has no resistors to ground. This maximization of input impedance, coupled with a characteristically low output impedance, results in a circuit which behaves nicely as an impedance converter. In this respect, it is much like a transistor emitter follower, but with a gain closer to unity. In fact, an operational amplifier follower offers all the benefits of impedance conversion at almost no loss of input signal amplitude.

FOLLOWERS WITH GAIN

In those cases where the unity gain follower is unsatisfactory due to a requirement for amplification, we can construct a follower with gain greater than unity. A modest example is offered in Fig. 2-2. This circuit uses a voltage-divider feedback network to deliver a fraction of the output signal to the inverting input. Unlike the inverting follower, this circuit has input signal applied to the *noninverting* input terminal. The feedback voltage divider provides a feedback factor (B) as indicated in Eq. 2-4.

Plugging Eq. 2-4 into Eq. 2-3 results in

$$A_V = \frac{A_{VOL}}{1 + A_{VOL}\left(\dfrac{R_{IN}}{R_F + R_{IN}}\right)} \tag{2-8}$$

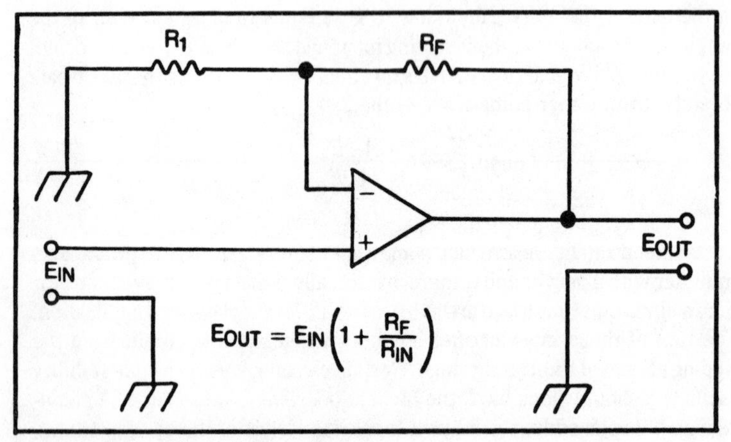

Fig. 2-2. Noninverting follower with gain.

Note that Eq. 2-8 can be used in its pure form without having to add an additional term to compensate for the fact that the input signal is attenuated on reaching the op-amp input terminal. In the noninverting gain follower, the signal is applied directly to the input, making unnecessary the $R_F/(R_F + R_{IN})$ term previously used in the numerator.

By a little algebraic manipulation, we can easily find the closed-loop gain as a function of the resistances in the feedback voltage divider: A_{VOL} is some value which is a very large number. In that case it is reasonably safe to state that

$$A_V \cong \frac{A_{VOL}}{A_{VOL}\left(\frac{R_{IN}}{R_F + R_{IN}}\right)} \tag{2-9}$$

This results in:

$$A_V = \frac{1}{\left(\frac{R_{IN}}{R_{IN} + R_F}\right)} \tag{2-10}$$

Invert and multiply:

$$A_V = \left(\frac{R_{IN} + R_F}{R_{IN}}\right) (1) \tag{2-11}$$

$$A_V = 1 + \frac{R_F}{R_{IN}} \tag{2-12}$$

Remember this equation: it will prove very useful in calculating resistances needed to set specific gain factors!

INPUT IMPEDANCE

What is the approximate magnitude of the input impedance and where does the figure come from? In the inverting follower, the minus (−) input was at virtual ground due to the action of feedback, and the fact that the noninverting input was grounded. In that case the input resistance, as seen by the source, was equal to the value of R_{IN}. In any case, R_{IN} will be equal to the quotient E_{IN}/I_{IN}. In the noninverting follower circuit, this is equal to the product of the loop gain and the impedance seen between the two inputs (R_D in Fig. 2-3). Since both figures can be very high, even in economy op amps, we have an impedance value which climbs out of sight. Compare this with the input impedance of the inverting amplifier. In those circuits, input resistor R_{IN} is responsible for the input impedance. In many cases, especially where closed-loop gains tend to be very high, this resistance can take on an uncomfortably low value. Even where high gain is not used, it seldom

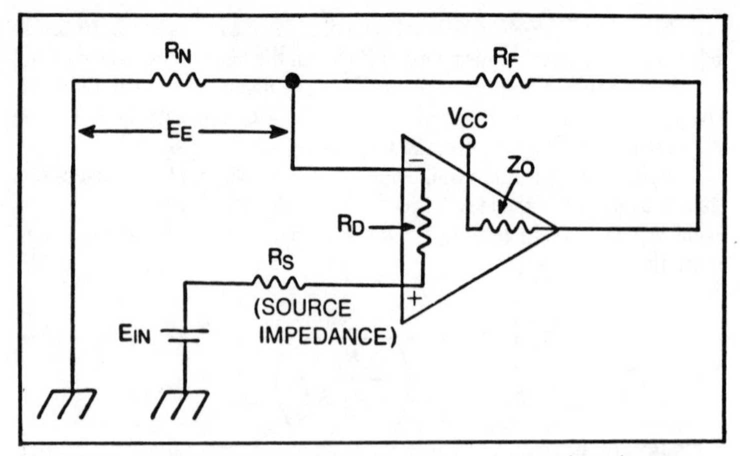

Fig. 2-3. Equivalent networks representing input and output impedances.

will have a value exceeding 100K and will, in fact, usually be quite a bit lower—an order of magnitude lower in many circuits.

AUDIO APPLICATIONS

The noninverting follower has proven popular in many audio applications. Figure 2-4 shows an example of one such application. Input transformer T_1 is a standard 600Ω input type with a high output impedance (typically 50K or so). The overall voltage gain of this circuit is equal to the voltage stepup of the transformer times the amplification of the op-amp circuit.

Figure 2-5 is a modification of the previous circuit, and this design might have some appeal to professional sound technicians and broadcast

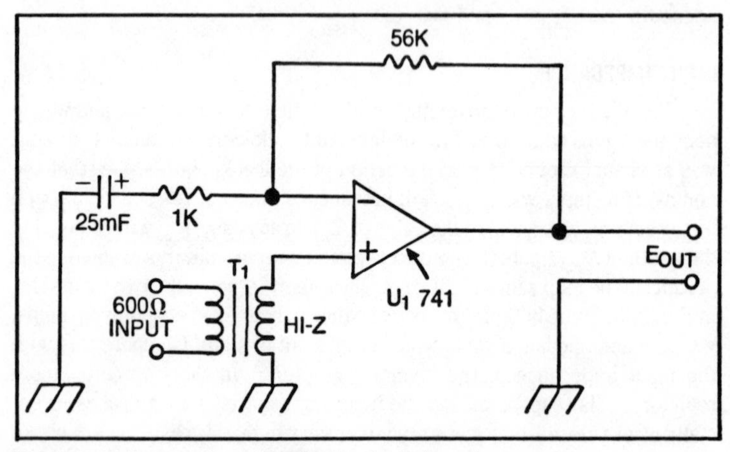

Fig. 2-4. Audio amplifier with 600-ohm input impedance.

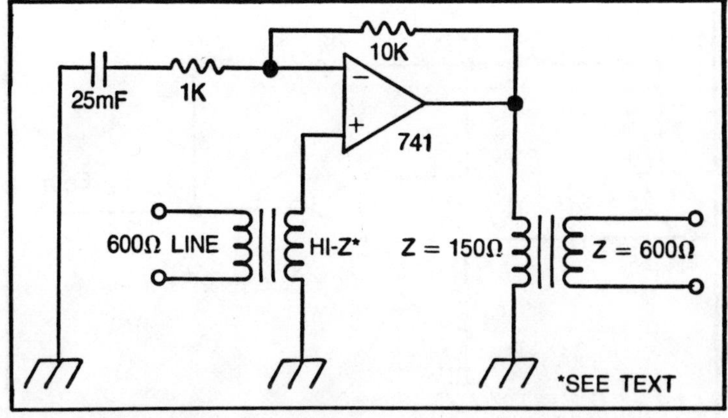

Fig. 2-5. 600-ohm audio line amplifier.

engineers. The circuit is a line driver amplifier. It features 600Ω input and output impedances so that it can be used to drive the 600Ω balanced lines frequently used in professional audio work. It must be noted that the user must not expect superior performance from a circuit such as this unless superior components are used. Avoid low-cost 600Ω audio transformers, such as often seen in blister packs. Instead, use high-grade components.

Although the transformer-coupled amplifier is technically an ac amplifier, we usually reserve that term for capacitor-coupled types. This leads us to a bit of confusion over what constitutes an ac amplifier. When speaking of the RC-coupled types, it is often stated, somewhat in error, that these are really nothing more than simple dc amplifiers (such as we have been discussing) with a couple of capacitors blocking the input and output terminals. This is true in the sense that the capacitors are there and they do keep dc out of the amplifier. It is not, however, the complete story and a lot more can be done. Also, those capacitors at the input tend to cause problems such as op-amp latchup due to accumulation of bias current. These must be taken care of in ac amplifier design.

The circuit of Fig. 2-6 is an effort to secure the advantages that an ac amplifier can provide. Notice that the inclusion of resistor R_1, not used in the previous noninverting follower designs, prevents the accumulation of bias current charge on capacitor C_1. The other capacitor, C_2, provides a low-impedance path to ground for ac signals within the desired passband, but blocks dc. This is necessary to ensure that both inputs see a similar situation with respect to ground.

Unfortunately, the resistor that bleeds off the charge on C_1 also acts to lower apparent input impedance—a fact that might tend to upset a driver stage if too low a value is used. Circuits such as Fig. 2-6 tend to suffer greatly if the resistance takes on relatively low values. A better circuit is shown as Fig. 2-7; it is called the *bootstrapped* ac amplifier. It offers superior stability and a higher input impedance.

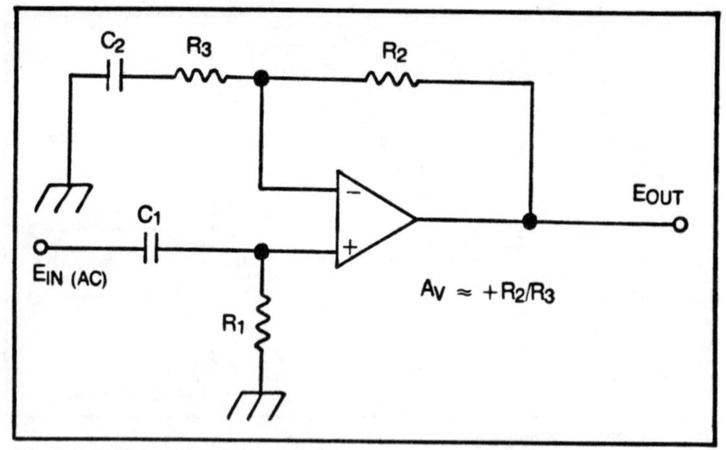

Fig. 2-6. Typical ac amplifier circuit.

Figures 2-8 and 2-9 are practical examples of audio applications for ac amplifier circuits. Both are preamplifiers which prove useful in the construction of audio equipment. Figure 2-8 is a broadband preamp essentially flat between 50 Hz and approximately 25 kHz. The gain of the circuit is 40 dB ($A_V = 100$). Use of a frequency-compensated op amp will insure retention of this flat response with no chance of unwanted oscillations which could possibly be well into the low ultrasonic range.

Figure 2-9 is actually three separate preamplifiers which can be tailored to specific needs by connecting the correct feedback network between points A and B. One network will produce a preamplifier with a frequency response (RIAA) suitable for phonograph reproduction. The remaining circuits are two different response characteristics for NAB tape equalization. One variety is for 3¾ ips tape speed while the other is for 7½ ips.

IC operational amplifiers have become increasingly popular among audio circuit designers because of the inherently easy design procedure and the low cost per unit. The existence of dual (stereo) op amps on a single chip is a powerful argument for this approach to design—and at low cost, too!

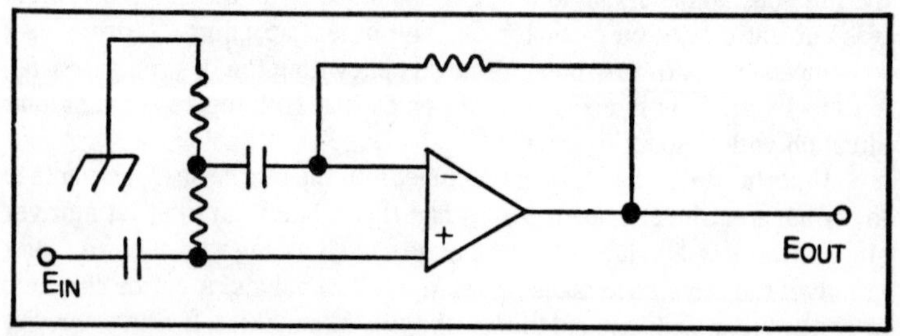

Fig. 2-7. Bootstrapped ac amplifier.

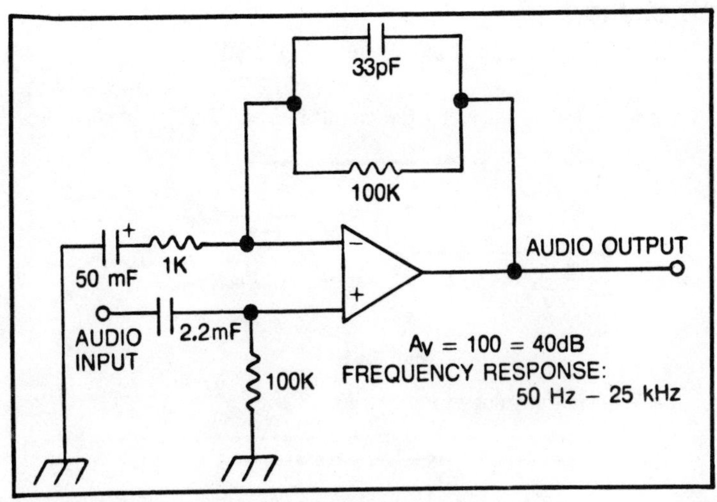

Fig. 2-8. Practical 40 dB gain audio amplifier.

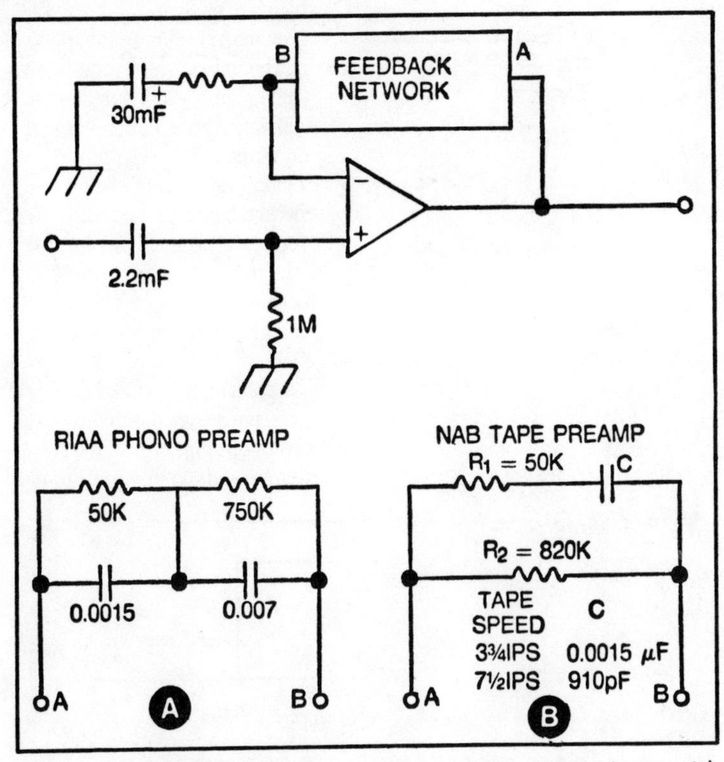

Fig. 2-9. Audio preamplifier which uses different feedback networks to match RIAA and the two NAB response curves.

TEST QUESTIONS

2.1 What is the gain of the circuit in Fig. T2-1?

2.2 What are two uses for the circuit in Fig. T2-1?

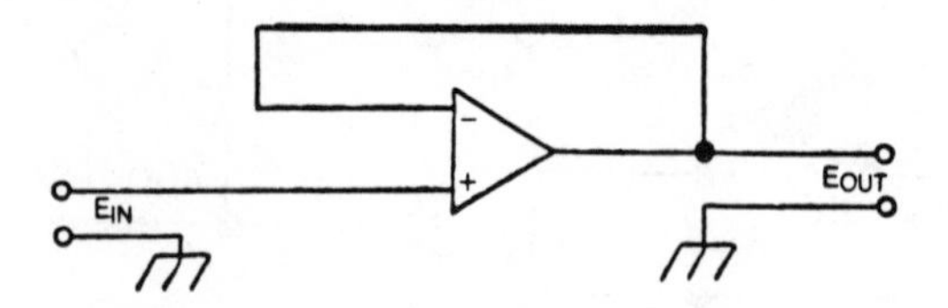

Fig. T2-1.

2.3 What is the value of E_{OUT} in Fig. T2-2?

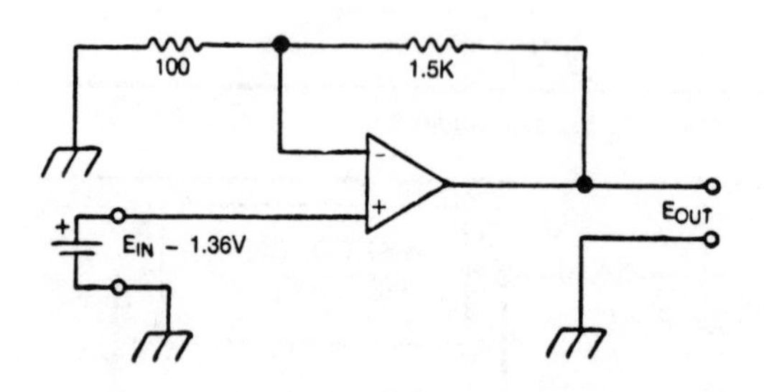

Fig. T2-2.

Answers to test questions are in the back of the book.

Chapter 3

Differential Amplifiers

It is quite easy to make use of the dual-input nature of the operational amplifier to form a *differential amplifier*. Such circuits deliver an output voltage proportional to the *difference* between the voltages seen by the respective inputs. Figure 3-1 shows an op amp connected to a pair of input voltage sources. From Eq. 1-5 we know that

$$E_{OUT} = A_V (E_1 - E_2) \quad (3\text{-}1)$$

When E_1 and E_2 are equal, then,

$$E_{OUT} = A_V(0) = 0$$

For any nonzero value of $(E_1 - E_2)$, then, an output voltage will be generated at a level proportional to the amplification gain, A_V.

Assume:

$$A_V = 100$$
$$E_1 = 2.0\text{V}$$
$$E_2 = 1.9\text{V}$$

From Eq. 3-1:

$$\begin{aligned} E_{OUT} &= (100)\,(2.0 - 1.9) \\ &= (100)\,(0.1) \\ &= 10 \end{aligned}$$

This relationship is shown vectorially in Fig. 3-2. As long as E_1 and E_2 are equal, as indicated in Fig. 3-2A, the vectors V_1 and V_2 will also be equal, but will have opposite directions. The resultant, of course, equals zero in those cases. Where E_1 and E_2 are not equal, as in Fig. 3-2B, there will be a

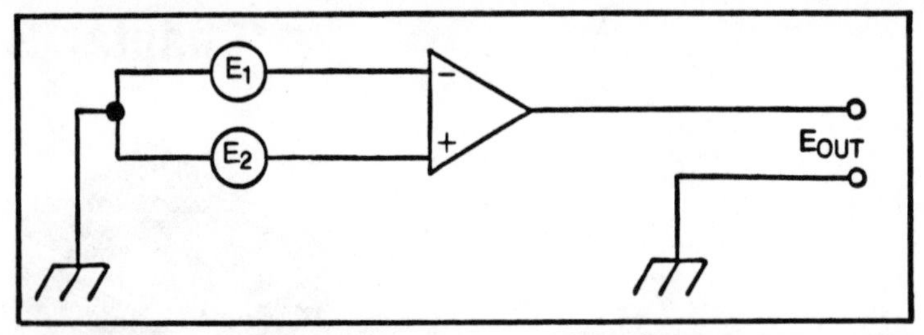

Fig. 3-1. Op amp connected with each input to separate signal voltage sources delivers an output voltage proportional to their difference.

resultant other than zero. This resultant, when multiplied by the gain factor, A_V, will equal the output voltage.

The utility of this characteristic becomes excitingly apparent wherever tiny signals must be acquired and amplified in the presence of large interfering signals. Power lines, for example, radiate 60 Hz energy which can be picked up by any electrical conductor. This can be heard in the form of the buzz generated in the loudspeaker whenever you touch (or have an unshielded connection to) an audio amplifier input line. Normally, if both input wires from a remote voltage source to an op amp are of equal length, the interference signals relative to ground presented at the op-amp input terminals will be equal. Ideally, these voltages, even though quite large relative to the actual signal voltage, will have no net effect on the output. The relationship of the interfering voltage to the normal input voltages is illustrated in Fig. 3-3. This diagram is essentially the same as Fig. 3-1, with the exception of an added voltage source labeled E_3. Since those signals represented by E_3 are common to both inputs, they are called *common-mode* signals.

In a perfect operational amplifier, the equal but opposite action of the respective inputs on the output level will tend to null to zero any common-mode signals. Unfortunately, real op amps are neither ideal nor perfect; some output voltage will be generated by a common-mode signal. The

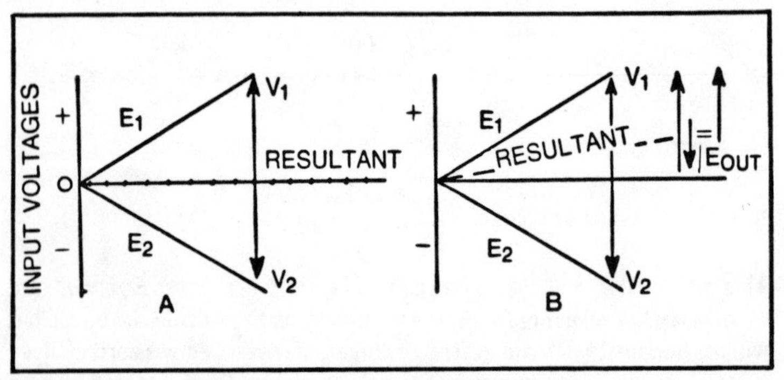

Fig. 3-2. Vector relationship between E1, E2, and EOUT.

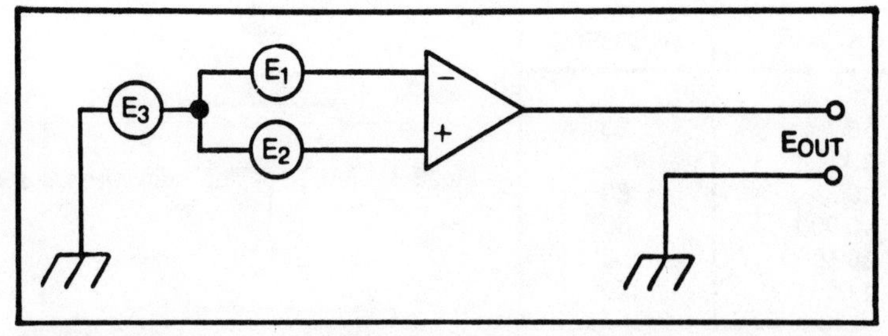

Fig. 3-3. "Common mode" voltages are those in series with both inputs (E_3).

capability of any particular device to reject common-mode input voltages is called the common-mode rejection ratio (CMRR).

The common-mode voltage (E_3 in Fig. 3-3) is the average of the two input voltages under those fortunate conditions when no blatant interference exists. This is

$$E_3 = \frac{E_1 + E_2}{2} \tag{3-2}$$

This voltage will produce some small output in normal op amps.

The common-mode gain of an op amp is calculated in the same manner as any other gain ($A_V = E_{OUT}/E_{IN}$). In this case:

$$A_{V(CM)} = \frac{E_{OUT(CM)}}{E_{IN(CM)}} \tag{3-3}$$

Where $A_{V(CM)}$ = common-mode gain, $E_{OUT(CM)}$ = output voltage generated by $E_{IN(CM)}$, the common-mode input voltage labeled E_3 earlier.

Common-mode rejection ratio (CMRR) is defined as the ratio of normal differential gain (A_V) to common-mode gain ($A_{V(CM)}$). Common-mode rejection (CMR) is the most often seen expression of CMRR and is merely that quantity converted to decibel form by the traditional formula:

$$\text{dB} = 20 \log_{10} (A_V/A_{V(CM)}) \tag{3-4}$$

or simply,

$$\text{dB} = 20 \log_{10} (\text{CMMR})$$

Figure 3-4 shows a chart of CMR for several orders of value for CMRR.

MAINTAINING HIGH CMRR

Any number of errors (or other factors not properly classed as errors) will deteriorate CMR to a point which renders the circuit useless. In biological and medical applications, for example, differentially connected op

CMRR	DECIBELS
1	0
10	20
100	40
1000	60
10,000	80
100,000	100
1,000,000	120

Fig. 3-4. CMRR—decibel conversion.

amps are often used to pick up bioelectric potentials such as ECG and EEG, which typically have maximum amplitudes under 1.0 mV. The interference from 60 Hz power-line radiation, on the other hand, can reach amplitudes of 1.0 mV per foot of input cable! Clearly, then, the common-mode interference may well be many times greater than the desired signal. In such cases it is absolutely essential to maintain a high CMR. There are several main causes of CMR deterioration; namely:

- Mechanical anomalies in connections.
- Improper connections.
- Component mismatches in the op amps causing poor initial CMR.
- Generation of differential signals manufactured from existing common-mode signals.

The first of these, the purely mechanical problem, is easily resolved in most cases by merely insuring the integrity of all connectors. In medical monitoring, stick-on adhesive electrodes attached directly to the patient's chest are frequently used. A low-resistance jelly is applied between the skin and the electrode to insure a good contact. If left in place over several days, the jelly will tend to dry somewhat, and the respective electrodes may have unequal resistance connections with the skin. This will allow a band of 60 Hz signal to obliterate the desired tracing on the monitor scope. Even in a less harsh environment with less dynamic subjects, the matter of CMR maintenance is of concern. The obvious solution is to maintain proper contacts.

Occasionally, improper connection results from the input wires actually being connected to the wrong points! Again, the operator of the equipment or the technician exercising good lab/bench practice can avoid the obvious.

Somewhat more difficult to cope with are component mismatches in the actual differential amplifier circuitry. Regardless of the differential amplifier circuit used, there will be at least some degree of component matching necessary. In most designs, there are certain resistances which should be equal, or at least nominally so. For most common applications which require only moderate CMR, use of resistors with a 1 percent tolerance will suffice (5 percent can be allowed only in those cases where a little sloppiness is of no importance). In highly critical applications, espe-

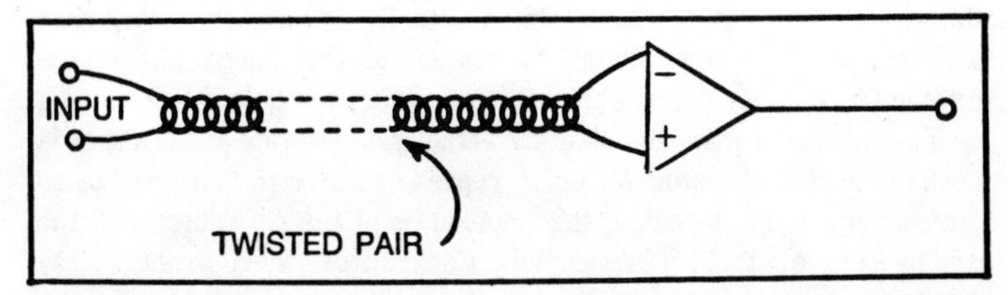

Fig. 3-5. "Twisted pair" wiring for input cable reduces interference pickup in relatively short signal lines.

cially when the circuit will be used in demanding environments, it might be necessary to use 0.1 percent or even 0.05 percent tolerance resistors; a move which adds considerable cost. Some value trimming using potentiometers can be done, but this is usually limited to one resistor.

In some instances, an existing piece of equipment using a differential input will have to be used in an unusually noisy environment. We can alleviate some CMR problems through the use of certain wiring techniques. For very short runs, it may prove possible to use a "twisted pair" for the input leads (see Fig. 3-5). On longer runs, through an area where a lot of fast rise time impulse noise exists, it might be wise to employ a technique used in the data transmission business. In Fig. 3-6, we see a pair of three-winding baluns connected in such a way as to cancel some of the noise. Two baluns are used, one at each end of the cable run, with their grounds connected to oppose the signal coils.

Shielding has often been shown to be the most successful method for eliminating unwanted interference. This holds true, but not without some qualification for differential as well as single-ended inputs. For short runs and where low frequencies (near dc) are used, it may well be that simple shielding is sufficient. This sort of wiring uses a pair of insulated conductors inside a braid of foil shielding conductor.

On longer runs, or anyplace where higher frequency signals are being processed, it is often found that simple shielding not only is less effective, but it may cause some deterioration on its own. In many scientific and

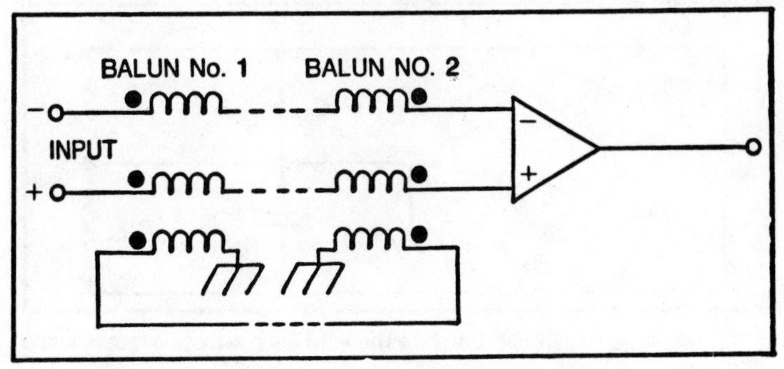

Fig. 3-6. Balun coils at either end of line reduces noise pickup.

industrial applications, a simple shield actually aggravates, rather than alleviates, interference problems! Certain circuit techniques, lumped unceremoniously under the heading *input guarding*, can help, however.

The way that simple shielding can actually deteriorate performance is shown in Fig. 3-7. Resistors R_1 and R_2 represent the sum of all resistances in the input circuit, including the impedance of the E_1 source and the resistance of the actual wire conductors. Capacitors C_1 and C_2 are the stray capacitance existing between the shield (which is grounded) and the two conductors. R_{IN} and R'_{IN} are simply the input impedances of the op amp which are usually high enough to be ignored here. Everything is fine as long as $R_1C_1 = R_2C_2$. If this equality is not maintained, however, common-mode rejection deteriorates and interference can result. The amount of difference in these relationships need not be too great for trouble to occur—especially where high op-amp gains follow the creation of a differential signal from a common-mode voltage. This signal is caused by different charges across the two capacitances. Ideally:

$$E_{C1} = E_{C2}$$

or

$$E_{C1} - E_{C2} = 0 \qquad (3\text{-}5)$$

In the case where the voltages are not equal this becomes

$$E_{CM}\left[\frac{X_{C1}}{R_1 + X_{C1}}\right] - E_{CM}\left[\frac{X_{C2}}{R_2 + X_{C2}}\right] = 0 \qquad (3\text{-}6)$$

where E_{CM} is the common-mode interference voltage (60 Hz) and X_{C1} and X_{C2} are the reactances of C_1 and C_2. If the relationship of Eq. 3-6 does not hold true, the common-mode signal becomes a differential signal which will be amplified by the high differential A_V of the amplifier. There are several tactics which can be used to eliminate this sort of thing; some are better than others but they all have a degree of merit.

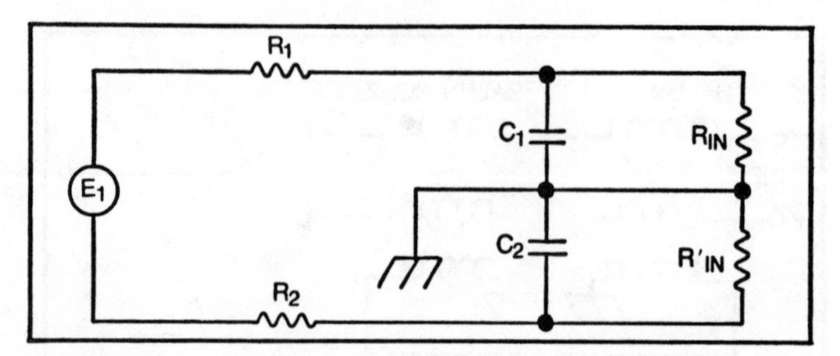

Fig. 3-7. Simple equivalent network shows how shielding can actually deteriorate performance.

One method is to use a double-shielded cable. This is a special form of signal cable with a pair of inner conductors for the differential voltage, and two separate, concentric shields insulated from each other (see Fig. 3-8A). The equivalent circuit is shown at Fig. 3-8B. Here we have an apparent parallel combination of source or wire resistances, and the capacitances between inner shield (also called *guard shield* for obvious reasons). One of these parallel combinations is in series with each of the op-amp inputs. There are superior methods, but at least this approach is inexpensive and it can be used on equipment where redesign is uninviting.

Figure 3-9 shows a CMR enhancement scheme often seen on biomedical and high-gain scientific equipment using differential inputs. In its simplest implementation, which is admittedly easier in differential amplifier designs using two or three op amps, we sum the signals from each input through resistors R_A and R_B at point A. This combination signal is then used to drive the input line shield. Some versions use either a unity or greater than unity noninverting follower to drive the shield (see the phantom amplifier of Fig. 3-9).

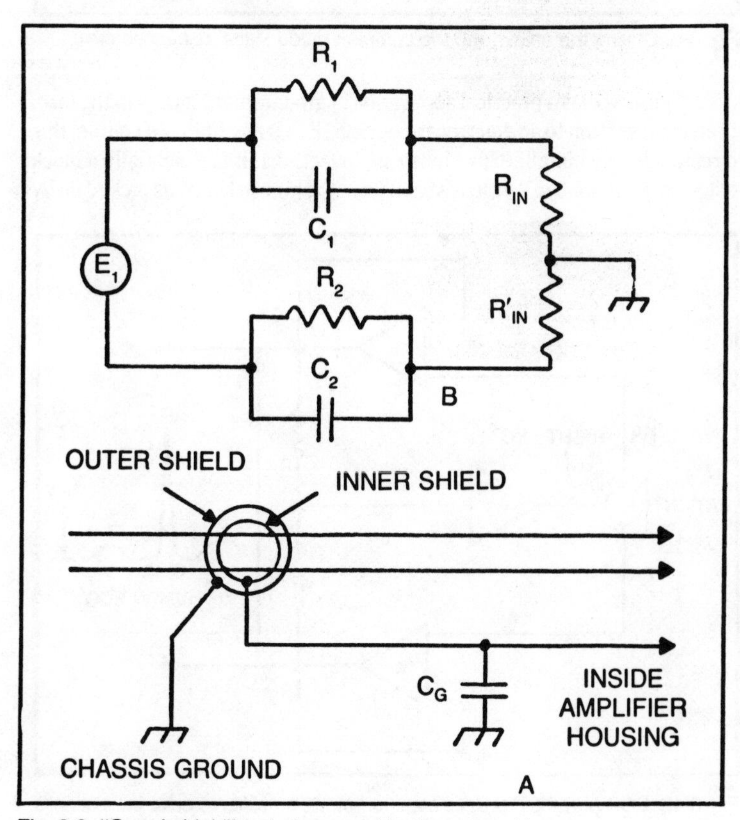

Fig. 3-8. "Guard shield" technique used in the input wiring.

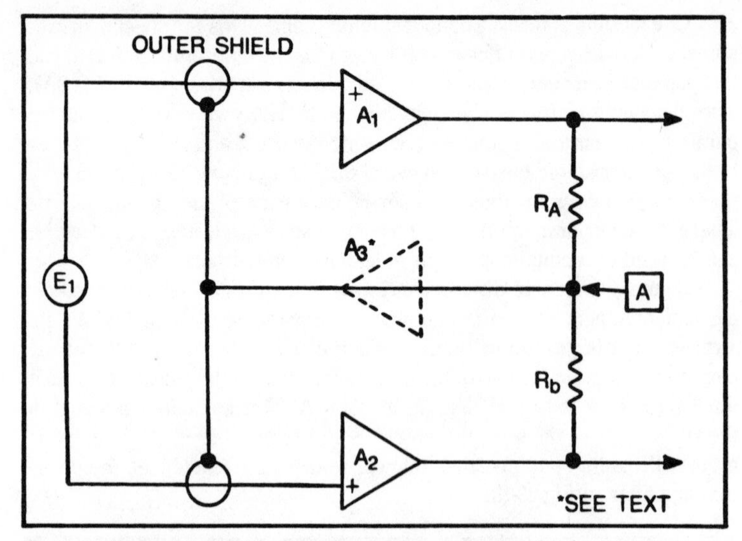

Fig. 3-9. Driving the shield with the common mode signal enhances CMR.

Figure 3-10 is a practical application of ground guard theory in the form of an input section to an electrocardiograph (ECG) amplifier. Of course, this circuit is highly simplified; so much so, in fact, that it is essentially a block diagram. E_1 is a 1.0 mV or less signal from the human heart, as picked up by

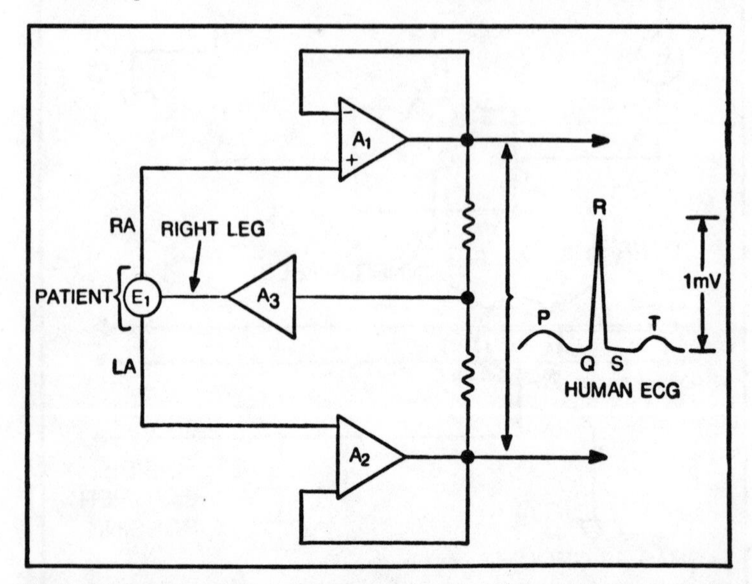

Fig. 3-10. ECG preamplifier uses common-mode amplifier to drive the patient's right leg both for patient safety and to enhance CMR.

surface electrodes, and is a differential voltage between left and right arms. In this case, right leg is ground.

A_3 is sometimes referred to as a guard amplifier, and in some cases as a common-mode amplifier, but medical electronic literature usually refers to it as a *right leg drive amplifier*.

Also used in medical amplifiers—more for safety rather than CMR—is the input preamplifier with floating power source. Although in medical equipment its main application is for safety to patients, the technique of using an isolation amplifier circuit also improves CMR. The floating power supply accounts for the enhancement. The common of the two supplies is connected not to ground but to the cable shields, and the output of the common-mode amplifier is used to drive the shields.

SINGLE OP AMP AS DIFFERENTIAL AMPLIFIER

Figure 3-11 shows one of the simplest types of differential amplifier using a single op amp. The differential gain of this circuit is given by:

$$A_V = R_2/R_1 = R_4/R_3 \qquad (3\text{-}7)$$

Where $R_2 = R_4$ and $R_1 = R_3$, this last requirement isn't strictly obligatory, but it is highly desirable. Only the *ratio* of Eq. 3-7 need be equal.

In order to maintain a high CMRR, it is necessary that resistors be matched as closely as possible. This is why it is best to use equal resistors. Actually, R_4 is often a 10-turn potentiometer, thus allowing a high degree of trimming. Adjustment is made by simultaneously connecting a signal to both inputs (Fig. 3-12) and then adjusting R_4 (R'_F) to provide minimum output.

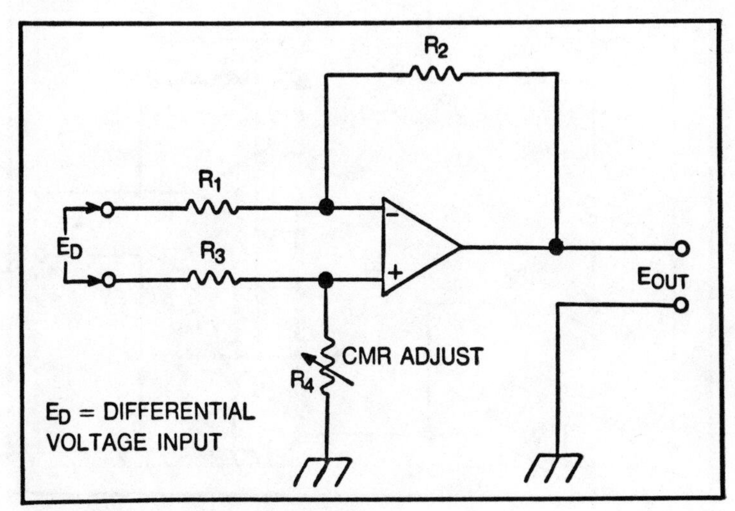

Fig. 3-11. Simplest differential amplifier.

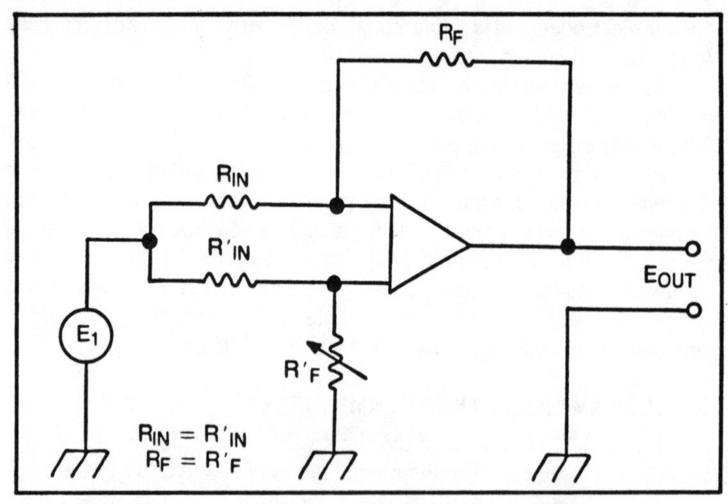

Fig. 3-12. Test circuit for balancing the amplifier for best CMRR.

INSTRUMENTATION AMPLIFIERS

A somewhat more involved differential amplifier is shown in Fig. 3-13. This is called the instrumentation amplifier (IA). It uses three operational amplifiers rather than the single op amp of the previous design. The

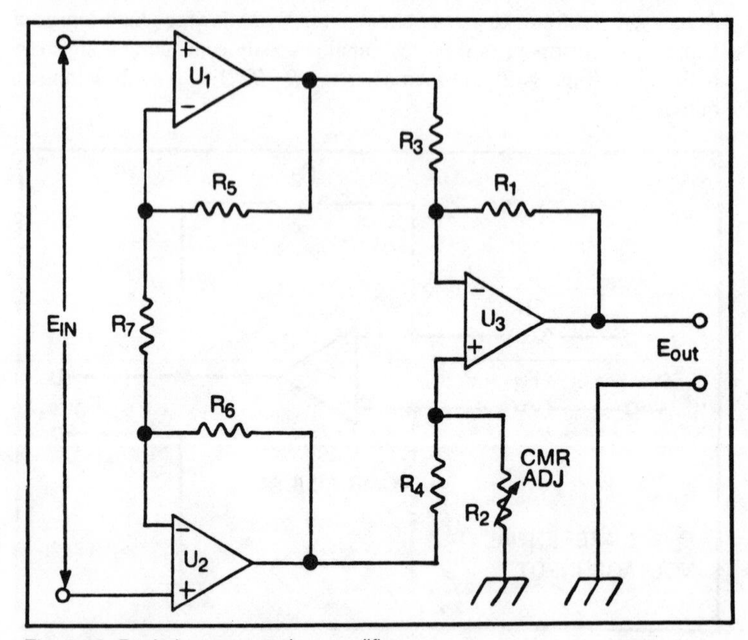

Fig. 3-13. Basic instrumentation amplifier.

noninverting amplifier input configuration results in a very high input impedance. The circuit is also capable of very high differential gain with both good stability and a high CMRR.

Principal applications for the IA include all uses where a superior-grade differential amplifier is indicated. They include amplification of Wheatstone bridge output voltages and the amplification of bioelectric potentials from living organisms. The gain for the IA is given by:

$$E_{OUT} = (E_1 - E_2)\,(1 + 2R_5/R_7)\,(R_1/R_3) \tag{3-8}$$

where $E_1 - E_2$ is the differential input signal and R_1/R_3 is the gain factor for the output stage.

IA ADJUSTMENTS

One interesting and almost unique characteristic of the IA is that common-mode rejection does not suffer excessively when resistors R_5 and R_6 are not perfectly matched. To be sure, a gain factor error will exist but it results in a minimal deterioration of CMRR. What does matter, however, is matching of R_1 and R_2, R_3 and R_4. For all but the most critical applications, use 1 percent tolerance resistors for R_3 and R_4. Use a 10-turn potentiometer at R_2 so that CMR can be optimized.

The use of a second potentiometer, this one at R_7, provides a handy means for adjusting gain. Typical values for R_7 range from 500 to 10,000Ω with 1000Ω being most popular.

ALTERNATE IA

Figure 3-14 shows a popular alternative instrumentation amplifier which has gained some favor because it allows the use of one less operational amplifier. In this circuit, provided that $R_2 = R_3$, we can approximate the gain, A_V, by:

$$A_V \cong 1 + \left[\frac{R_4\,(2R_3 + R_g)}{(R_3 R_G)}\right] \tag{3-9}$$

The classical IA of Fig. 3-13 is relatively easy to understand from a knowledge of both inverting followers and single op-amp differential amplifiers. However, this alternate IA (Fig. 3-14) may bear a brief explanation.

Let us consider the circuit by examining the smaller subparts. First, ignore gain control resistor R_G. Also, let us temporarily ground the + input. Under this set of conditions, amplifier A_1 is able to work as a simple noninverting follower with a gain greater than unity. In fact, the voltage at point A will be equal to:

$$E_A = E_{(-)}\,[1 + (R_3/R_4)] \tag{3-10}$$

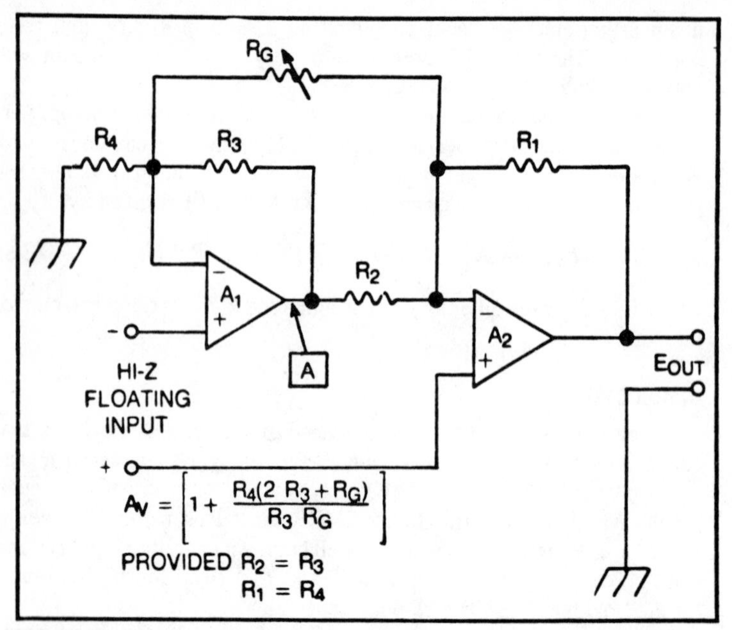

Fig. 3-14. Alternate instrumentation amplifier.

where $E_{(-)}$ is the voltage applied to the negative (–) input with respect to ground. This voltage is being applied to an inverting follower with a gain of $-R_1/R_2$, comprised of A_2 and the associated resistors. Since the overall gain of amplifiers in cascade is the product of the respective individual amplifier gains, we can state that:

$$A'_V = [A_{V(A1)}] \times [A_{V(A2)}] \tag{3-11}$$

$$= \left[1 + \frac{R3}{R_4}\right] \times \left[\frac{-R_1}{R_2}\right]$$

$$= \frac{-R_1}{R_2} + \frac{R_3 R_1}{R_4 R_2}$$

$$= \frac{-R_1 + R_3}{R_2} \quad \text{(Recall that } R_1 = R_4\text{)}$$

$$= \frac{-E_1 + R_3}{R_2}$$

But, since $R_2 = R_3$:

$$A'_V = \frac{-R_1}{R_2} + \frac{R_3}{R_2}$$

$$= (-R_1/R_2) + 1 \qquad \text{(Eq. 3-12)}$$

Now let's consider the case where the minus input is grounded. In that situation, amplifier A_1 makes no contribution to the output voltage, but point A is effectively at ground potential through the internal circuitry of A_1. In this case, amplifier A_2 can act as a noninverting follower with a gain of

$$A_{V(+)} = 1 + \frac{R_1}{R_2} \qquad \text{(3-13)}$$

Since we have a circuit whose minus input has a gain equation which is the negative of the gain equation for the + input (equal but opposite), we can say that a true differential amplifier exists.

The gain trimming resistor, R_G, has the ability to affect the voltage gain over a wide range. It can be either switch-selected or in the form of a potentiometer (if variable gain is needed). As with other similar designs, best results occur if A_V is greater than 10.

WHEATSTONE BRIDGE APPLICATIONS

One of the more common IA applications is the amplification of the output voltages from a Wheatstone bridge. Such circuits are used extensively in science, medicine, and engineering to measure unknown values of resistance, reactance, impedance, and physical parameters such as strain, pneumatic, and hydraulic pressures (including blood pressure), temperature, and displacement. These circuits are used to measure a host of other variables which can be converted by one means or another to a change in resistance, or either capacitive or inductive reactance. This is an area where many measurements can be made from a few basic, seemingly unrelated phenomena.

Figure 3-15 is one version of the classic Wheatstone circuit. Although not strictly obligatory in the overall scheme of things, let us simplify by assuming there is equality among the resistor arms. It will, however, become almost immediately apparent that the ratios, rather than the actual values, are most important.

Resistance h associated with resistor R_4 in Fig. 3-15 is a graphic device used to depict a small change in the value of R_4. Resistor R_4 will change by amount h whenever the bridge arm is changed by whatever parameter is being measured. Under *normal* or *at-rest* conditions, all of the resistors will have equal values. Also equal at this time will be voltages E_2 and E_3. The latter is given by:

$$E_3 = E_1/2$$

because

$$\frac{R_3}{R_1 + R_3} = ½$$

and

$$E_3 = E_1 \left[\frac{R_3}{R_1 + R_3} \right] = E_1(½) = E_1/2$$

Still assuming equilibrium where $R_1 = R2 = R_3 = R_4$,

$$E_3 = E_1 \left[\frac{R_4}{R_2 + R_4 + h} \right]$$

or, since all resistors are equal:

$$E_3 = E_1 \left[\frac{R}{2R + h} \right] \tag{3-14}$$

Output voltage E_0 is given by:

$$E_0 = E_3 - E_2 = \left[\frac{E_1 R}{2R + h} \right] - \left[\frac{E_1}{2} \right] \tag{3-15}$$

$$= - \frac{E_1 h}{4R + 2h} \tag{3-16}$$

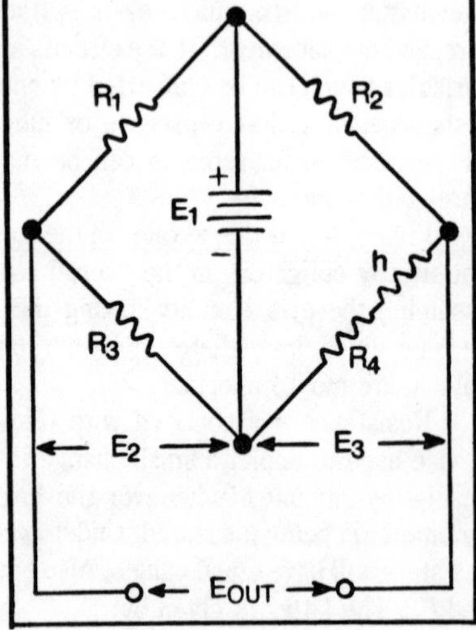

Fig. 3-15. Basic Wheatstone bridge.

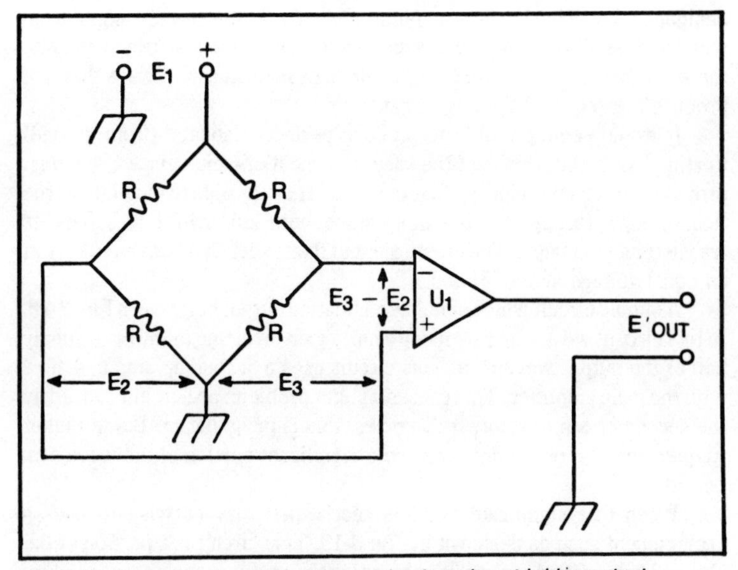

Fig. 3-16. Using the op-amp's differential gain to boost bridge output.

In many cases, the Wheatstone bridge cannot practically be made to produce enough voltage to directly drive a meter movement or any other significant load. The differential amplifier is seemingly just made for this application! An example is shown in Fig. 3-16. Sensitivity of this system is controlled by varying the gain of amplifier U_1.

It should be noted that regulation of bridge excitation voltage E_1 directly affects the value of E'_0. This can lead to serious problems if the value of data being extracted is proportional to E'_0 rather than the position of the potentiometer set to null. For this reason, good regulation of the excitation voltage is mandatory.

Figure 3-17 shows a practical instrumentation amplifier useful for a wide variety of applications. To prevent or minimize loading of the source, it would be wise to use a low-input-current op amp.

FLOATING OUTPUTS

So far, the differential and instrumentation amplifiers we have considered have been of the single-ended variety. In many cases, however, an instrument or circuit design may call for a differential output circuit. There are several ways in which this can be provided. The easiest is to simply buy an op amp designed with a differential output; there are several on the market. While the simplicity of this approach may be appealing, let us quickly point out the main drawback to that idea: money. While there are any number of good differential output op amps available, they share one almost universal property, and that is high cost. Many of the devices were designed for service in video amplifier chains or as the vertical amplifier in wideband oscilloscopes. To the user with more modest requirements, there are circuits which use low-cost devices in magnificent ways that will produce the required floating output.

It would seem possible to produce perfectly isolated (from ground) floating inputs, but this isn't the case. For most op-amp devices, we must provide a ground path for the bias currents. It is possible to simulate a true floating input through the use of op amps, with either FET or superbeta transistor input stages. The practical input floats such that both inputs are at an equal voltage above ground.

A simple circuit which simulates a floating output is shown in Fig. 3-18. In this circuit, we are merely using a unity gain inverting follower to supply half of the output waveform. This circuit uses a second op amp cascaded with the main amplifier. This causes a slight problem: phase shift caused by the second op amp. At low frequencies, this is insignificant. But at higher frequencies, the phase delay can be a significant portion of the waveform period.

When that significant point is reached, it may be wise to use an arrangement such as is shown in Fig. 3-19. This circuit is a portion of the classic IA described earlier. It overcomes the problem encountered in Fig. 3-18, yet still requires only a single pair of op amps. Since the input signal is

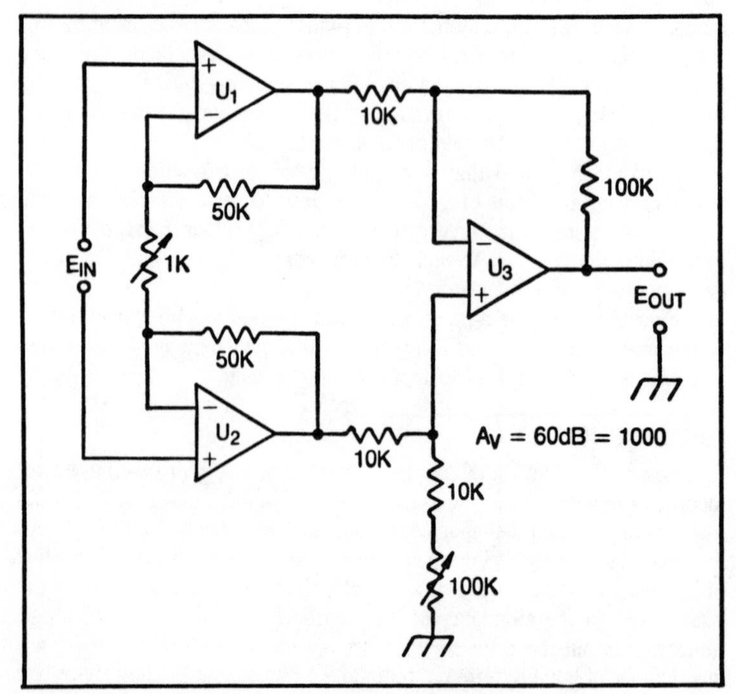

Fig. 3-17. Instrumentation amplifier with 60 dB gain.

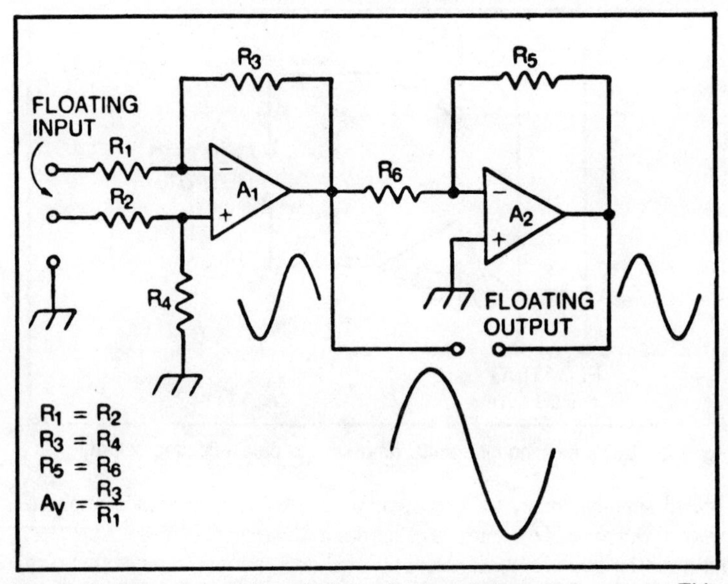

Fig. 3-18. Easy method for obtaining floating (differential) outputs. This technique can be used with either floating or single-ended input.

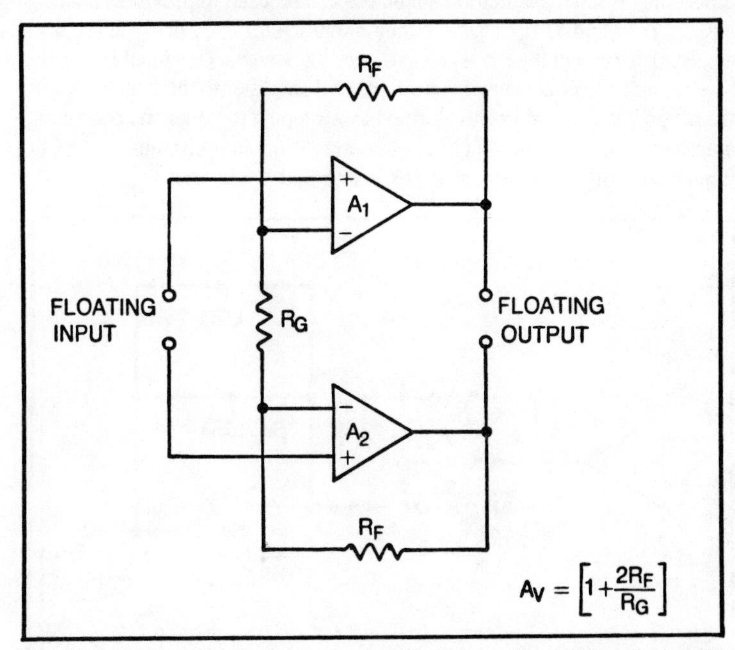

Fig. 3-19. "Half instrumentation amplifier" provides differential outputs with minimum phase delay.

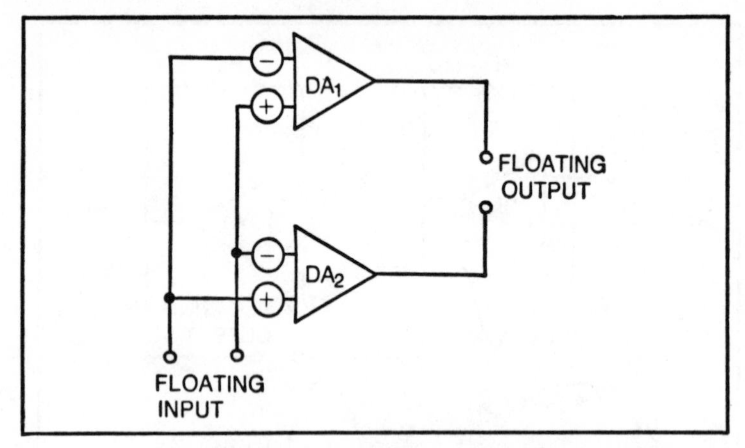

Fig. 3-20. Using existing differential amplifiers to obtain floating output.

applied simultaneously to both op amps, there is no difference in phase delay to worry us. To be sure, a phase delay always exists in any amplifier, but here the two are equal. Also, thermal drift, a topic to be explored in Chapter 4, is better controlled in this circuit.

Figure 3-20 is a block diagram to illustrate how a pair of existing differential or instrumentation amplifiers can be used to provide a floating output. DA_1 and DA_2 can be either simple (single device) differential amplifiers or one of the more sophisticated IA designs. One input is formed by strapping the plus input of one differential amplifier to the minus input of the other. The second input is formed by strapping together the remaining amplifier inputs. If the amplifiers are single op-amp circuits, the input impedance will be somewhat lower than might be desired.

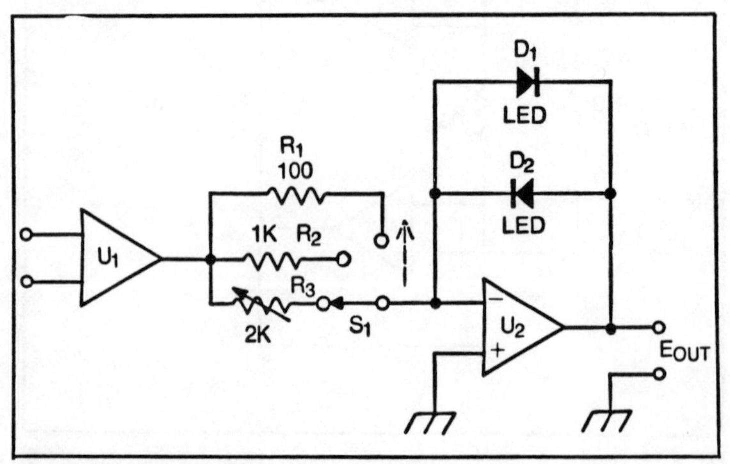

Fig. 3-21. LED null detector.

Figure 3-21 is a null indicator circuit. It can be used following a differential amplifier that is being driven by the output of a Wheatstone bridge or other null-seeking device. Diodes D_1 and D_2 are light-emitting diodes (LEDs). They will light up on alternate swings of the output voltage polarity. The null is located when they both extinguish or when they both glow dimly but equally. Resistors R_1, R_2, and R_3 are used to adjust the sensitivity of the null indicator. An output voltage, E_{OUT}, is provided as an option so the user can drive an analog or digital panel meter if desired.

TEST QUESTIONS

3.1 The ability of a differential amplifier to reject signals common to both inputs is called ________.

3.2 What is the gain of the circuit shown in Fig. T3-1?

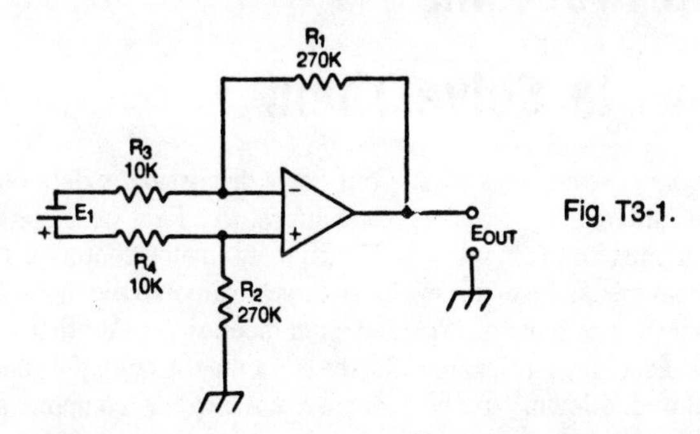

Fig. T3-1.

3.3 If E_1 = 50 mV (Fig. T3-1), what is the value of E_{OUT}?

3.4 List two important uses for the instrumentation amplifier.

3.5 What is the gain of the instrumentation amplifier circuit of Fig. T3-2?

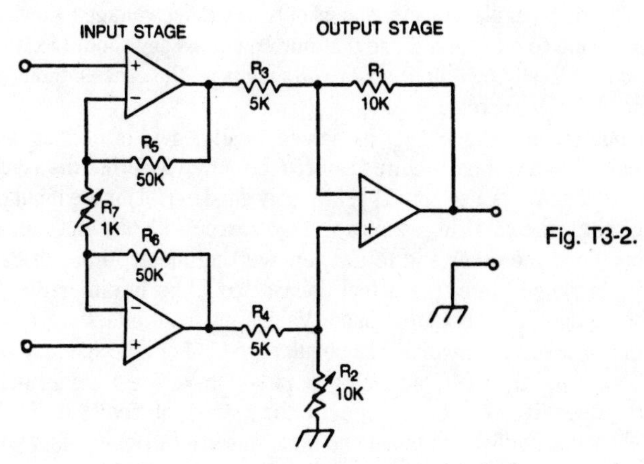

Fig. T3-2.

Answers to test questions are in the back of the book.

Chapter 4

Op-Amp Problems and How to Solve Them

The ideal op amp, which was part of our early discussion, exists only in flights of imagination and in advertising literature. Real op amps have defects which must be taken into consideration by anyone contemplating a design. In many cases, the error will be so large relative to the input signal level that some means must be provided for compensation. At other times, notably in stages with high signal levels, the error may be negligible and can be safely ignored, allowing us the economy of a few less components.

DC ERRORS

The dc error factors result in an output offset voltage E_{OO}, which exists between the output terminal and ground at a time when it should be zero. This helps explain discrepancies between those voltages which actually are found to exist and those that our equations say should exist. One method for classifying output offset voltages is by the causes: input offset voltage and bias current.

Input offset voltage E_{IO}, as shown in Fig. 4-1, is defined as the differential input voltage required to force the output to zero. This assumes, of course, that E_{IN} is also zero. A reasonably good model for the input offset voltage phenomenon (Fig. 4-2) is a voltage source with one end connected to ground and the other end to the noninverting input. Although battery polarity is shown here, the actual polarity could be in either direction, depending upon the op amp at hand. Values for input offset are typically from one to several millivolts. The popular type 741 op amp spec sheet lists the E_{IO} as typically 2 mV, but the range is 1—5 mV. The designer must be able to either live with or compensate for a range of from 1 to 5 mV.

The value of the output offset voltage caused by an input offset voltage is equal to:

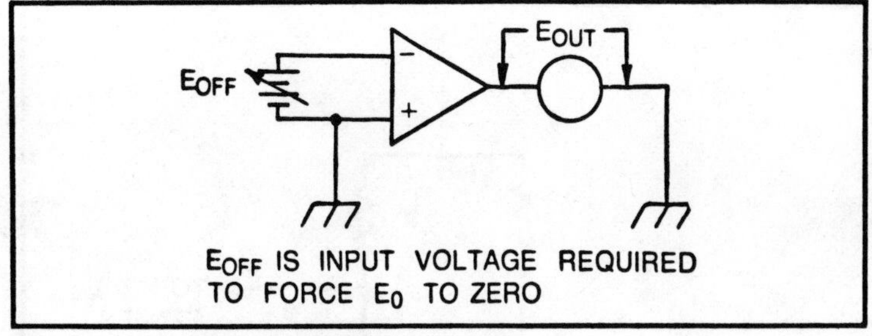

Fig. 4-1. Input offset voltage test configuration.

$$E_{OO} = \left[\frac{R_{IN} R_F}{R_{IN}} \right] E_{IO} \tag{4-1}$$

$$= R_F E_{IO}$$

If the circuit gain is low and E_{IN} remains within relatively high values, the input offset voltage may be of little consequence. It is primarily where either high values of A_V or low values of E_{IN} are encountered (and they are usually encountered in tandem) that the input offset becomes a problem.

The second major cause of output offset voltage is spurious input current. This can be further subdivided into two more classes: normal input bias current and input offset current.

Figure 4-3 shows a typical op-amp input stage. Whenever bipolar transistors are used in this stage, some small base bias current will be required for normal operation. This is one of those unavoidable conditions inherent in the nature of the transistor rather than any deficiency in the internal op-amp circuitry. The value of the bias current of interest to us is the average of the current in each transistor:

$$I_{BT} = \frac{I_{B1} + I_{B2}}{2} \tag{4-2}$$

No really stupendous problems occur in this circuit until you actually try and use the op amp. What fouls things up is connecting the input and

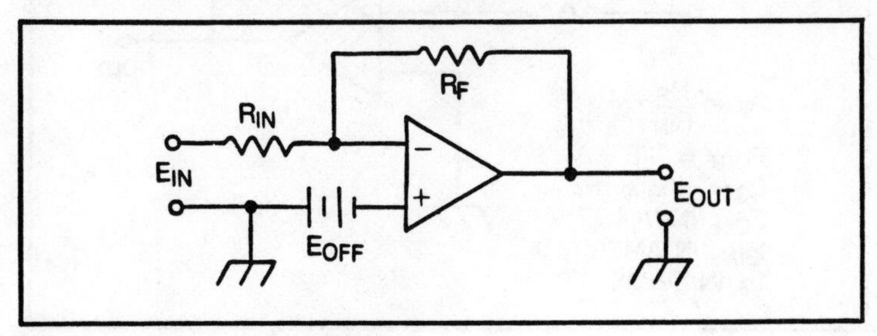

Fig. 4-2. Input offset voltage model.

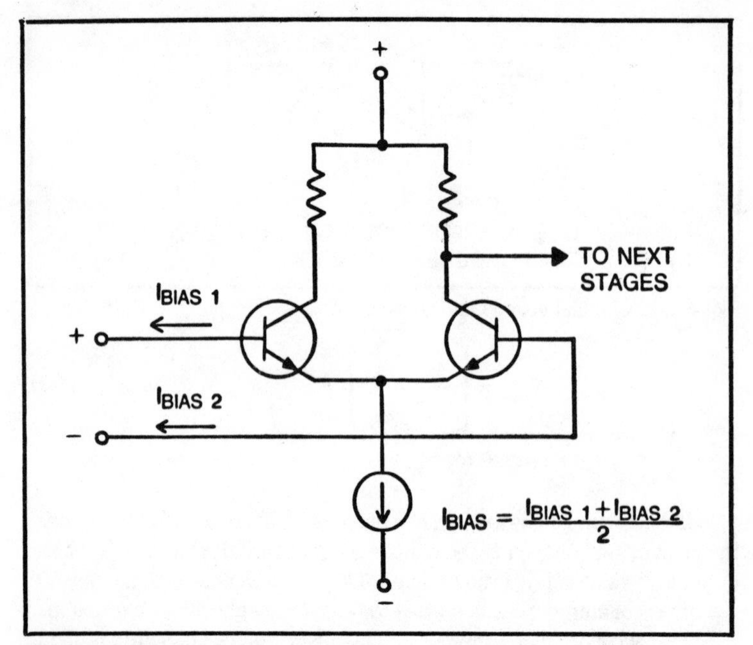

Fig. 4-3. Simplified version of typical op-amp input stage.

feedback resistors (Fig. 4-4). When these are in the circuit, the bias current causes a voltage drop across R_F and R_{IN} with no corresponding voltage applied to the alternate input. The value of the output offset voltage created by this is:

$$E_{OO} = I_{BIAS} R_F \tag{4-3}$$

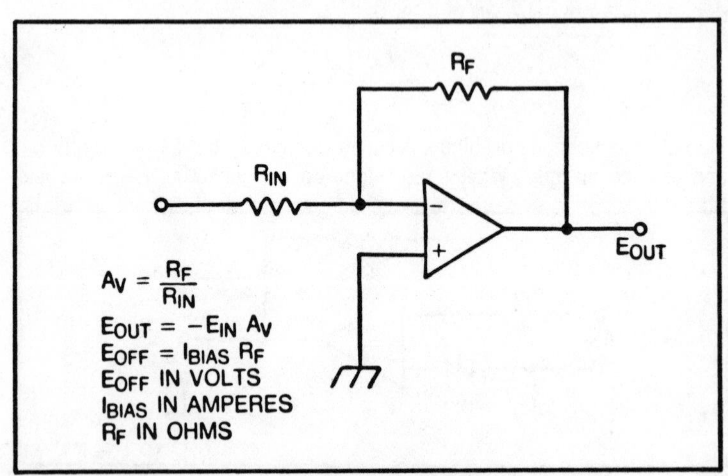

Fig. 4-4. Computation of output offset due to input bias currents.

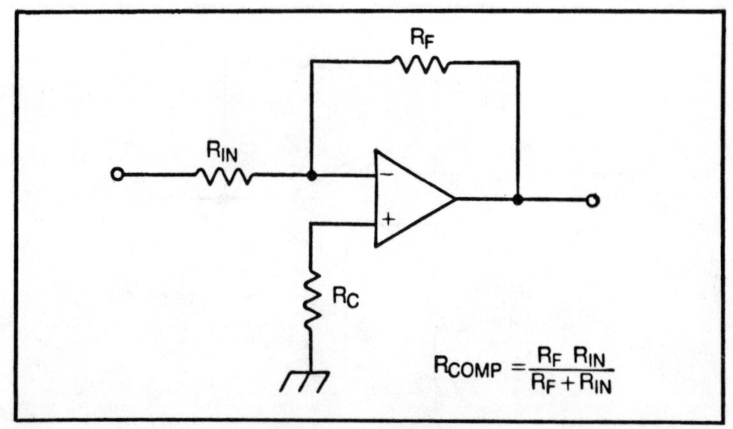

Fig. 4-5. Compensation resistor in noninverting input circuit reduces offset due to bias currents.

The most immediately obvious solution for this is to place an equal voltage in the noninverting input circuit. One quick means for implementing this is to add a resistor as shown in Fig. 4-5. The value for this compensation resistor is:

$$R_C = \frac{R_F R_{IN}}{R_F + R_{IN}} \tag{4-4}$$

In other words, the compensating resistor is equal to the value of the parallel combination of the feedback and input resistors.

Should the use of the resistor still fail to reduce the offset to zero, try using either of the circuits in Figs. 4-6 and 4-7. These techniques afford

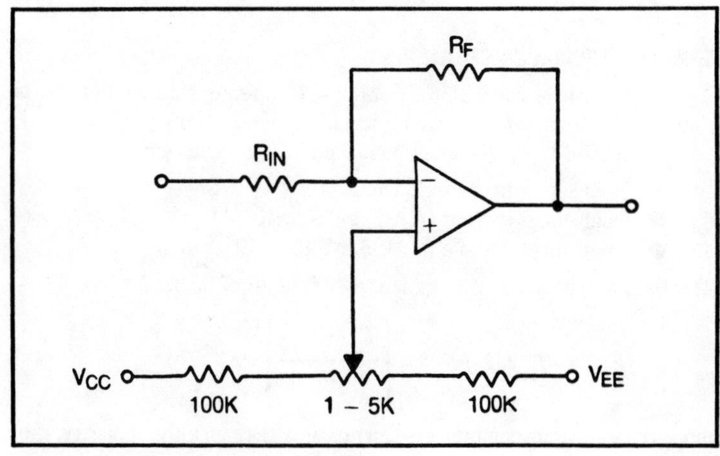

Fig. 4-6. External suppression of offsets.

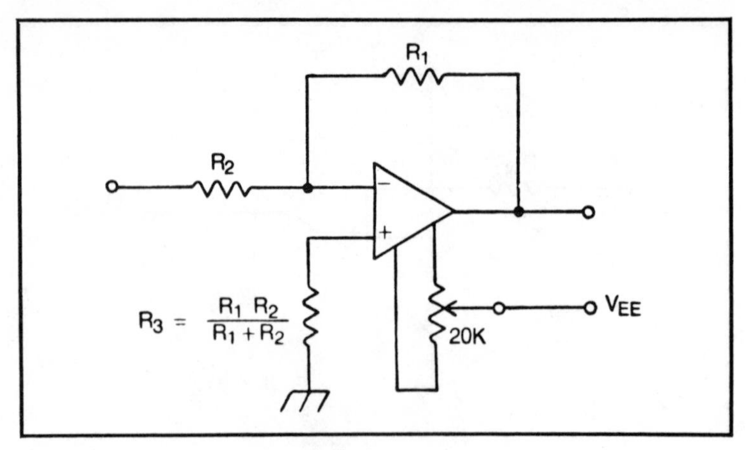

Fig. 4-7. Internal suppression of offsets.

methods by which the offset can be dropped to zero. The circuit in Fig. 4-7 is only applicable on those op amps which provide special offset null terminals. An example is the 741.

The last type of input current error we will consider is the input offset current. This current is the difference between the two bias currents. Ideally, the two bias currents will be exactly equal, making their difference zero. But the ideal is a rarely reached goal.

In modern op amps, the inherent close match between the transistors that are formed on the same chip reduces the severity, but does not completely eliminate the defect. Values for the input offset will be either:

$$I_{IO} = I_1 - I_2 \qquad (4\text{-}5)$$

or

$$I_{IO} = I_2 - I_1 \qquad (4\text{-}6)$$

SAMPLE DC ERROR CALCULATIONS

Let us assume that a Motorola MC1437G operational amplifier is to be used in an inverting follower circuit with a gain of 100.

From the MC1437G sheet published by the manufacturer:

- Input bias current (I_B): 15 nA (15×10^{-9}A)
- Input offset current (I_O): 5 nA (5×10^{-9}A)
- Input offset voltage (E_{IO}): 5 mV (5×10^{-3}V)

The total output offset voltage is the sum of all of these, or:

$$E_{OO} = (I_B \pm I_O)\, R_F \pm \left[\frac{R_F + R_{IN}}{R_{IN}}\right] E_O \qquad (4\text{-}5)$$

Since these various components can possibly take on either polarity, they may add or subtract. Since we must be cognizant of the worst possible case under which the device must still function, we must assume that they will add.

Since A_V has been stated to be 100, we can assume that $R_F = 100\ R_{IN}$. We will arbitrarily (for ease of calculation) assign values of $1000\Omega (10^3)$ to R_{IN} and $100{,}000\Omega\ (10^5)$ to R_F:

Output offset voltage due to average I_B:

$$\begin{aligned} E_O &= R_F I_B \\ &= (10^5)(1.5 \times 10^{-8}) \\ &= 1.5 \times 10^{-3} \\ &= 1.5\ \text{mV} \end{aligned}$$

Output offset voltage due to I_O:

$$\begin{aligned} E_O &= R_F I_O \\ &= (10^5)(.5 \times 10^{-8}) \\ &= 0.5 \times 10^{-3} \\ &= 0.5\ \text{mV} \end{aligned}$$

Output offset voltage due to E_{IO}:

$$\begin{aligned} E_{OFF} &= \left[\frac{10^5 + 10^3}{10^3}\right] (5 \times 10^{-3}) \\ &= (1.01 \times 10^2)(5 \times 10^{-3}) \\ &= 5.05 \times 10^{-1} \\ &= 0.505\text{V} \\ &= 505\ \text{mV} \end{aligned}$$

Adding these together:

$$E_{OO} = 1.5\ \text{mV} + 0.5\ \text{mV} + 505\ \text{mV} = 507\ \text{mV}$$

Clearly, the offset in the output level due to input offset voltage, E_{IO}, is predominant. The effects of the other two sources of output offset will increase as values of R_F and R_{IN} are increased. This is because the output offset results from the action of the voltage drop across these two resistors created by the offending currents. The input offset voltage will worsen the condition at the output if the ratio R_F/R_{IN} is increased. In this case, a compensating resistor would probably be insignificant since it would alleviate only 2.0 mV out of a total 507 mV defect!

THERMAL DRIFT

Our less than perfect operational amplifier suffers from yet another dc defect: thermal drift. This parameter is usually given in the data sheets relative to the input conditions. The specification is usually related to the change of input offset voltage per degree Celsius. Typical figures for popular operational amplifier types range in the 1—5 μV/C° region (typically 3μV/C°). Keep in mind, however, that this is usually an expression of the drift in steady-state circuits and may not accurately represent drift under dynamic conditions. These may well be a lot higher than the drift given in the spec sheet. There are actually two sources of drift in the input circuit; both the current and the voltage are at fault.

When signal levels are high, we can ignore small changes due to drift. At lower levels, however, drift can easily become highly significant. Added to this we have a magnification of drift (for inverting circuits) due to attenuation of the signal. Inverting amplifier circuits do not apply the signal direct to the inverting input of the amplifier, but instead only a fraction of the signal equal to $R_F/(R_F + R_{IN})$ is actually applied to the amplifier. If the gain is 10, for example, then the drift figure is increased by a factor of 10 percent. The situation is even worse for unity-gain inverting amplifiers where the drift factor is effectively doubled. In that case a 5 μV/C^0 drift would actually become 10 μV/C^0. In such cases we may easily find it preferable to use a higher grade operational amplifier device.

Another source of increased drift figure is in the use of resistor networks to null offset voltages. The current passing through the null network adds to the drift, deteriorating the overall drift performance.

Although drift may not be too important in some circuits, it can become critical where low-level signals are being processed. If an amplifier has a drift of 10 μV/C^0 and the circuit is expected to maintain its performance over a large temperature range, we may easily have a significant drift component. For example, a temperature change of 20°C will result in a 200 μV error, or 20 percent of a 1 mV input. Generally, noninverting amplifiers do not have as high a drift factor because the input signal is applied directly to an amplifier input without undergoing any attenuation. Use of the noninverting input, where possible, and a transistor base-emitter junction in the dc compensation network (because of its temperature coefficient) will aid significantly in control of thermal drift problems. For those cases where the inverting input is required, try the use of a compensation resistor to ground in the plus input lead. As in the cases previously mentioned, it should have a value equal to

$$R_C = \frac{R_F R_{IN}}{R_F + R_{IN}} \tag{4-7}$$

Although this may introduce some common-mode problems, it should help the drift situation.

OSCILLATION AND INSTABILITY

There are several factors that conspire toward allowing an operational amplifier to oscillate at times when this is highly undesirable. Quite often these oscillations occur at frequencies far in excess of the passband of the associated circuit. Two of these factors, both of which can be overcome, are positive feedback via the dc power supply, and spurious internal phase shift.

If the power supply presents a high impedance at any frequency where the overall circuit gain exceeds unity, positive feedback sufficient to cause oscillation may exist. The obvious answer to this problem is to make the impedance of the power supply somewhat lower. The quickest and least expensive, yet very effective, method for accomplishing this is to bypass the supplies with capacitors as is shown in Fig. 4-8. Separate bypassing for each supply is used. The only real rule of thumb to follow is to use a sufficiently high value of capacitor that is placed as close as possible to the power supply terminals of the IC package. This especially holds true when using op-amp devices capable of operating at frequencies well into the upper HF and medium VHF ranges.

Thus far our op-amp discussions have dealt mostly with circuits assumed to be purely resistive as would befit a well behaved ideal device provided with no external reactances. In actuality, there will be some unwanted capacitance involved in our circuits. One source is the junction capacitance of the transistors in the input amplifier, and another is the capacitance between the actual chip and ground. Regardless of the source, the result is the same: unwanted RC phase shift. In an ideal inverting amplifier, the output is precisely 180° out of phase with the input; a really nice situation since we are looking for negative or *degenerative* feedback. Those internal phase shifts, however, cause the actual output signal to be something other than 180° relative to the input. At some frequency, the extra phase shift will be exactly 180° (see Fig. 4-9). When added to the 180° caused by the op amp's normal inversion process, we have a 360° phase shift. This situation, with feedback, is the phase criterion required for oscillation (provided, of course, that greater than unity gain is available). If

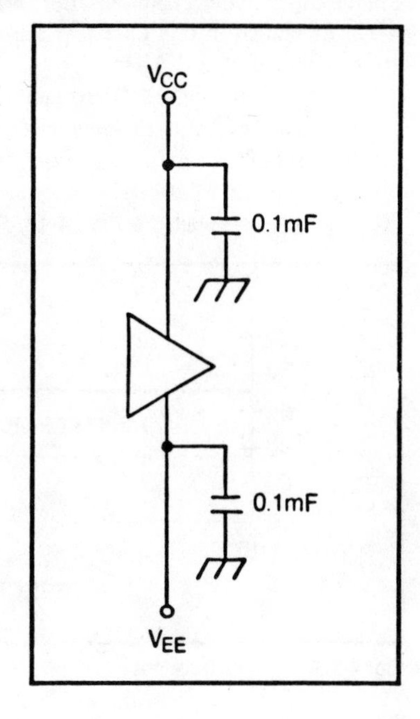

Fig. 4-8. Bypass power supply leads with capacitors located as close to the op-amp case as possible.

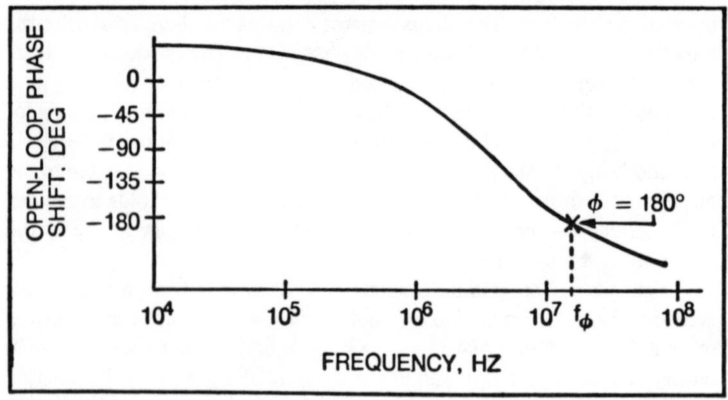

Fig. 4-9A. Phase shift vs frequency.

the frequency at which the internal phase shift is 180° is below the frequency where the natural gain of the op amp drops to unity, then oscillation may occur. Frequency compensation is the technique of identifying the frequency at which oscillation can occur and then reducing the gain at that point to some figure less than unity.

The *lag* technique of frequency compensation (see Fig. 4-10) involves using a fairly large value capacitor to shunt to ground some of the signal amplitude fed to the output amplifier stage. This point is usually available as a special terminal marked *lag* (Fig. 4-11) on the base diagram. Effect of simple capacitive lag compensation on frequency response is shown in Fig. 4-12. As shown in this example, the circuit gain drops to unity at some frequency less than 1 MHz.

Although it might not be readily apparent, an amplifying device requires capability to much higher frequencies, even when the overall required passband is relatively modest, because of the high levels of feedback supplied. These wider bandwidths can be effectively obtained by using an RC lag network such as Fig. 4-13. The graph in Fig. 4-14 shows the

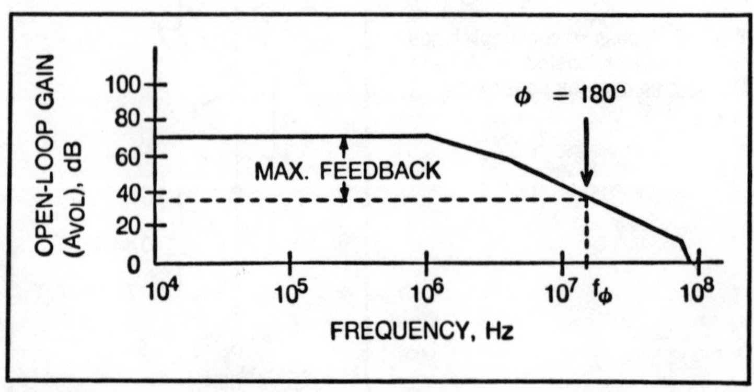

Fig. 4-9B. A_{VOL} vs frequency.

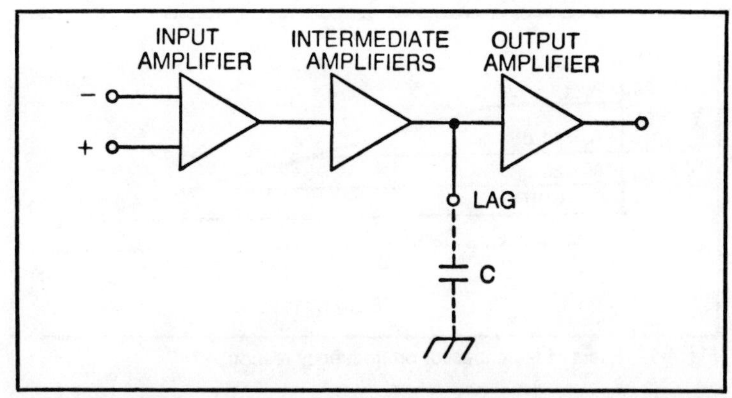

Fig. 4-10. Location of the lag bypass capacitor in op-amp's internal stage chain.

approximate gain vs bandwidth characteristics of a type 702 op amp using several different values of R and C. Note that the circuit bandwidths are considerably wider in these cases.

In some circuits, especially but not exclusively those using a differential input, it is sometimes preferred to place the lag network such that it shunts the two input terminals (see Fig. 4-15). This technique can also be used where compensated op amps, which do not usually possess a lag terminal, need an assist.

Lead (as opposed to *lag*) compensation (Fig. 4-16) involves using a small value capacitor to move the point at which the internal phase shifts reach 180° to some higher frequency. This allows us to take advantage of the amplifier's normal frequency rolloff to supply some of the compensation. Typical values for this capacitor are in the 50—100 pF range in most applications, but values to 0.05 μF have been used.

Figure 4-17 shows a fully compensated operational amplifier device capable of a voltage gain of 10 (20 dB) out to frequencies in excess of 10 MHz. This extremely wide bandwidth makes the stage useful for application as a video amplifier, or to process waveforms with either high harmonic content or fast repetition rate. The active device is the 702 op amp. Voltage gain is set by the ratio R_1/R_2 = 100K/10K = 10. Two forms of frequency compensation are employed: capacitor C_1 offers lead compensation, while

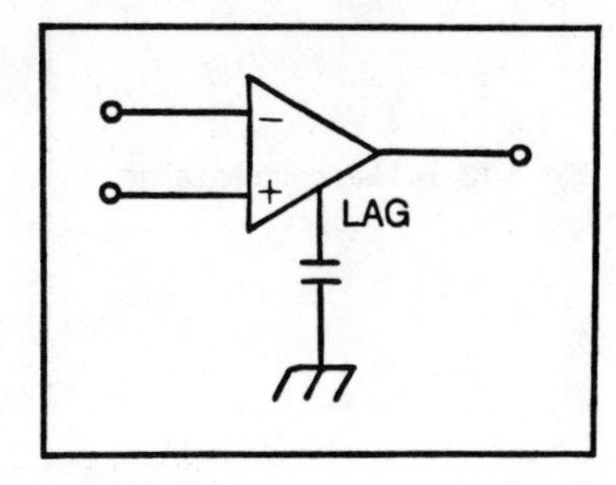

Fig. 4-11. Lag capacitor in schematic.

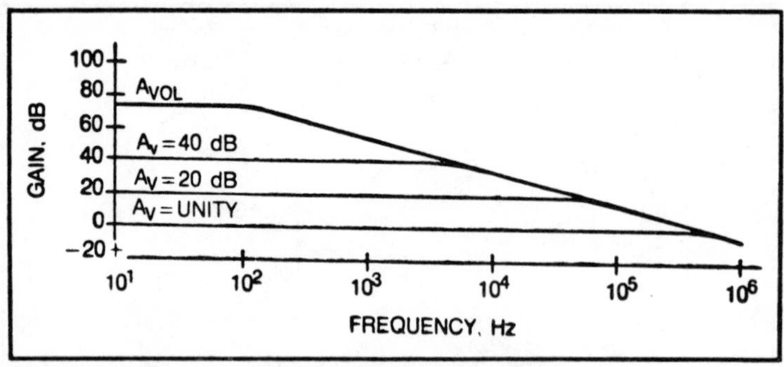

Fig. 4-12. Effect of lag capacitor on frequency response.

the series network of R_4 and C_2 forms a lag network shunting the inputs. The dc offset is, for the most part, canceled by the use of resistor R_3 in the noninverting input circuit. Positive feedback through the power supply is eliminated by capacitors C_3 and C_4. These components must be better grade types offering low lead inductance, and should be physically located as close as possible to the 702 case. In most instances, Mylar, polyfilm, or ceramic capacitors will do nicely. To the inexperienced constructor, the low overall gain (20 dB) may be a temptation to accept sloppy construction techniques. Keep in mind, however, that positive feedback great enough to cause oscillation can occur whenever frequencies exceed low audio and gains exceed unity.

LAYOUT PRACTICE

All electronic circuits can suffer somewhat from inappropriate layout and construction techniques. In operational amplifier circuitry, this wisdom can doubly apply because of the extreme gains and bandwidths often encountered. Generally, the only advice usually given in this matter is to follow something called "good layout practice," although most advisors seem to forget to let the reader know exactly what constitutes such

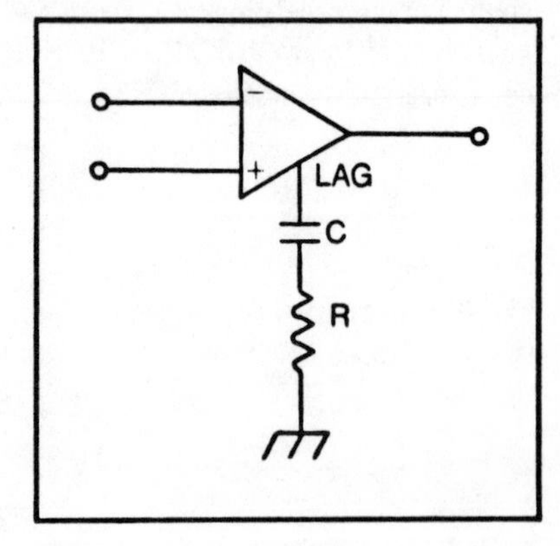

Fig. 4-13. RC lag compensation.

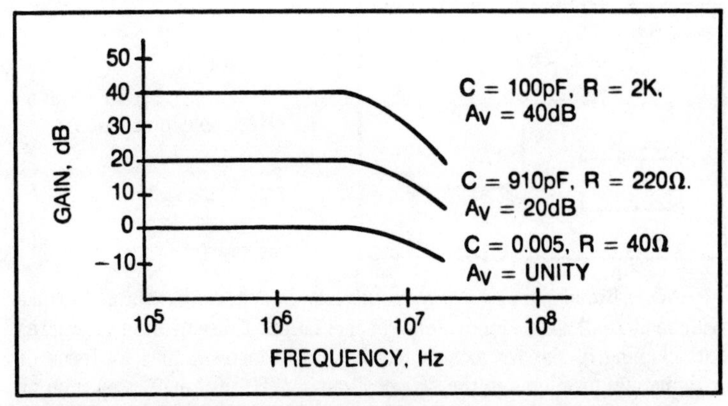

Fig. 4-14. Effects of different RC combinations on gain and frequency.

practice. Perhaps this is to be excused since this concept will take on different meanings (situations alter cases) from one situation to another. This is little solace, though, to the guy at a workbench trying to layout a breadboard or build a project. In general, the only really helpful advice is to avoid layout tactics which allow stray capacitive coupling between input and output. This is a real problem in op-amp circuits because the device is so small relative to the overall circuit. It is all too tempting to make the physical layout of a circuit as tight as possible. In many circuits, though, we'll do better if we don't worry too much about component density, unless that is an overwhelming consideration.

Repeated emphasis on bypass capacitor placement may seem a little redundant, but it is important enough to bear frequent reiteration. Those capacitors must be as close as possible to the op amp in order to eliminate the possibility of oscillation.

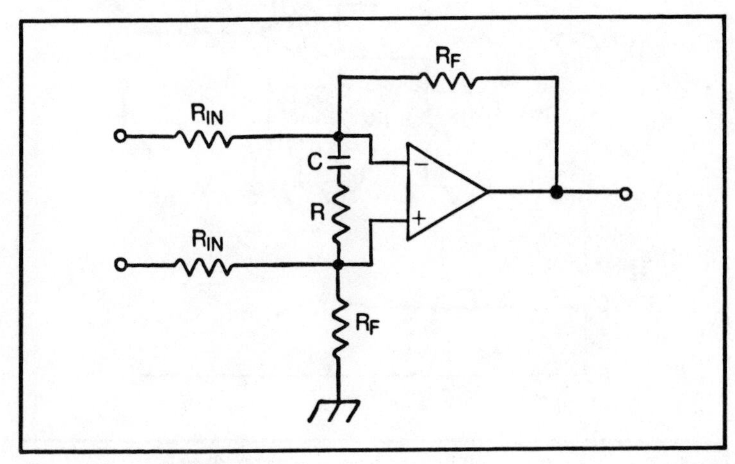

Fig. 4-15. Input RC compensation.

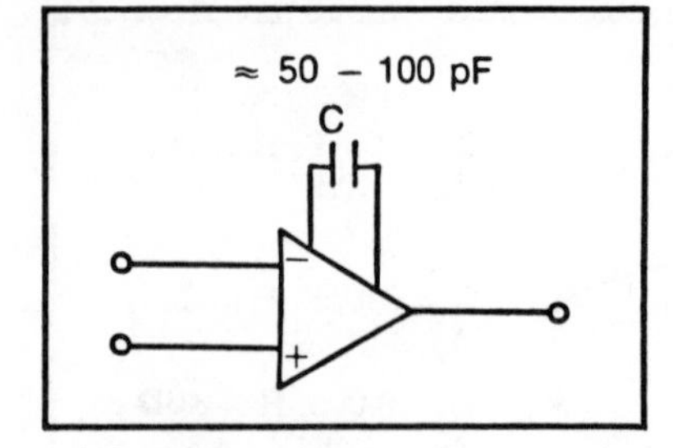

Fig. 4-16. Lead compensation.

When breadboarding a new circuit, examine the output waveform on a wideband oscilloscope for evidence of oscillation. This will often show up as a thickening of the trace, and may easily be taken as lack of focus or astigmatism problems in the scope. Examine the thickened region on an expanded time base. If it is an oscillation, the individual cycles will show up. A burst of oscillations can occur anyplace on the trace, but appear most frequently at or immediately after regions where the derivative (rate of change) of the signal is highest. This takes the form of ringing in square waves and distortion near the peaks of sine waves.

Breadboarding is an art which, alas, cannot be learned from a book, at least not very easily. There are some points, though, which are reasonably

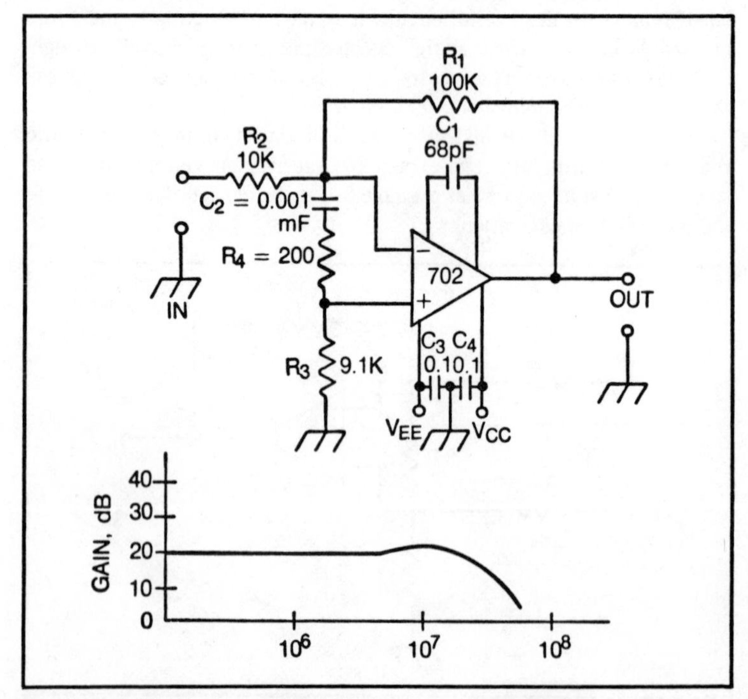

Fig. 4-17. Fully compensated op-amp inverter with 20 dB gain.

universal. One is to keep leads short and your work neat (those "good" layout practices). Other points include use of single point grounds, a ***ground plane*** design for the printed circuit board, and (if applicable) use of ferrite beads in the supply leads. This latter technique is used mostly in video amplifiers and other circuits operating well into the HF region of the spectrum. If any given op amp has closed-loop gain capability to 4 or 5 MHz, as required of a video amplifier, you can bet that its open-loop characteristics extend to the low VHF region! Be forewarned, though, that an op-amp circuit forced to stability by the use of ferrite beads in the supply leads may have a fundamental defect in either the layout or the design of the compensation networks.

One last point, before we move on to some other topics, is that of lab practice. The op amp can make the chores of the designer a lot easier if he exploits its capability to the fullest. Even a relatively unsophisticated designer (and who will admit that?) finds his overall circuit design acumen enhanced when he uses operational amplifier techniques.

Now, some bench experiments are usually in order—especially if a departure from standard methods is planned. In this respect, it is important that all work be documented. First, a drawing is made of the circuit as originally designed. As new things are tried, component values are changed, as appropriate, from the working diagram for optimum operation. If a change was counterproductive ("...it didn't work") the diagram is changed back to its original state. The problem is that when the circuit is in its final state, it may be several generations removed from the original diagram. The next step, if duplication or eventual repair efforts are to be successful, is that the circuit board is carefully gone over and a final drawing prepared. Waiting days or even weeks after a change was made may result in fuzzy memory and fuzzy drawings! Record-keeping may be a pain, but it is far easier than hand-making a final drawing—especially if more than a few components are used in the design.

SLEW RATE

Slew rate is a measure of the capability of an operational amplifier to rapidly switch from one output extreme to the opposite extreme while delivering full output load current. This parameter is usually expressed as so many volts per units of time (i.e., $30/\mu s$).

A saturating square-wave input is used to measure slew rate. The square wave must have a rise time that exceeds the slew-rate capability of the op amp. The value is actually found by examining the output slope (with a large value square wave applied to the input) on an oscilloscope. A determination is made of the time required for the output to switch from the 10 percent to the 90 percent points on the waveform. It must be noted that slew rate can be affected by gain. Therefore, the same value at unity gain that was obtained under open-loop conditions cannot be expected. Once the switching time is known, the slew rate (S_R) is approximated by:

$$S_R = \frac{V_{CC} + |V_{EE}|}{t_S} \quad (4\text{-}8)$$

where t_S is the switching time. Since most manufacturers specify slew rate (open-loop) in op-amp data sheets, we can use this relationship to find approximate switching times of certain op-amp digital circuits.

It is possible to improve the closed-loop slew rate at any given gain figure through the use of appropriate lag compensation techniques. We generally do not get much advantage out of using lag terminals but should, rather, use input lag techniques (Fig. 4-15). Keep the values of R_F and R_{IN} low when trying to improve slew rates; values under 10K will be best. The compensation capacitor will have a value of:

$$C = \frac{R_F + R_{IN}}{4\pi R_F R_{IN} \left[\frac{f_{01}}{10^m}\right]} \quad (4\text{-}9)$$

where f_{01} is the half-power point—the frequency at which the uncompensated or natural gain drops 3 dB and

$$m = [A_{VOL(dB)} - A_{V(dB)}]/20$$

The resistor value is found by the usual $R = 1/(2\pi f_{01}C)$.

OP AMP SELECTION

Every text on operational amplifiers seems to render advice on which amplifier is best suited for many different purposes. In keeping with this tradition, we will now examine selection criteria with respect to applications problems.

There seems to be at least two schools of thought about what sort of op-amp device constitutes the all-purpose selection. This, unfortunately, reflects a somewhat optimistic approach. On the one hand, we will occasionally be advised to keep on hand large stocks of the very least expensive types, since these are to be universally applied to every conceivable project. To those who give us this advice, the venerable type 741 is the be-all and end-all! On the other hand, we have the op-amp purist who insists that only the types which closely approximate the ideal op amp are suitable for any purpose. The first philosophy is viable only in those cases where the general circuit requirements will tolerate the moderate specs of the typical 741 (see Table 4-1). If this is the case, then the 741 and related types (such as the dual 741 devices marketed as the 747 or 5558) are a good selection. Where higher performance is needed, due to circuit requirements, then it is wise to forego the cost attractiveness of the 741 family and look to certain higher performance types.

Higher grade devices are needed when input impedances are critical.

Table 4-1. 741 Specifications

Maximum supply voltages:	±18V
Power Dissipation:	500 mW
Maximum differential input voltage:	±30V
Maximum single-ended input voltage:	±15V*
Output short circuit time:	Indefinite
Input offset voltage:	2 mV
Input offset current:	20–200 nA
Input bias current:	80 nA
CMRR:	90 dB (min)
Output short circuit current:	25 ma
Slew rate:	0.5 V/μs

*or supply voltage if supply voltage is less than ±15Vdc

This can be the case in certain types of instrumentation applications where the source impedance of the external circuit may be very high. Of course, to optimize input impedance means to use the noninverting follower configuration. Even here, though, we can realize an improvement over similar circuits using 741-class devices. Most bipolar input op amps cannot offer terrifically high input impedances. Of course, types such as the 5556/1456 sometimes exceed the performance of the 741, but we do not have maximum impedance until we go to Darlington (a special bipolar type) or FET input devices. Certain FET types, such as the 536, have become very popular in recent years, but a manufacturer's data book and price guide should be consulted to ascertain which current types offer the best performance/cost tradeoff; such changes occur monthly in this fast moving market.

In some cases, an amplifier might be required which will be able to offer unconditionally stable operation from dc to ultrasonic with a minimum of external parts and design hassle. In those instances, one should consider a fully frequency compensated type. These devices, however, suffer from a lack of gain at even moderately high frequencies not too far into the ultrasonic range. Where it is necessary to process either high frequency analog signals or pulses with fast rise times and rapid repetition rates, it is best to use a device capable of operating at high frequencies. Some op amps can operate into the high frequency or low VHF region. Wideband capability is not without cost in that we generally pay more for the IC and have to be careful of proper layout and compensation technique.

Amplification of microvolt or low-millivolt level signals brings to the fore problems associated with thermal drift. This almost universally means the use of both low drift rate devices and certain preferred circuit configurations. The circuit requires the use of the low drift noninverting follower and, possibly, either chopper- or varactor-stabilized input configurations (Chapter 9). The chopper circuit is generally conceded to be superior where the worst effects are from voltage drift. The varactor input type is preferred where current drift must be eliminated even at the expense of a worsened voltage drift.

Applications can place further constraints upon the designer in his selection of the operational amplifier. Take, for example, the matter of noisy environments. Typical industrial and scientific measurements, which usually require some sort of transducer, suffer from the twin defects of noise pickup from a hostile environment and low signal levels.

In the measurement of pressure, for example, a typical resistive or inductive Wheatstone bridge transducer may offer output levels in the neighborhood of a few millivolts per torr (millimeter of mercury) per volt of excitation (mV/T/V). Since no one has successfully repealed Murphy's law (*if anything can go wrong, it will!*), there is a reasonably good chance that this low-output transducer will be physically located at least 10 feet from the amplifier in the noisiest environment possible. Both 60 Hz and impulse signals from motors and other sources will tend to interfere with the transducer signal. Added to the noise picked up by radiation is 60 Hz interference generated by differences in ground potentials.

Fortunately, all of these signals will appear to the amplifier as common-mode voltages. The transducer can be (and usually is) built so that the desired signal is differential mode. Use of an amplifier which features good low-signal-level performance (low drift, high Z_{IN}) and very high common-mode rejection ratio will all but eliminate such problems. Of course, it will be necessary to use one of the differential amplifier configurations.

Automotive electronics—along with other applications where the designer is constrained by low-voltage, single-polarity power supplies—presents another set of design headaches. This situation lowers the output voltage swing. This is not the only problem. Another is the fact that many op amps require certain minimum levels of voltage for V_{CC} and V_{EE}. The actual minimum values for any op amp are related to the number of base-emitter and base-collector junctions used in the internal circuitry. Typically, minimum values are in the dc range of 3—6V. If a 12—14V automotive supply is used, the op amp may well starve for voltage under low battery conditions. This will become especially apparent in those applications where a pair of resistor/zener voltage dividers are used to simulate a dual-polarity supply against a floating ground. To overcome these problems, we might find it useful to select either a device designed to be used in single-polarity supply circuits (a few types do exist) or one of the dual-polarity micropower numbers which seem perfectly content with ±1.5V.

Certain medical electronic applications require a very special kind of operational amplifier—the *isolation* amplifier. When a patient in a hospital has an in-dwelling catheter, currents as low as 20 μA can prove fatal if allowed to get to the heart. To guard against accidental electrocution of patients, it is necessary to use electrocardiograph amplifiers which have extremely high isolation from the ac power mains. This implies use of a very high input impedance configuration. Usually, this latter criterion is satisfied by using a three-device instrumentation amplifier (IA) made with FET input op amps. Figure 4-18 shows the block diagram of a typical

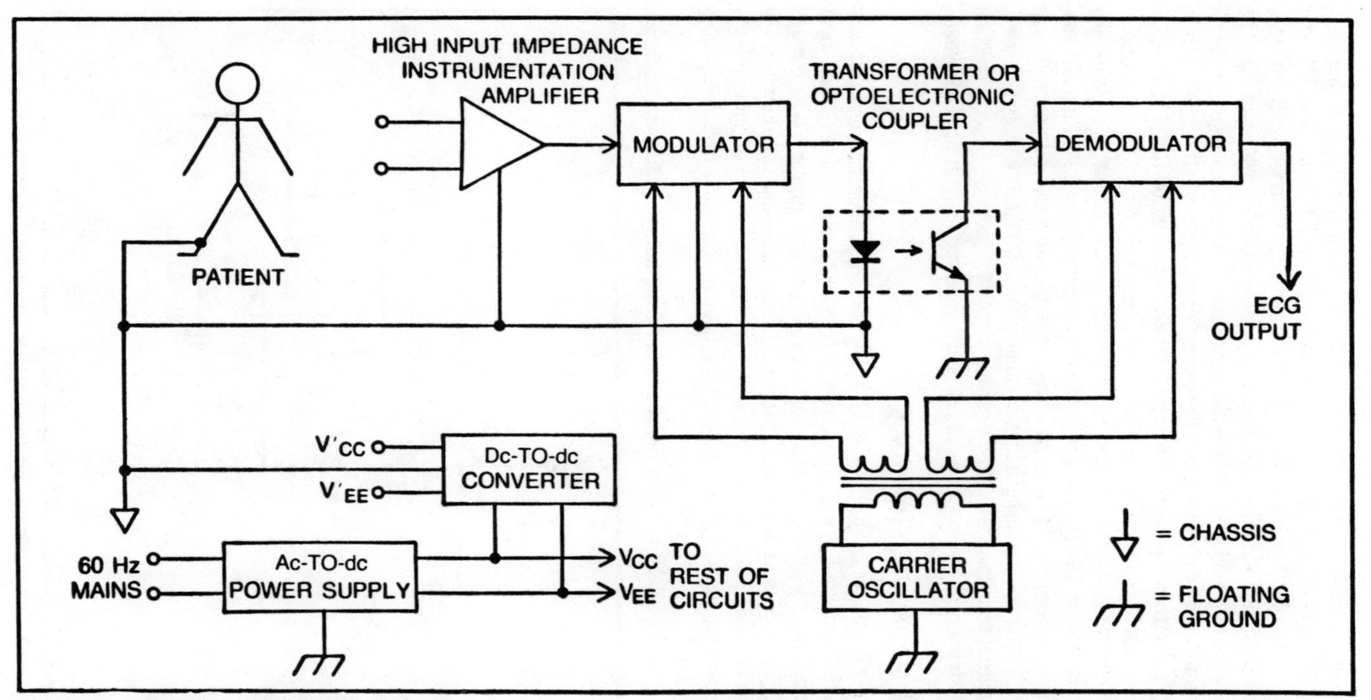

Fig. 4-18. Isolation amplifier block diagram.

isolation amplifier. The output of the IA is fed to a modulator. Although an AM circuit is shown here, some equipment uses an FM audio range VCO for better results. In those circuits we can eliminate the carrier oscillator since the FM detector can be one of the new phase-locked-loop decoder ICs. The modulated signal is coupled to the demodulator, and to the rest of the circuit through either a transformer designed to pass little 60 Hz signal or to an optoelectronic coupler. Power mains isolation of up to $10^{12}\Omega$ is possible using such circuits. This figure is maintained by driving a dc-to-dc converter from the normal-equipment dc power supply. These circuits usually consist of a 15-kHz oscillator and an associated rectifier-filter. Transformers designed for that range can still operate efficiently even though their core material is such that minimal amounts of 60 Hz energy is passed. Several manufacturers offer isolation amplifiers as potted-epoxy function modules, while at least one offers it in a patented monolithic IC package.

INCREASING INPUT IMPEDANCE

The use of an op amp with FET, Darlington, or superbeta input circuits is the preferred design where it is necessary to supply a very high input impedance. However, this is not always possible. Figures 4-19 through 4-21 are circuits which offer increased input impedance. Although these circuits may have originated before the easy availability of modern high-impedance devices, their continued popularity seems ensured by repeated use.

Figure 4-19 shows a technique used in many scientific instruments,

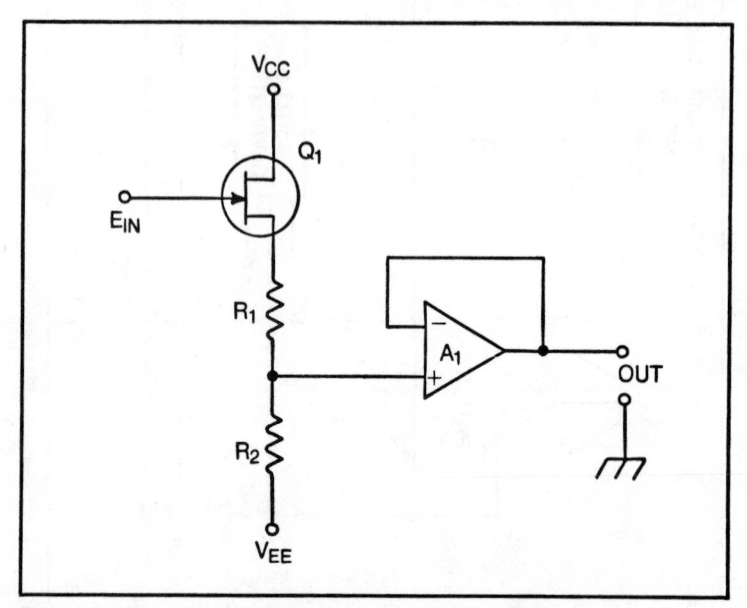

Fig. 4-19. Using external JFET to boost amplifier input impedance.

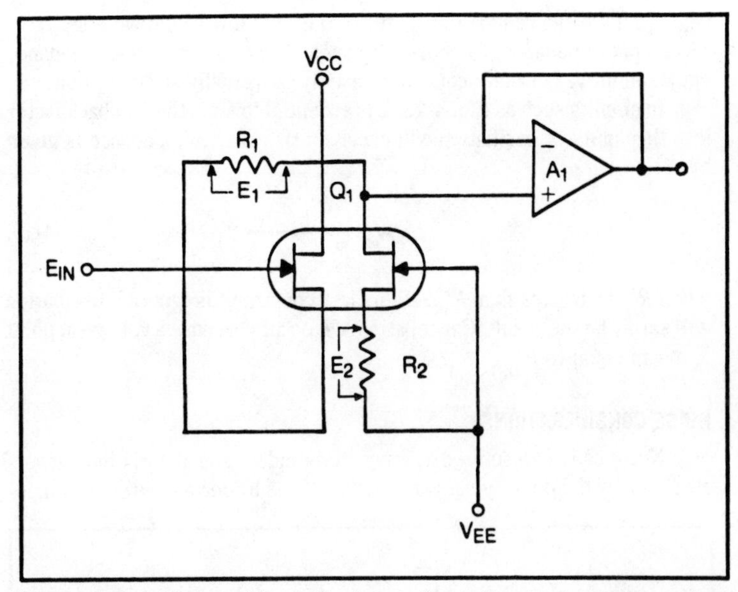

Fig. 4-20. Dual JFET providing both a boost of input Z and an improved constant current source.

test equipment designs, and at least one construction project in a popular magazine aimed at the hobbyist. In this circuit, the impedance seen by the input source is essentially that of Q_1. For most JFET types, this value is typically very high. In this circuit, Q_1 is connected as a source follower. The offset voltage created by this arrangement is substantially nulled by a quasi constant-current source (CCS) from V_{EE} through resistor R_2. Generally, R_2 is much higher in value than R_1.

A modification of the circuit to include an improved CCS is shown as Fig. 4-20. In this circuit, a second JFET is used as an electronic CCS. Almost perfect thermal tracking is obtained if both JFETs are part of the same substrate in the form of a dual JFET. As in the previous case, some offset may be produced equal to $E_1 - E_2$. The ideal case is for the current in the signal JFET to remain constant. Since the channel resistance varies with signal input voltage, we might ordinarily find both the channel current and E_1 varying. The use of a resistor CCS simulates (but only poorly) true CCS operation; the JFET design more nearly approximates the ideal.

Figure 4-21 shows a similar tactic used to raise the apparent input impedance of a differential amplifier. The CCS should be another JFET such as used in the previous example. Maintenance of a high CMRR over a wide range requires the use of a dual JFET for the input transistors. If a triple JFET becomes available, the third section can be used to form the CCS.

The circuit of Fig. 4-22 uses a small amount of regenerative feedback to cancel part of the input current. This feedback is supplied by a second operational amplifier, A_2. Remember that input impedance is equal to

E_{IN}/I_{IN}. If we can reduce the I_{IN} term to a very low value, we effectively raise input impedance. Of course, it appears that if $I_{IN} = 0$, the impedance equals infinity, but don't count too heavily on actually attaining that.

In circuits such as Fig. 4-22, it is essential to keep the feedback factor less than unity or oscillation will occur. In this circuit impedance is given by:

$$Z = \frac{R'_F R_{IN}}{R'_F - R_{IN}} \tag{4-10}$$

when R'_F is greater than R_{IN}. If this last constraint is ignored, oscillation will surely be the result. Cancellation of I_i occurs because a voltage at point A exists equal to E_{OUT} (R_1/R_2).

NOISE CONSIDERATIONS

Noise can be described as unwanted random signal variations generated both by the operational amplifier itself and by certain external compo-

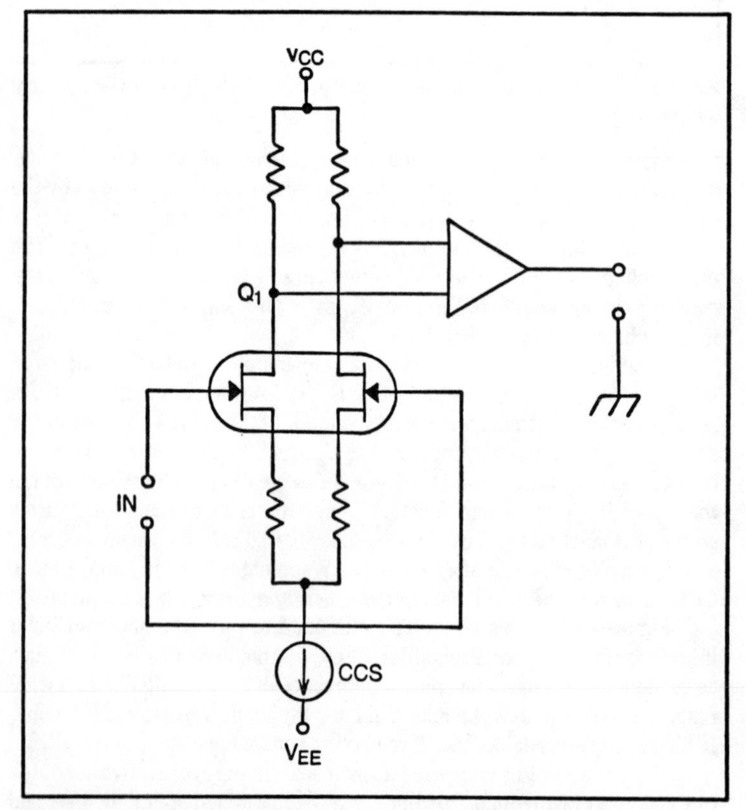

Fig. 4-21. Dual JFET used to boost differential input impedance.

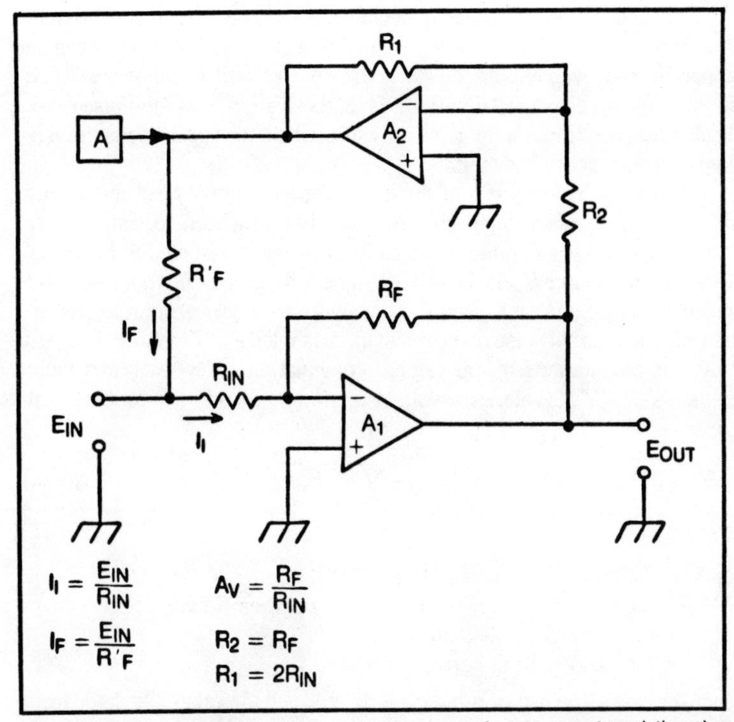

Fig. 4-22. Regenerative feedback circuit reduces input current and thereby increases input impedance.

nents. For low-level signal applications, noise considerations can be of overriding importance when selecting which operational amplifier to use in any particular circuit.

Internal noise is generated in an operational amplifier mostly by the same mechanisms which cause noise in regular transistor circuitry. Consider the typical differential input operational amplifier. The input circuitry for such a device will use at least one transistor for each input terminal. The noise contribution of the input circuitry is proportional to the square root of the number of input transistors actually used in the particular device.

Noise figure (NF) is an often quoted parameter which, while still being meaningful, can lead to problems if misunderstood. It seems that a good noise figure and good over-all noise performance do not always go hand in hand. In fact, for many operational amplifier circuits, the noise figure is actually somewhat misleading. It is a measure, in decibels, of the power signal-to-noise ratio (S/N) at the input divided by the power signal-to-noise ratio at the output:

$$NF(dB) = 10 \log_{10} \frac{(S/N)I}{(S/N)_O} \quad (4\text{-}11)$$

Noise figure is expressed in decibels. It requires little imagination to see from Eq. 4-11 that an increased amplifier noise level can result in an apparent improvement in the noise figure, yet will simultaneously be responsible for an overall deterioration of the system signal-to-noise ratio. Under that condition, a poor circuit can be made to appear considerably better than it actually deserves.

Figure 4-23 shows several noise sources as input voltages or currents driving one of those impossible to make but delightful to contemplate "ideal" operational amplifiers, which in this case is assumed to be noise-free. Voltage source E_{IN} is the regular signal voltage and does not represent noise signals. Sources E_1 and E_2, however, are noise generators representing the thermal noise of the resistances labeled R_C. These are, incidentally, representations of the parallel combination of feedback and input resistors ($R_F \| R_{IN}$). Values for voltage sources E_1 and E_2 are proportional to:

$$E_{NOISE} = \sqrt{4kTR_C\beta} \quad (4\text{-}12)$$

where:

k = Boltzmann's constant (1.38×10^{-23})
T = the temperature of the resistor in degrees Kelvin (°K).
R_C = the parallel combination of R_F and R_{IN}
β = the bandwidth in hertz.

In many cases, the bandwidth term is deleted and the value calculated from Eq. 4-12 is in terms of volts of noise per $\sqrt{\beta}$.

Voltage sources E_{N1} and E_{N2} represent that component of the noise existing in the output whenever R_C is equal to zero. Currents I_1 and I_2 are needed to account for noise generated by the operational amplifier, in

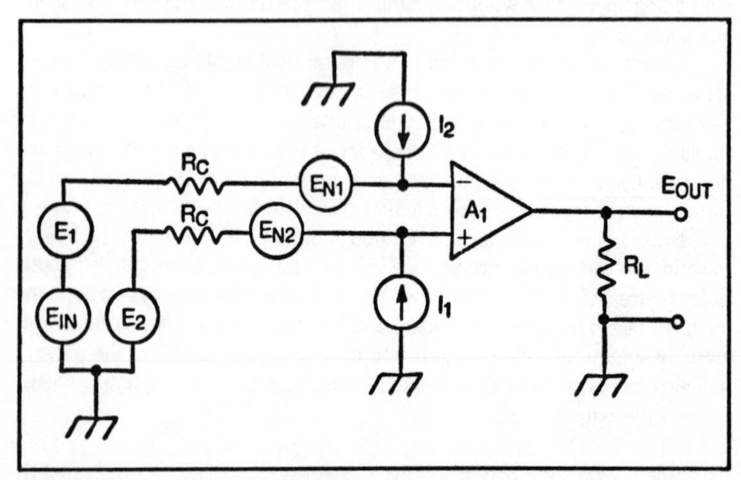

Fig. 4-23. Model showing relationship of noise sources and signal voltages.

addition to E_{N1} and E_{N2}, when R_C is *not* zero. Total noise is proportional to the sum of the individual noise components. Because the respective sources have somewhat random phase relationships, which is the nature of noise, these sources must be added together in the *root mean square* (RMS) manner. With similar noise sources combined to reduce the terrible complexity, we can express the total RMS noise picture as:

$$\frac{E_N}{\beta^{1/2}} = 2(4kTR_C) + (\overline{E_{N1} + E_{N2}}) + [\overline{(I_1 - I_2)R_C}]^{1/2} \quad (4\text{-}13)$$

where the bar indicates the RMS value.

Provided that the noise is fairly evenly distributed with respect to frequency (as is usually the case), total noise can be determined by multiplying the noise voltage by the square root of the circuit bandwidth.

Internal Noise Sources

Noise sources represented by the E_N and I terms in Fig. 4-23 are created by several different phenomena inside the operational amplifier. One source contributing to E_N is the thermal noise of the input transistor base spreading resistance, R'_{BB} (not shown in this figure, as it is internal to the op amp.) This noise is also described by Eq. 4-12 if the R_C term is replaced by the base spreading resistance. Other sources of noise are shot voltages created by direct current flowing in the base and emitter regions of the transistors used as inputs to the operational amplifier:

$$\frac{I_N}{\beta^{1/2}} = (2qI_E)^{1/2} + (2qI_B)^{1/2} \quad (4\text{-}14)$$

where:

I_N = noise current in amperes
q = the electric charge 1.6×10^{-19} coulombs
I_E = the emitter current in amperes
I_B = the base current in amperes

Field-effect transistors also suffer from internal noise problems, so expect noise in FET input operational amplifiers also. This noise is due chiefly to *thermal noise* $(4kTR)^{1/2}$ in the channel resistance and *shot noise* generated by dc leaking across the gate-channel barrier.

Low-Noise Operation

We have demonstrated that noise figure alone is insufficient for proper evaluation of an amplifier's noise performance. Consider Eq. 4-11 with the S/N terms replaced by their equivalent voltage and current terms:

$$(S/N)_I = (E_{IN})^2/(E_N)^2$$
$$(S/N)_O = (E_{OUT})^2/(E'_N)^2$$

where E_N is in this case noise at the input and E'_N is noise at the output.

$$\text{NF(dB)} = 10 \log_{10} \frac{(E_{IN})^2/E_N)^2}{(E_{OUT})^2/(E_N)^2} \tag{4-15}$$

Any method which tends to either reduce the value of the numerator in Eq. 4-15 or increase the value of the denominator will have the effect of reducing the noise figure. Paradoxically, increasing the noise voltage at the input (E_N in Eq. 4-15) has the effect of reducing the value of the numerator while simultaneously increasing the amount of noise in the circuit! Clearly, this is an unacceptable approach to reducing the noise figure and serves (only) to confuse the issue. Only those tactics which make the noise figure more attractive through reducing the noise at the output, while leaving the input noise either the same or less, are acceptable.

One common recommendation, which usually aids in reducing overall system noise, is to keep the value of R_C as low as possible within the gain requirements of the circuit and practical resistor values. If the required voltage gain (R_F/R_{IN}) can be maintained using lower values for feedback and input resistors, there should be a significant improvement in the noise performance of the operational amplifier. Remember that 10,000/100 gives the same voltage gain as 1,000,000/10,000, but will offer superior noise characteristics. It is also worthwhile to use resistors specially designed as low-noise types in the early stages of the amplifier chain. In most cases, it is the first stage or two in a cascade amplifier chain which sets the noise bounds for the entire amplifier. These must be treated carefully.

There are other methods which serve to reduce noise. One frequent recommendation is to select an operational amplifier type which has an E_N/I_1 ratio (which has units of resistance) approximately equal to the impedance of the source driving the amplifier. Alternatively, it is sometimes possible to use programmable operational amplifiers which allow some freedom to the user in the matter of trimming input current levels. With this type of device the level of bias current can be adjusted until the desired match is obtained. Of course, as source resistances dive significantly below 1,000Ω, the current required for such trimming may outrun the op amp's capability to deliver.

When the amplifier chain must use a low-gain first stage, it often proves necessary to follow this stage with a second stage also optimized for low-noise operation. Once the total gain exceeds a figure in the 50—300 range, we no longer have any real worries about noise performance. It is usually those first stages which determine the noise performance for the entire amplifier.

Recall that bandwidth was a part of the original expression for thermal noise in Eq. 4-11. This leads us almost inevitably to the use of a tiny capacitance shunting the feedback resistor, which has the effect of limiting bandwidth. It should have a reactance equal to about 10 percent of the feedback resistance at the highest frequency at which the amplifier is expected to operate. This tactic and other filtering schemes act to limit noise voltage amplitude by reducing bandwidth. Noise figure specifications are usually given in $V/\sqrt{\beta}$, so we can see why it is obligatory that the β term be limited to that actually needed for the amplifier to do its assigned job.

Chapter 5

Op Amps in Computation

It was in the field of electronic computation that the op amp originally began its long and illustrious career. That was the world of analog computers and computer-like instrumentation (make no mistake about it, this form of circuitry is still very much alive!). Such equipment uses the operational amplifier to perform predetermined (programmed) mathematic operations on specified electrical signals. These signals might be electrical analogs of simple numbers or they could be electrical quantifications of actual physical or biological phenomena. In either event, the operational amplifier was one of the leading factors that removed the analog computer from the realm of mechanical monsters that had little flexibility.

SUMMATION CIRCUITRY

As demonstrated in Chapter 1, the output voltage from an op amp is proportional to the voltage gain of the circuit and the *sum* of the input currents (see Fig. 5-1). The sum of the input currents in the circuit of Fig. 5-1 must be, by Kirchhoff's law:

$$I_6 - I_1 - I_2 - I_3 - I_4 - I_5 = 0 \tag{5-1}$$

Each of the currents is created by a voltage applied across the associated resistor. Except in the case of I_6, which is formed by E_{OUT}/R_6, the currents are created by input voltages E_1 through E_5 and the respective resistances. Keep in mind the fact that the inverting input is kept at virtual ground. The algebraic sign associated with each current will depend upon the polarity of the input voltage. What could be simpler?

The output voltage for a circuit such as Fig. 5-1 is given by:

$$E_{OUT} = (E_1(R_6/R_1) + E_2(R_6/R_2) + E_3(R_6/R_3) + E_4(R_6/R_4) + E_5(R_6/R_5)$$

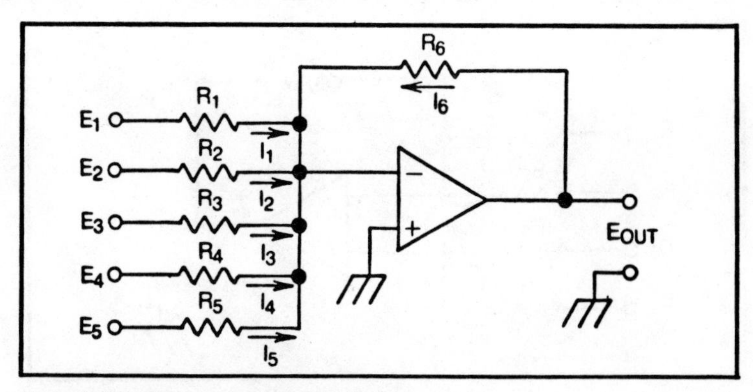

Fig. 5-1. Inverting summation amplifier.

Example:

$$R_6 = 10K$$
$$R_1 = R_2 = R_3 = R_4 = R_5 = 2000\Omega$$
$$E_1 = 1.0V$$
$$E_2 = 0.5V$$
$$E_3 = -1.0V$$
$$E_4 = 1.2V$$
$$E_5 = -0.9V$$

$$E_{OUT} = -\left[\frac{1.0(10)}{(2)} + \frac{.5(10)}{(2)} + \frac{(-1)(10)}{(2)} + \frac{1.2(10)}{(2)} + \frac{(-.9(10)}{(2)}\right]$$
$$= -[1.0(5) + .5(5) - 1(5) + 1.2(5) - .9(5)]$$
$$= -[5 + 2.5 - 5 + 6 - 4.5]$$
$$= -4.0V$$

The circuit of Fig. 5-1 is called a *summer* for obvious reasons. It is not, however, the only species capable of that function. Figure 5-2 is an alternate form of summer which uses both inputs to allow even more complex combinations.

In case of this circuit, it is especially necessary to be careful of the polarity lest an incorrect input be presented. The output for the circuit of Fig. 5-2 is:

$$E_{OUT} = E_3(R_5/R_3) + E_4(R_5/R_4) - E_1(R_5/R_1) - E_2(R_5/R_2)$$

NONLINEAR FUNCTIONS

Logarithms provide a powerful arithmetic device used in computation. They offer us a good method for handling multiplication and division in analog computer circuitry. They have also proven useful in compressing signals with a wide dynamic range so that they can be handled in circuitry

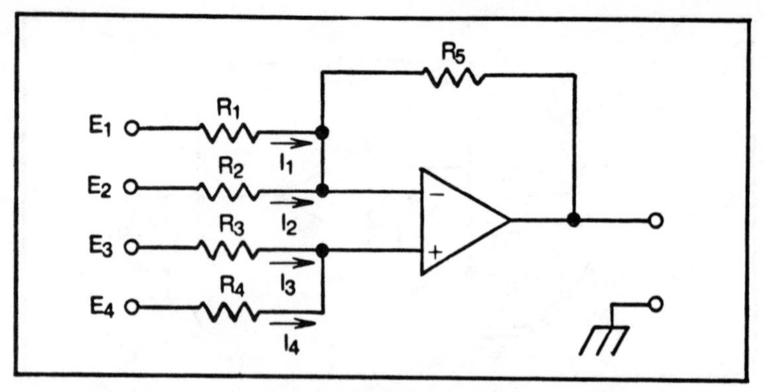

Fig. 5-2. Alternate form of summation amplifier using both inputs.

with a limited dynamic range. This is due to the fact that the logarithmic curve flattens out at the upper end of its range (Fig. 5-3).

One fortunate fact, at least for purposes of log conversion, is that the $V_{BE} - I_C$ curve for many transistors is a close approximation of the curve generated by graphing the natural logarithms. By using a selected transistor in the feedback path (Fig. 5-4), we can tailor an operational amplifier to generate an output voltage proportional to the logarithm of the input voltage.

For Q_1, seek a type with an exceptionally accurate $V_{BE} - I_C$ characteristic. The op amp should be one of the low input offset types such as the Motorola MC1456 or Signetics 5556. A lower cost op amp such as the 741 can be used if some means is provided for cancellation of the offending offset current. An example is shown in Fig. 5-5.

Some manufacturers offer ready-made logarithmic amplifiers. Many are regular op-amp chips in a standard IC package along with an appropriate transistor as part of the same substrate. This allows not only a smaller package and higher component density, but a closer match of characteristics and thermal tracking ability. This results in a superior op-amp log amplifier.

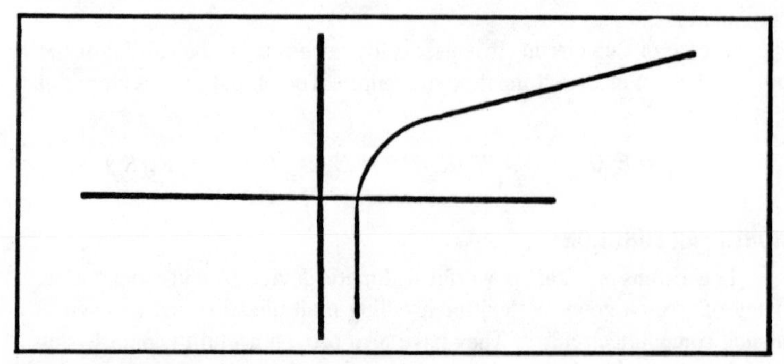

Fig. 5-3. Logarithmic characteristic curve.

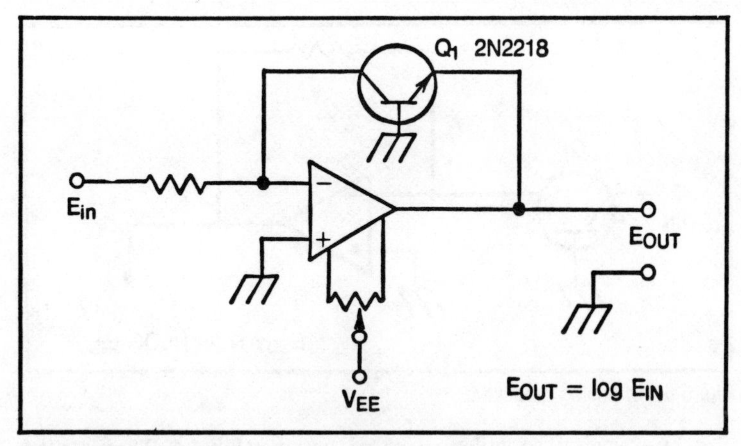

Fig. 5-4. Basic form for logarithmic amplifiers.

Another approach, taken by some manufacturers, is to use discrete components sealed in a case made of epoxy/fiberglass. This can then be mounted on a PC board as if it were a discrete component in its own right.

The antithesis of the logarithmic amplifier is, of course, the antilog amplifier. Such circuits deliver an output voltage that is proportional to the antilog of the input voltage. They are often used at the output end of an instrument that normally processes signals in log form so that the readout voltage is in the linear form recognized by the human world.

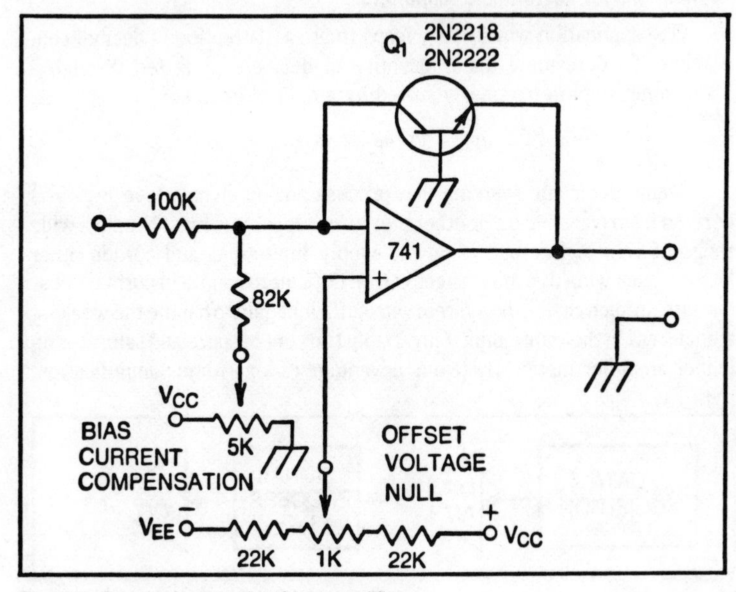

Fig. 5-5. Practical example of log amplifier.

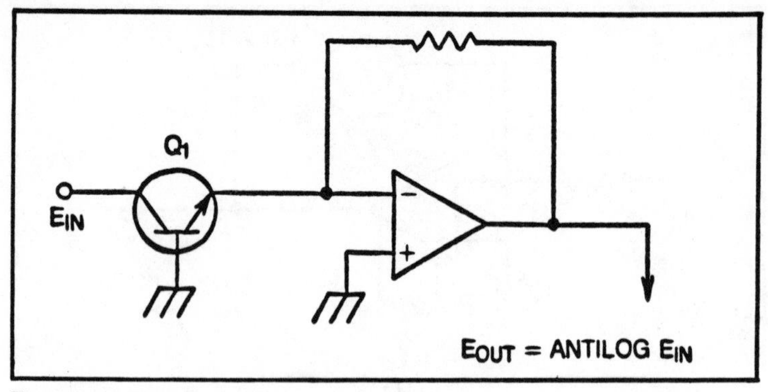

Fig. 5-6. An antilog amplifier.

An example of an antilog amplifier is shown in Fig. 5-6. Where the log amp uses a logarithmic element (transistor Q_1) in the op-amp feedback network, the antilog amplifier uses it in the inverting input circuit.

Calibration of Logarithmic Amplifiers

In the system of natural logarithms, the value for the log of 1 is 0. The component values in the log amp are trimmed until the output is zero when one unit of input voltage (a voltage to one unit of the number of quantity being measured) is applied.

Applications for Logarithmic Amplifiers

One application which fairly leaps to attract attention is decibel conversion. To determine linear quantity in decibels, it is fed through a logarithmic amplifier properly scaled by a multiplier to solve:

$$\text{dB} = 20 \log (E_1/E_2) \tag{5-2}$$

Many electronic systems that process analog signals (see Fig. 5-7) derived from transducers or other measuring apparatus must handle a wide range of values. Because of power supply limitations and certain other factors, such wide dynamic ranges can be difficult to handle in normal linear circuits. In such cases, the system with sufficient gain to handle the weakest signals within the range almost invariably runs out of space and saturates on higher amplifier inputs. By taking advantage of logarithmic amplification,

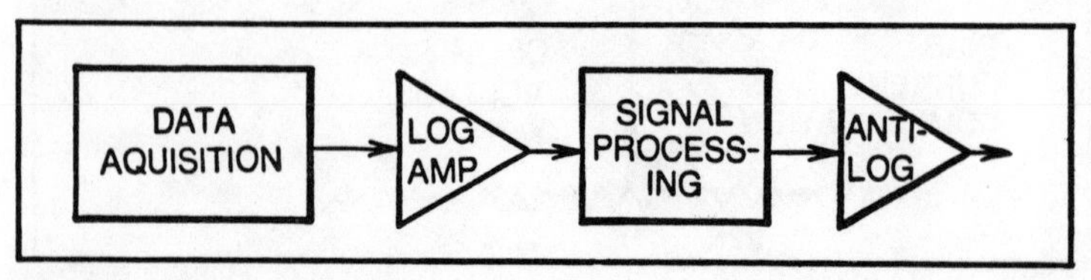

Fig. 5-7. Analog signal processor.

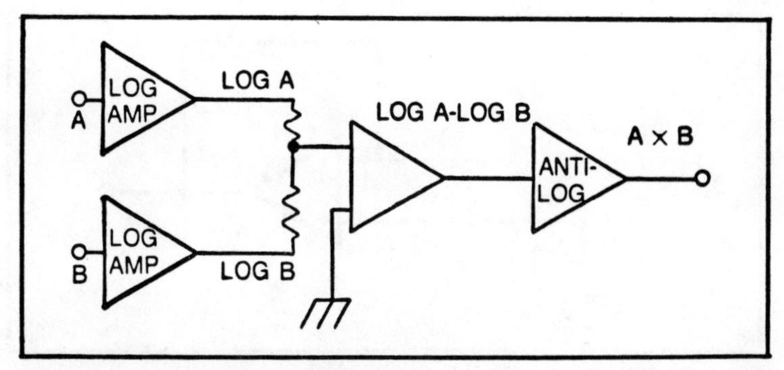

Fig. 5-8. Analog multiplier using log amps.

we gain the capability to process signals over an extremely wide range (10 decades and more have been seen) with only a relatively limited range of actual absolute voltage levels. After processing, we can pass the signal through an antilog stage, if necessary, for display in linear terms.

As demonstrated earlier, an op amp can easily handle problems in addition and subtraction as both are merely two different cases of summation. Op amps can also multiply, but only by a fixed constant equal to the voltage gain. Multiplication or division by two nonconstant quantities, however, is a little more difficult unless we resort to logarithms. This is because:

$$\text{Log}\,A + \log B = \log\,(A \times B) \tag{5-3}$$

$$\text{Log}\,A - \log B = \log\,(A/B) \tag{5-4}$$

Systems to implement these functions are shown in Figs. 5-8 and 5-9. In both cases the stages represented by Σ(Greek letter sigma) is a simple adder or subtractor as required. An antilog amplifier at the output returns the value computed to linear terms.

In some instances, potentiometers are used to simulate division, as shown in Fig. 5-10. In this case, the voltage applied to the input is proportional to the nth fraction of R times the input voltages.

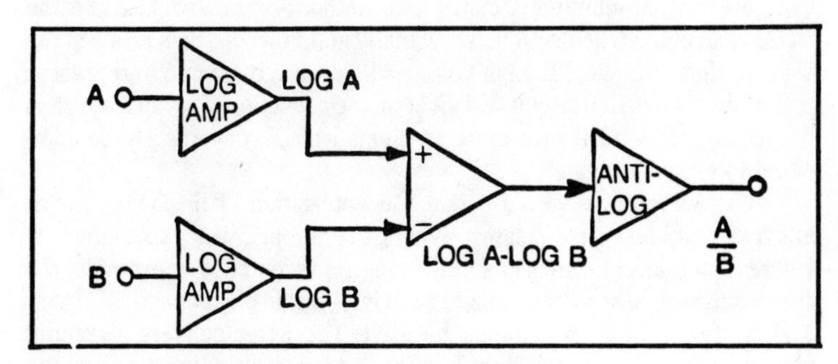

Fig. 5-9. Analog using log amps.

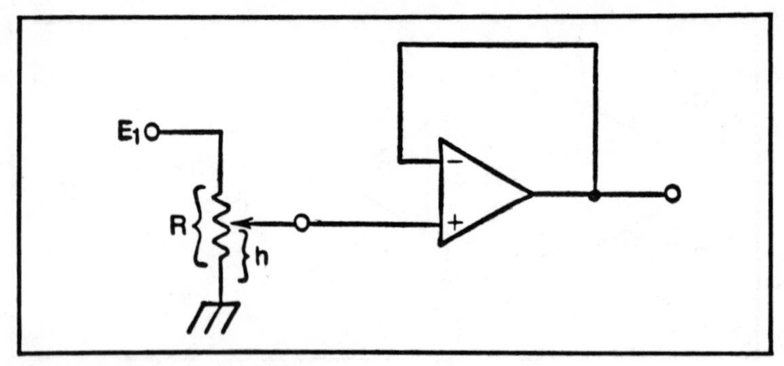

Fig. 5-10. Sine or cosine amplifier.

OTHER ANALOG MULTIPLIERS

There are actually several techniques for performing multiplication or division of analog signals. Some of these use operational amplifiers while others do not. One very popular form of analog multiplier uses a special form of modulator circuit utilizing a transconductance amplifier. An example of this sort of IC is the popular MC1595/μA795 four-quadrant multiplier. These chips have the advantage, lacking in many other forms of electronic multiplier, of being able to operate in all four Cartesian quadrants. Most analog multipliers can only operate in the first quadrant, or at most, in two quadrants. Most transconductance multipliers produce an output voltage proportional to $(XY)/Z$.

In the multiply mode, the term in the denominator becomes a constant, usually either 10 or 25. For typical 1595 circuits, the output voltage is equal to $XY/10$. A more sophisticated circuit allows division such that the output voltage will be equal to Y/Z with X being a constant. The 1595 chip, and most others of similar type, can also be used to produce an output equal to either the square or the square root of Y.

TRIGONOMETRIC FUNCTIONS

There are several ways to handle the various trigonometric functions using operational amplifier circuitry. One method is to take advantage of the fact that all of the trig functions are actually nothing more than ratios of the sides of right triangles. If input voltages levels can be scaled to represent those sides, a division circuit will yield that trig function. This approach has limited application because most problems cannot conveniently be compared to a right triangle.

It is sometimes the case that the application of mechanics to an electronic problem can assist in providing a solution. This is especially true where a mechanical displacement is being represented. For example, the sine or cosine of a shaft angle might be of interest. In that instance, a circuit such as Fig. 5-10 or 5-11 might be used. The latter delivers an output voltage proportional to the input voltage and inversely proportional to the

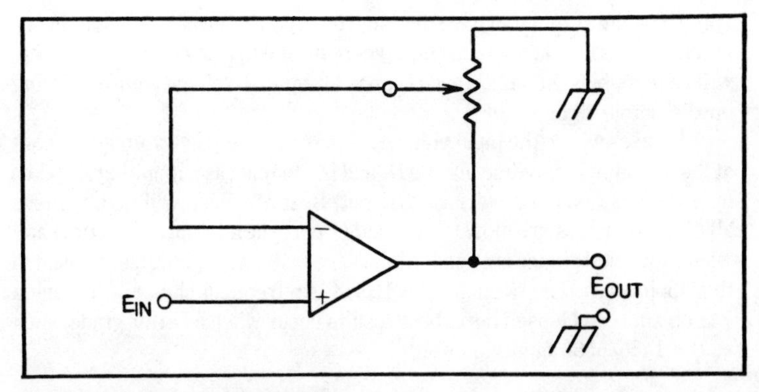

Fig. 5-11. Sine or cosine amplifier.

sine of the shaft angle. This occurs because the potentiometer is a special type which exhibits a resistance proportional to the sine of the wiper angle.

Absolute Value Circuit

In many applications, a circuit or measurement function requires the absolute value of the input voltage without regard to the polarity. An example of such a circuit is given in Fig. 5-12.

Suppose that an input voltage is presented which has a negative polarity. Amplifier A_2 is a noninverting follower. This means that the

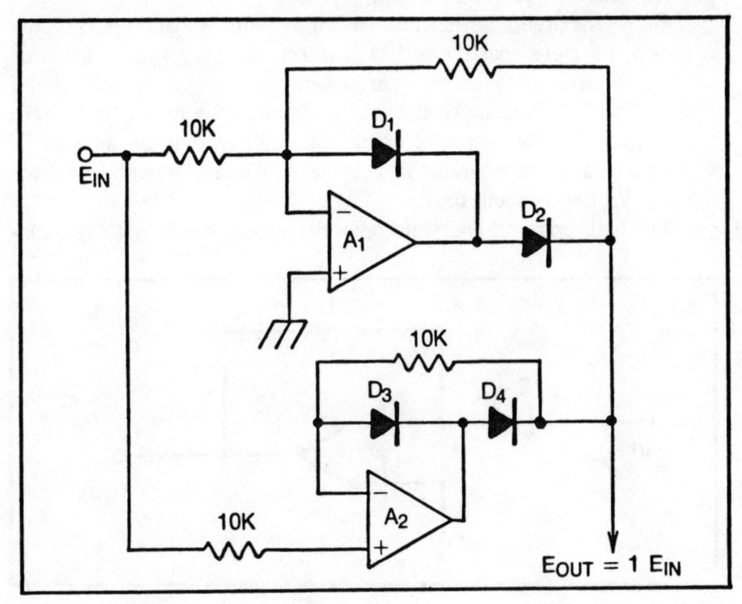

Fig. 5-12. Absolute value amplifier.

voltage on the output will have the same polarity as the input voltage. In our present example, the input is negative, resulting in a negative output. This will reverse bias diodes D_3 and D_4 prohibiting that voltage from appearing on the output line.

In cases where the input voltage is positive, a negative voltage appears at the output of A_1 reverse biasing D_1 and D_2. In that case, amplifier A_2 takes over the function of delivering an output. Best precision will result where all of the resistors are closely matched (1 percent tolerance or better) and where matched diodes are used. Almost any fast-acting diode can be used in this application. The popular type 1N914 is a frequent choice. Although a 741 op amp can be used here, best results occur when a better grade, such as the 1456/5556 family, is used.

Integration and Differentiation

Operational amplifier circuits can be arranged to perform the mathematical operations usually associated with calculus, called integration and differentiation.

Differentiation is the process of finding instantaneous rates of change by finding the slope of a line tangent to the point of interest on the graph of the function. Figure 5-13 is an example of a simple electronic differentiator using an op amp. This circuit finds the negative (inverting input used) of:

$$\frac{de_{IN}}{dt} \tag{5-5}$$

provided that the RC time constant is proper.

One of the first requirements of a differentiator is that it respond only to *changes* in input signal (the derivative of a constant is zero). To meet this criterion, a capacitor is placed in series with the negative input. Ideally, if the input voltage function changes value instantaneously (i.e., has a zero transition time), the output of a true differentiator will be infinite. Of course, no real operational amplifier produces an infinite output. In fact, for most, 15V or so is about tops!

For both practical and philosophical reasons, we do not even con-

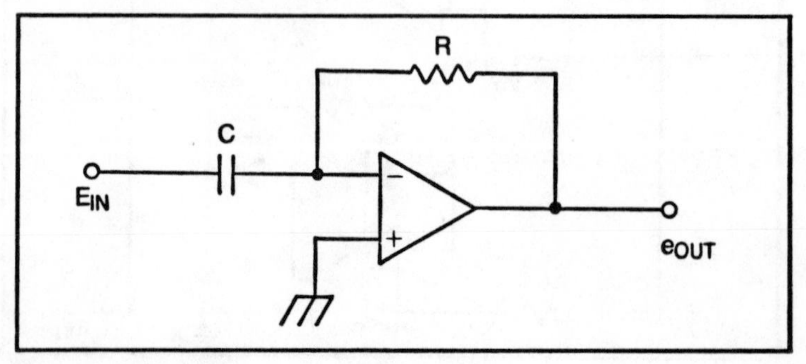

Fig. 5-13. Differentiator.

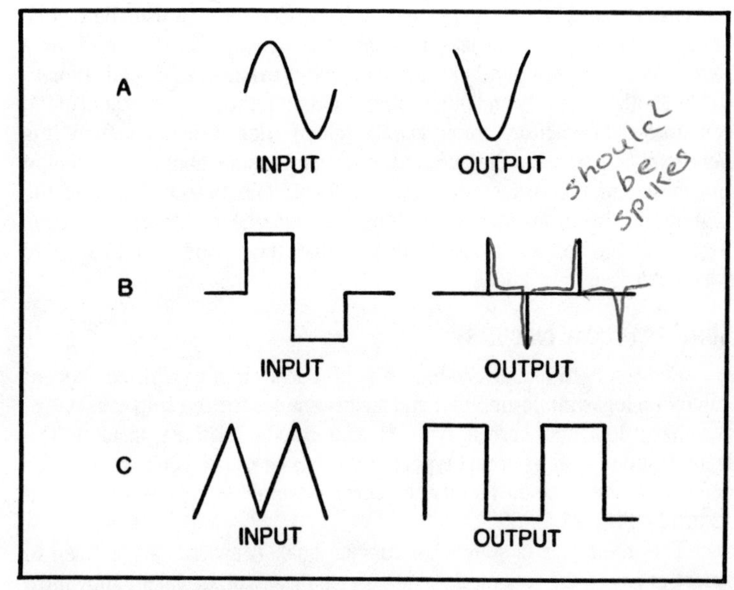

Fig. 5-14. Certain differentiated waveforms.

template a true differentiator. For real-world signals, fortunately, we will not see instantaneous transitions. In fact, the square wave is the fastest available, and even it has a finite transition time. Even though we cannot cry too much over the loss of our realistically impossible differentiator, we can use the electronic differentiator to perform a wide variety of tasks in analog computers and in instrumentation, using analog computer techniques for highly sophisticated applications.

One way to describe a circuit such as the differentiator is to examine its effects on various types of waveforms (see Fig. 5-14). A sine wave, for example, when fed through a differentiator, will produce at the output the cosine of that wave. A cosine, on the other hand, will produce the "minus sine" at the output. A square wave is affected in a special way that produces a bipolar train of sharp pulses (examine the waveform and you will see why).

Another frequently seen circuit is the Miller integrator of Fig. 5-15. Such circuits are used to perform the mathematical operation of integration which is, essentially, to find the area under the curve generated by the input waveform. For the op-amp integrator, the output voltage will be equal to the integral of the input waveform divided by the RC time constant. Also present in some cases is a portion of the output, due to any initial charge either existing from a previous operation (due to design intent) or preloaded for a special purpose. Since the capacitor in the circuit may well continue to accumulate a charge as long as the input signal does not charge reverse polarity, we must provide a means for limiting the charge to a certain period of time, as determined by the needs of the circuit design purpose at hand. To accomplish this, it is necessary to use the switch shown. This can be a relay or pushbutton in very slow circuits, or a field-effect transistor or other electronic switch in more rapid applications.

In both integrator and differentiator circuits, the time constants of the resistors and capacitors are crucial. Although rules of thumb abound, it is generally safe to make the differentiator time constant about 10 percent of the period of the expected input waveform. The time constant of the integrator is handy for scaling the output, but it can be made too short. Again a general rule applies: make it not less than the period of the expected waveform.

SOME PRACTICAL CIRCUITS

Figures 5-16 and 5-17 show two practical circuits with component values—a logarithmic amplifier and an integrator. The log amp uses one of the bipolar low input current types of op amp and a 2N2218 transistor. The transistor need not be of that type, but this has been a selection popular for some years because of the nice log curve generated by transistors in the 2N2218—2N2222 family.

The integrator is somewhat conventional. A switch can be used to select either of the capacitor values given, or any other value, allowing a wide-range integrator with a selectable time constant.

Comparator Circuits

A comparator is a circuit that compares two input voltages and issues an output indicating whether the inputs are equal or unequal. Consider the circuit in Fig. 5-18. It is a simple *ground state* comparator. One immediately apparent feature is the lack of a feedback loop because it is an open-loop amplifier. Such circuits essentially have a gain equal to the open-loop gain of the device. This causes the amplifier output to saturate when even minute input voltages are presented. Because of this, some instructors and at least

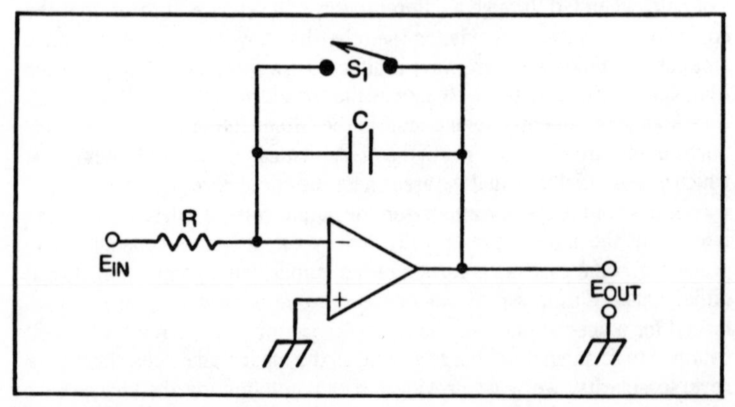

Fig. 5-15. Integrator.

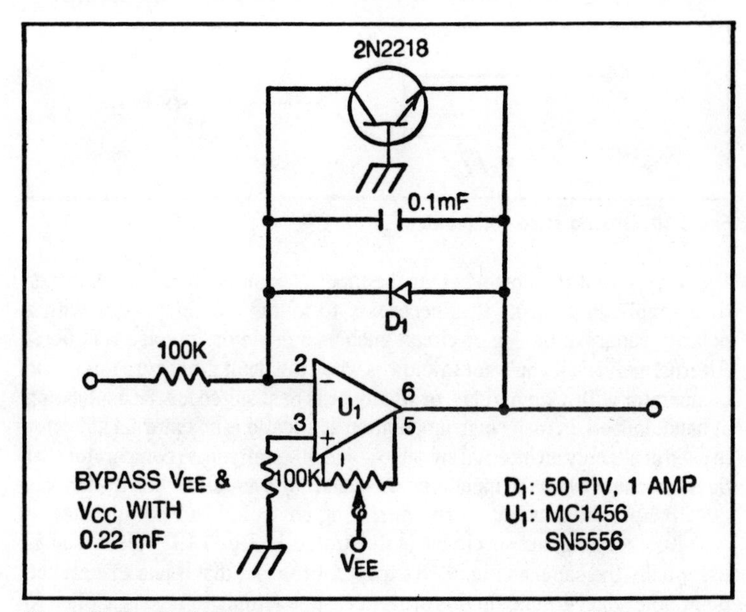

Fig. 5-16. Practical log amp.

one textbook author have referred to the comparator as an "amplifier with too much gain."

In the circuit of Fig. 5-18, zero output voltage can exist, as in any operational amplifier, whether closed- or open-loop, only when the differential input voltage is zero. Since the noninverting input is grounded, this can only occur when E_{IN} equals zero. If E_{IN} is even slightly more positive than ground, the output will assume a high negative level. Alternatively, when the input is negative with respect to ground, the output will be at a high positive level. Absence of an output signal indicates that the input is at ground potential.

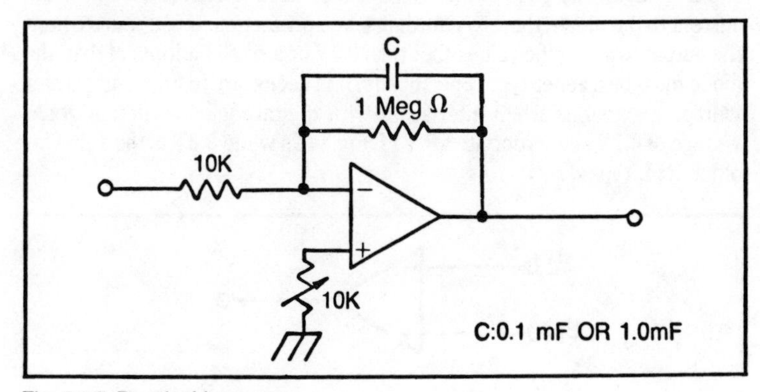

Fig. 5-17. Practical integrator.

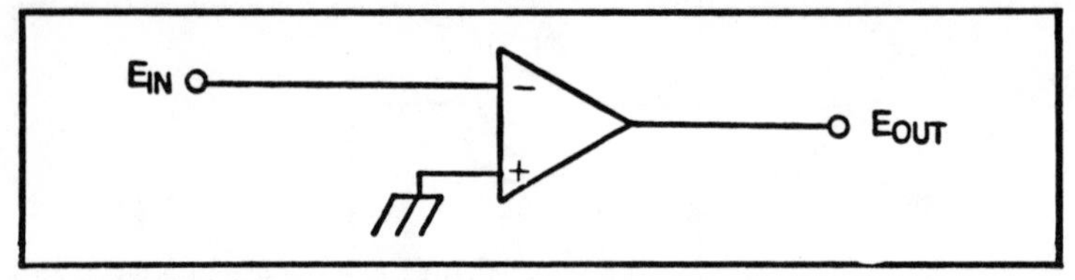

Fig. 5-18. Ground state comparator.

If you want to know whether the input is positive or negative, rather than simply "not zero," it is necessary to follow the comparator with a polarity-sensitive device or circuit such as a diode or "precise rectifier." Alternatively, if all you want to know is when the input is not zero follow the comparator with a lamp, relay, or whatever is best suited for the application at hand. Indeed, in many instrumentation applications no external indicator is used at all; only an internal signal to some other circuit. A comparator that does one thing when the input is positive and quite another when the input is negative provides us with some intriguing control-circuit possibilities.

Another comparator circuit is illustrated in Fig. 5-19. This circuit is essentially the same as Fig. 5-18 except for the fact that it has a reference point other than ground. In this present case, the limit voltage is applied to the inverting input while the unknown is applied to the noninverting input. When $E_1 = E_{IN}$ the output voltage will be zero. A differential input voltage other than zero ($E_1 \neq E_{IN}$) will produce a high-level output (i.e., terminal voltage) of a polarity determined by the usual op-amp rules.

It is occasionally necessary to limit the output of a comparator. In one case, it might be preferred that only a single-polarity output be produced or recognized. If only one output polarity is wanted, but you want it to be present any time an output is called for, the comparator should be followed with an *absolute value* amplifier. If, on the other hand, only those outputs generated by inputs of specific polarities are to be recognized, the circuit in Fig. 5-20 can be used. Should the output level be somewhat unimportant or at a high level, any good silicon diode can be used. The resistor limits the current to the diode, thereby affording some protection. If you want to limit the output to a specific value other than 0.7V or a small multiple of that, the diode must be a zener type. Specifically, it is necessary to limit comparator voltage excursions when interfacing with digital logic circuits. A zener voltage of 4.7V is appropriate for TTL logic ICs while 3.6V is the value for older RTL types.

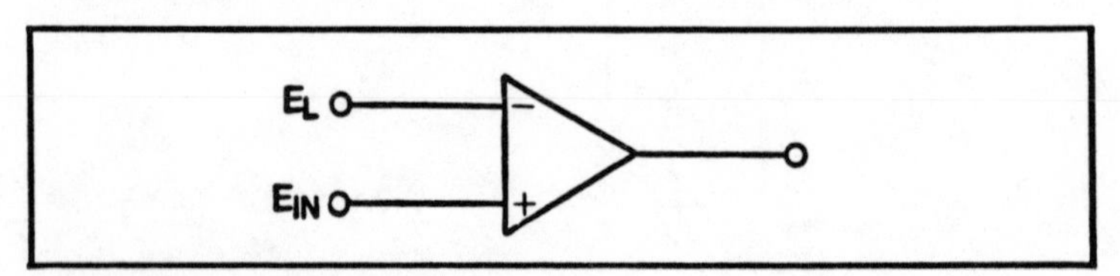

Fig. 5-19. Voltage level comparator.

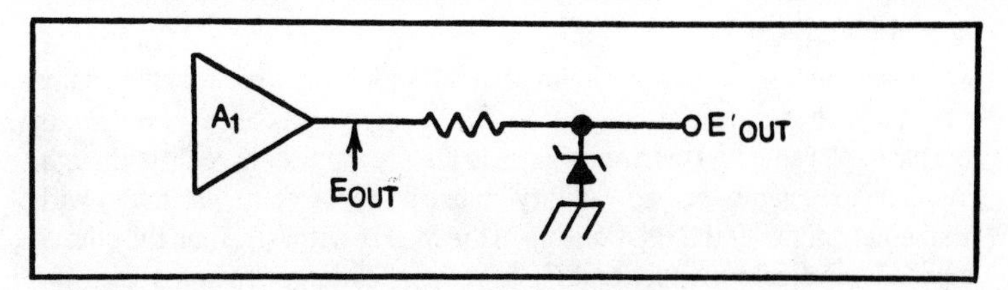

Fig. 5-20. Zener diode used to limit output voltage excursions.

The last comparator circuit we will consider is the double-limit job of Fig. 5-21. Amplifier A_1 is a unity-gain follower used mostly to buffer the input. The upper limit is set by the reference voltage on amplifier A_2, while amplifier A_3 handles the lower limit. The output is coupled through a NOR gate. If either limit is exceeded, an output will occur. As long as the input voltage remains within the limits imposed by the two reference voltages, no output will occur. Examples of this application can be found wherever a signal must be produced or an alarm given, should some measured factor go out of bounds. Electronic medical instruments, for example, are designed to generate a dc voltage that is proportional to some physiological parameter such as heart rate or blood pressure. In these cases, a potentiometer will allow the medical user to set limits on a double-ended limit comparator. Because of this, a single circuit can serve to give a warning for either high or low alarm contingencies.

Unit Comparators

It is sometimes necessary to convert units in an electrical instrument from one type to another. This can take the form of current-to-voltage, voltage-to-current, voltage-to-frequency, and so forth. There are several circuits developed using operational amplifiers which serve these purposes admirably.

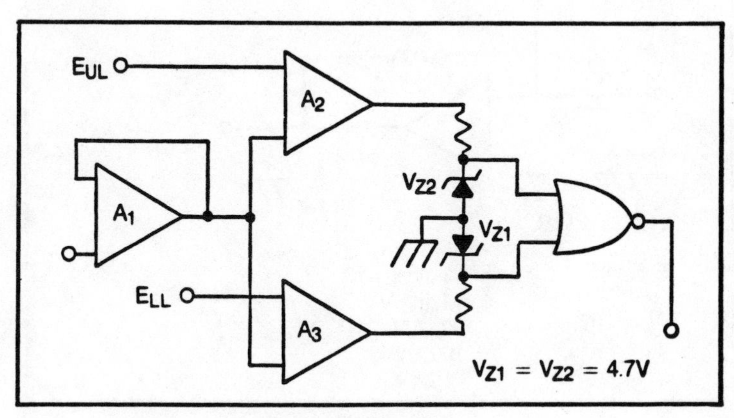

Fig. 5-21. "Window comparator" with TTL output.

Current-to-Voltage

A current source is a circuit that provides a current that remains constant with wide variations in load. The source impedance Z_S (or R_S, in this case) of a constant-current source is ideally infinite. In reality, though, this is unachievable, and so "infinity" must be replaced in our model with "extremely high." If the relationship of the load resistor (R_1) and the source impedance reflects the fact that R_S is very much larger than R_1, then the current through the combination $R_S + R_1$ is almost independent of changes in R_1.

Figure 5-22 shows an op amp current-to-voltage converter which offers almost zero loss to low values of input current. This is due to the fact that the minus input is held to virtual ground by having the plus input strapped to ground.

The input impedance can be approximated by

$$Z_{IN} \quad \frac{R_F}{A_{VOL} + 1} \tag{5-6}$$

Since A_{VOL} is very large, this can offer a very low impedance; just the ticket for a "lossless" current passer.

For example, assume a 1 mA input current and a 10K feedback resistor, resulting in a maximum value of 10V output when the 1 mA full-scale input current is present. If the output op amp is a relatively modest type with a value of A_{VOL} around 100,000 (10^5), we would have

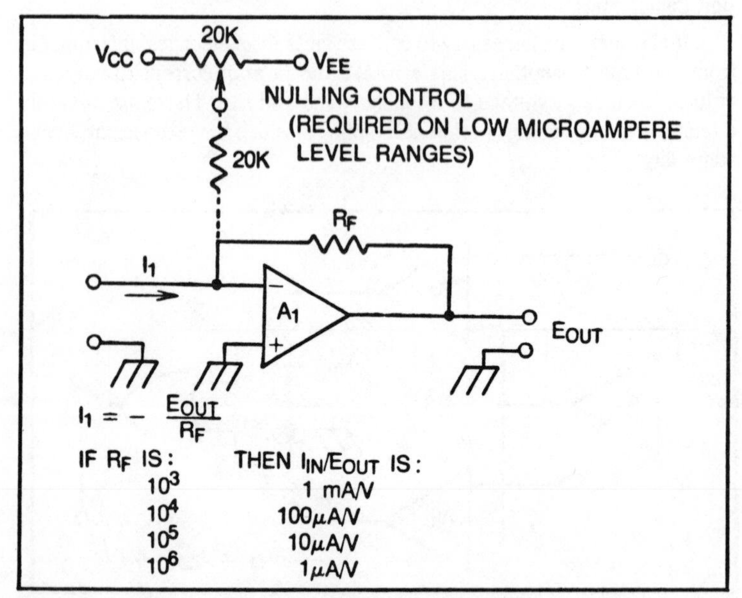

Fig. 5-22. I-to-E converter functioning as microammeter.

$$Z_{IN} = \frac{10^4}{10^5 + 1} \cong \frac{10^4}{10^5} \cong 10^{-1} \cong 0.1\Omega \qquad (5\text{-}7)$$

indeed, a "lossless" current-to-voltage converter.

Some of the most common uses for a current-to-voltage converter are in the realm of scientific instruments. Several chemical measurement schemes, for example, require the application of a constant voltage from a small battery or power supply to a solution, and then the resultant current is measured. Typically, the electrodes used in such measurement equipment have impedances that are quite high: usually well over 100K. This makes them appear as a current source when followed by a circuit with only a fraction of an ohm input resistance. This type of circuit proves especially useful for measurement of currents normally too low to measure with an ordinary current meter.

One of the more annoying aspects of instruments of this kind is the appearance of high-frequency noise and interference at the output. To prevent this sort of thing, assuming that it may be a problem in the first place, shunt the feedback resistor R_F with a capacitor having a reactance of less than $R_F/10$ at the lowest frequency at which interference will be normally expected. This can be as low as 25 to 40 Hz when the circuit is used for measurements close to dc. The capacitor will reduce the gain of amplifier A_1 at the offending frequencies by a considerable amount, because the feedback factor at those frequencies is approximately 100 percent.

Voltage-to-Current

At least as popular as current-to-voltage conversion is the opposite, or voltage-to-current conversion. This is primarily used where the output will be an analog meter movement, a galvanometer pen mechanism in a strip chart recorder, or some similar arrangement.

Perhaps the simplest method of voltage-to-current conversion is that shown in Fig. 5-23. This circuit is a simple inverting amplifier in which the load resistor (through which the current must flow) is used as the op-amp feedback resistor. Input voltage E_{IN} sets up a current flow in the resistor R_{IN}. By Ohm's law, $I_1 = E_{IN}/R_{IN}$. A second current, I_2, is set up in the load (feedback) resistor equal to I_1 in order to satisfy Kirchhoff's law. The value of E_{OUT}, although a bit irrelevant since we are interested in a current (I_2), is given by the $E_{IN} A_V$ rule in which A_V is equal to R_1/R_{IN}.

Another floating load voltage-to-current converter is shown in Fig. 5-24. This is essentially very similar to the previous design in that it is an inverting follower. The difference is in the placement of the load resistor. The circuit of Fig. 5-24 uses a separate feedback resistor. A load resistor, the output for a current driver device, is series connected between the op-amp output terminal and the feedback voltage divider. For purposes of analyzing the circuit, this can be considered as a voltage source driving a resistor network. Since these circuits have a transfer function that relates a

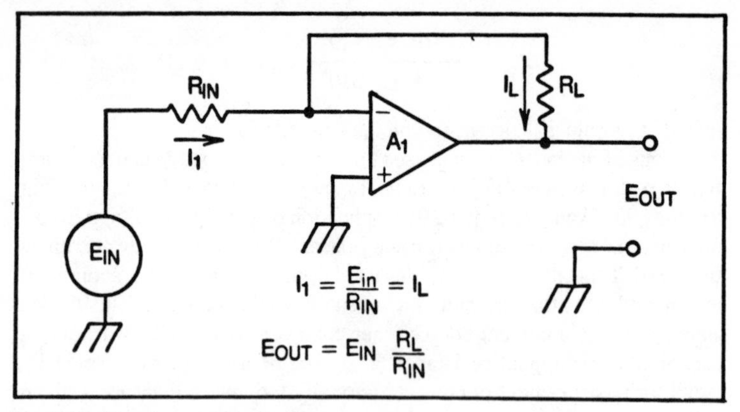

Fig. 5-23. E-to-I converter.

change in output current to a proportional change in input voltage, it is basically a transconductance amplifier. For the specific circuit of Fig. 5-24:

$$I_L = \frac{E_{IN}(R_1 + R_F)}{R_{IN}R_1} \tag{5-8}$$

Since all of the resistors are constant, we can rewrite this to show the transconductance nature of the circuit:

$$\Delta I = k\,(\Delta E_{IN}) \tag{5-9}$$

The symbol Δ is the Greek letter delta, used to mean "small change in...".

We can also describe the action of the amplifier with respect to its behavior relative to input current by replacing E_{IN} with it's Ohm's law equivalent:

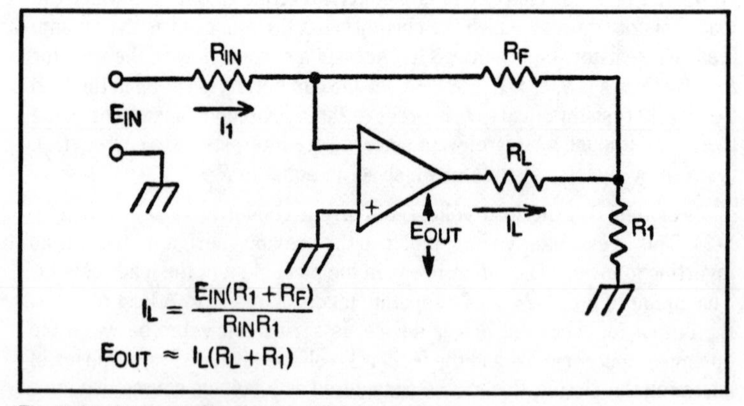

Fig. 5-24. Alternate floating load E-to-I converter.

$$I_L = \frac{I_{IN} R_{IN}(R_1 + R_F)}{R_{IN} R_1}$$

$$I_L = \frac{I_{IN}(R_1 + R_F)}{R_1}$$

$$R_1 I_L = I_{IN} (R_1 + R_F)$$

$$I_{IN} = \frac{R_1 I_L}{R_1 + R_F} \tag{5-10}$$

We can trim the values of the currents flowing, then, by varying the value of resistor R_1. The output voltage capability of both the op amp and its power supply must be able to sustain and output voltage of $E_{OUT} = I_L (R_L + R_1)$, assuming that R_F is much greater than R_1.

So far we have only considered circuits in which the load resistor is floating above ground potential. In practice, though, not all possible loads can be ungrounded. To be sure, devices such as galvanometer pens and meters can be made to float, but in those cases where the load must be grounded, the type of circuit shown in Fig. 5-25 can be employed. Here we have a situation in which the load current is equal to:

$$I_L = -\frac{E_{IN}}{R_2} \tag{5-11}$$

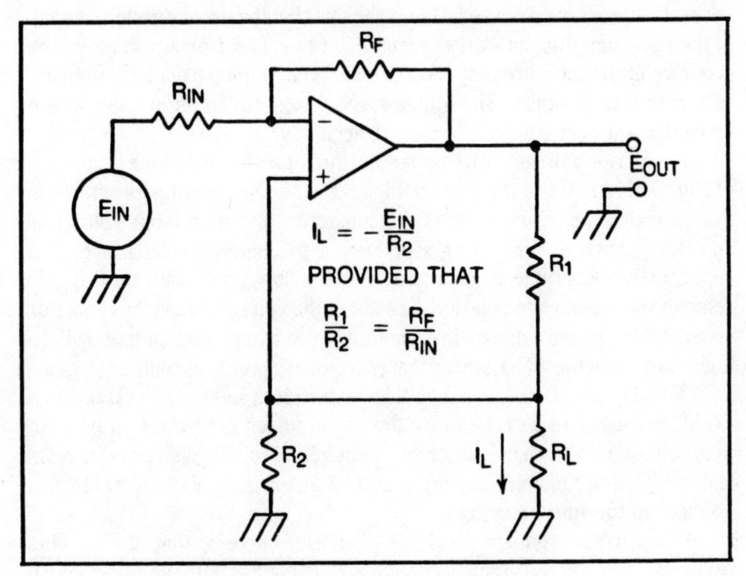

Fig. 5-25. Grounded (unbalanced) load E-to-I converter.

provided that $A_V = R_F/R_{IN} = R_1/R_2$. We need not worry about the actual absolute values—only the ratios.

Voltage-to-Frequency

There are any number of reasons for wanting to convert a voltage level into a proportional frequency or a pulse train. These include measurement of a voltage (or current), computation, and telemetry; this latter referring to both the transmission and tape recording of analog data.

The digital voltmeter (DVM) is an example of the measurement application of voltage-to-frequency converters. The same circuit can, however, be used in other applications where a voltage-to-frequency converter may be indicated. Figure 5-26 shows a single-slope integrator voltage-to-frequency converter. Amplifier A_1 is connected as a comparator with the converted voltage applied to the terminal marked E_{IN}. A ramp function voltage is applied to the alternate input. The initial conditions at time t_0 are: switch S_1 in the grounded position and ramp voltage equal zero. As soon as the ramp voltage rises a few millivolts above zero, the comparator output will snap to its *high* state—applying an input to the AND gate. This will allow the passage of clock pulses through the gate to the voltage-to-frequency converted output. Also occurring at this time (t_0) is the toggling of switch S_1. This switch will usually be a JFET or CMOS (digitally driven) analog switch. When this occurs, E_{IN} is applied to the comparator input. When the ramp voltage equals E_{IN}, the comparator output snaps back to 0V (ground state) closing the gate to clock pulses. The number of pulses passed through the gate is proportional to the input voltage. This circuit has several inherent weaknesses. One is the fact that the linearity and accuracy of the ramp function, as well as accuracy of the clock frequency, affect the accuracy of the measurement. Also, this circuit is not particularly immune to errors due to noise. The single-slope integrator is often used where economy is a necessary tradeoff with accuracy.

A superior voltage-to-frequency converter is the dual-slope integrator of Fig. 5-27. Amplifier A_1 is operating as a voltage-over-time integrator in the normal manner, while A_2 is a comparator. When an input voltage is applied through S_1, the integrator begins to charge its capacitor. The capacitor will continue to charge at a reasonably linear rate until E_{IN} is removed or reversed in polarity. As soon as the voltage across the capacitor rises above ground (almost immediately), the comparator output will go high, turning on the AND gate so that pulses can pass to the counter stages.

The digital counter, which will have decoders and readouts if this is a DVM, is caused to increment by the clock pulses until it overflows. An overflow signal will cause electronic switch S_1 to toggle, disconnecting E_{IN} and applying a constant-current source, formed from a stable reference voltage, to the integrator input.

The current from the CCS has a polarity opposite that of E_{IN}. This reversal, shown in the graph occurring at t_1, coincides with the (overflow +

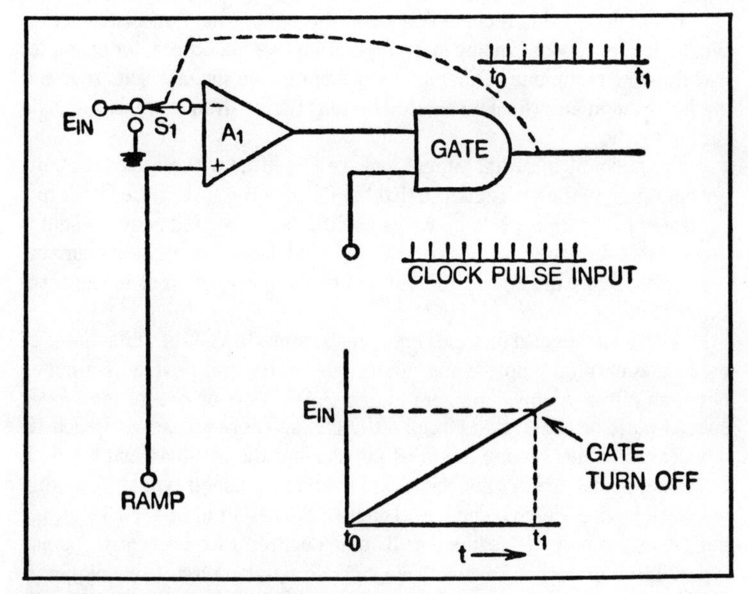

Fig. 5-26. Single slope V-to-F converter.

1) state of the counter which is all zeros. The clock pulses continue, however, and they will continue to increment the counter until time t_2, when the integrator capacitor has been completely discharged. This causes the comparator output to revert to the ground state.

The number of pulses entered into the counter during the t_2/t_1 interval is proportional to the input voltage. In nonvoltmeter applications, a second switch (S_2) is used to connect the pulse train at the gate output to the outside world. This switch is closed at time t_1.

Among the reasons for the popularity of the dual-slope integrator is the elimination of the difficult-to-control ramp voltage and relative independence from clock accuracy. Also, the low-pass-filter characteristic of the integrator acts to limit noise interference.

We have lumped together both analog data transmission and tape recording, not because these are the same thing but, because they make related use of voltage-to-frequency converters. In both cases near-dc analog data cannot be transmitted over normal audio channels (either in tape recording or radiotelephone), because of the normal limitations placed on audio passband. A useful method for overcoming these problems is to convert or translate the low-frequency data signal to a higher audio frequency within the passband of the device or equipment in use. This can be done easily by using the signal to modulate a voltage-controlled oscillator (VCO) to produce an FM signal with a carrier frequency within the audio spectrum. In these cases, the instantaneous carrier frequency is proportional to the instantaneous input signal amplitude.

Examples of this technique abound throughout modern instrumentation technology. Most analog instrumentation tape recorders, for example, use the FM technique. Other areas of application include scientific and medical equipment which is required to transmit low-frequency data signals through radio.

In a hospital, a cardiac patient may well be fitted with a radio transmitter operating in the vhf region so that his ECG can be transmitted back to a central nurse station while he walks about in a designated zone. In equipment of this sort, the data signal frequency modulates the telemetry carrier, which frequency-modulates the vhf or uhf radio carrier; hence, the term FM/FM.

There are several methods for using op amps in VCO circuits. Some of these use only op amps, while others use an op-amp device as a buffer between either a unijunction transistor (UJT) VCO or one of the newer special-purpose integrated circuit VCO chips. There are several such IC devices available. Among the most popular are the MC4044 and the 566. Several manufacturers offer these and even more useful types. Since this may well be the design technique of choice, the reader is advised to consult the data sheets of the respective IC manufacturers for currently popular types. In other cases, however, we can use op-amp circuit techniques.

One method for using op amps in a V is simply a variation on the dual slope integrator. In circuits such as this, the input voltage causes a current, I_{IN}, to flow in the integrator input resistor, thereby charging the capacitor.

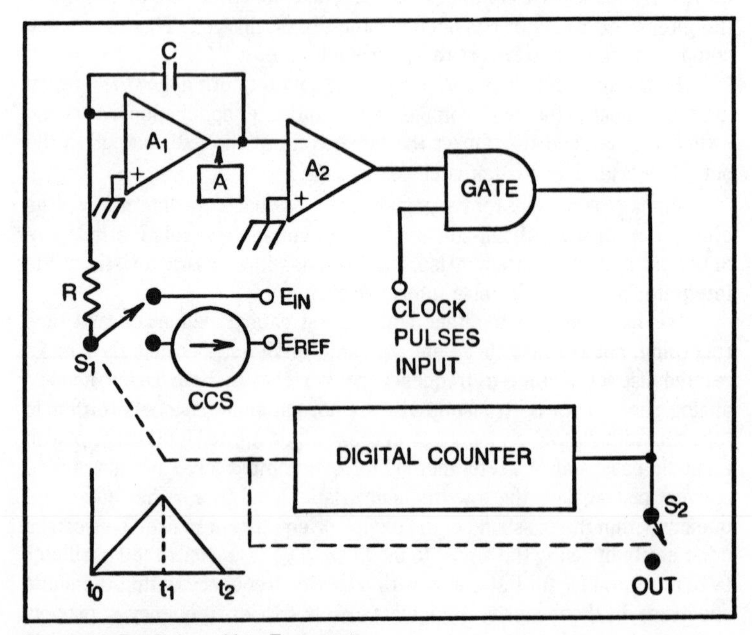

Fig. 5-27. Dual slope V-to-F converter.

The output of the integrator begins to go positive. In this circuit, the comparator is not referenced to ground but to a voltage level higher than ground, E_{REF}. When the input voltage (across the integrator capacitor) reaches the reference level, an output is generated to turn on a timer. This latter circuit issues a pulse of duration t. The pulse also switches on the CCS (allowing the integrator capacitor to discharge a bit). The charge removed from the capacitor is proportional to $I_{CS}t$. Frequency will be equal to $I_{IN}/I_{CS}t$.

We can show that this leads to a circuit which has an output frequency proportional to the ratio of two voltages. I_{IN} is created by E_{IN}/R_{IN}. The current source can be a resistor (R_{CS}) and a second voltage E_2.

The value of I_{CS}, then, is equal to E_2/R_{CS}. When these equivalents are substituted into the frequency equation:

$$\frac{I_{IN}}{tI_{CS}} = \frac{\dfrac{E_{IN}}{R_{IN}}}{\dfrac{E_2 t}{R_{CS}}} = \frac{R_{CS}E_{IN}}{R_{IN}E_2 t}$$

Since $R_{CS}/(R_{IN}t)$ is a constant, we can write:

$$f = k(E_{IN}/E_2)$$

Within a limited domain (E_2 near dc) this circuit can be used to perform a division (E_{IN}/E_2)

The control of a capacitor charge/discharge cycle is a fundamental method for making all sorts of frequency generators and, as can be seen from the above discussion, a VCO is no different. Any means by which an op amp, either alone or in conjunction with other devices, can be made to accomplish this using a control voltage as the source of the charge time, can be used as the basis for a VCO design. There are also several types of similar circuits other than the dual-slope integrator, shown above, which use other techniques.

ALTERNATE ANALOG MULTIPLIER CIRCUITS

Figures 5-28 and 5-29 show two methods for performing analog multiplication and division using a special dual-photoresistor control element. Under initial conditions, with input voltages X and Y equal to zero, the inverting input of amplifier A_2 will be held negative by current I_1, which is generated by a negative reference voltage applied to resistance R_b of photocell PC_1. This causes the output of the op amp to go positive, effectively cutting off PNP transistor Q_1. The output of A_2 is held to about 0.7 V by diode D_1 in the negative feedback path. If D_1 were eliminated, current I_1 would most likely cause amplifier A_2 to saturate at the $\pm V_{CC}$ supply level. When a first quadrant voltage is applied to input X, current I_2 will begin to flow. This will tend to counteract the effects of I_1, thereby

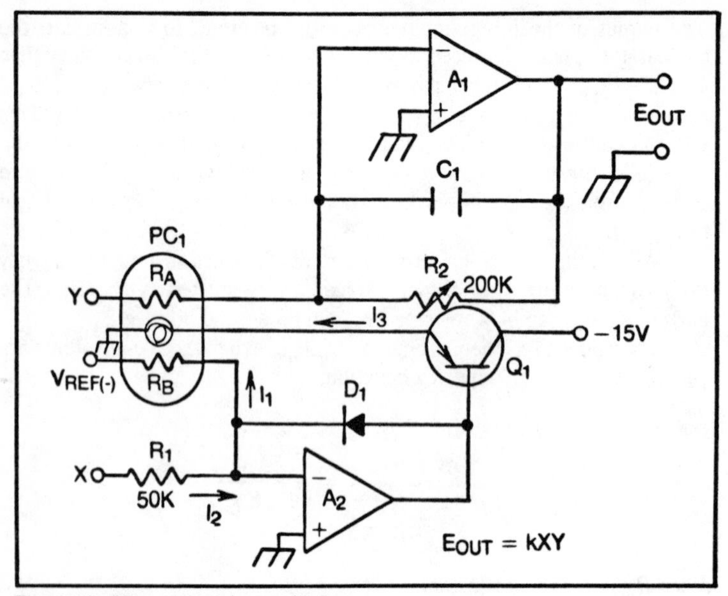

Fig. 5-28. Alternate analog multiplier.

causing the output to go more and more negative. This allows Q_1 to turn on, causing current I_3 to illuminate the lamp in the photoresistor assembly. Resistor R_b will drop in value when the PC_1 lamp is turned on until a point is reached where currents I_1 and I_2 null each other to zero:

$$I + I_2 = 0 \tag{5-12}$$

$$-\frac{V_{REF}}{R_B} + \frac{E_X}{R_1} \tag{5-13}$$

Or, by a little algebraic manipulation:

$$R_B = \frac{(R_1)V_{REF}}{E_X} \tag{5-14}$$

At this point, we must also take into consideration the fact that resistance R_A in PC_1 is also being reduced in value by the light from the lamp. Its resistance can be denoted by $R_A = k'R_B$ where k' is some constant (although different from k in Fig. 5-28). The output voltage for amplifier A_1 is calculated from Eq. 1-9:

$$E_{OUT} = -\frac{E_Y R_2}{R_A} \tag{5-15}$$

Replacing R_A with its equivalent statement:

$$E_{OUT} = -\frac{E_Y R_2}{k' R_B} \tag{5-16}$$

Now, we may substitute the expression for R_B from Eq. 5-14 into Eq. 5-15:

$$E_{OUT} = -\frac{E_Y R_2}{k' \dfrac{R_1 V_{REF}}{E_X}} \tag{5-17}$$

Let us now use the algebraic trick of inverting the denominator and multiplying by the numerator:

$$E_{OUT} = -\frac{E_X E_Y R_2}{k' R_1 V_{REF}} \tag{5-18}$$

We now have

$$E_{OUT} = -E_X E_Y k \tag{5-19}$$

where $k = R_2/(k' R_1 V_{REF})$.

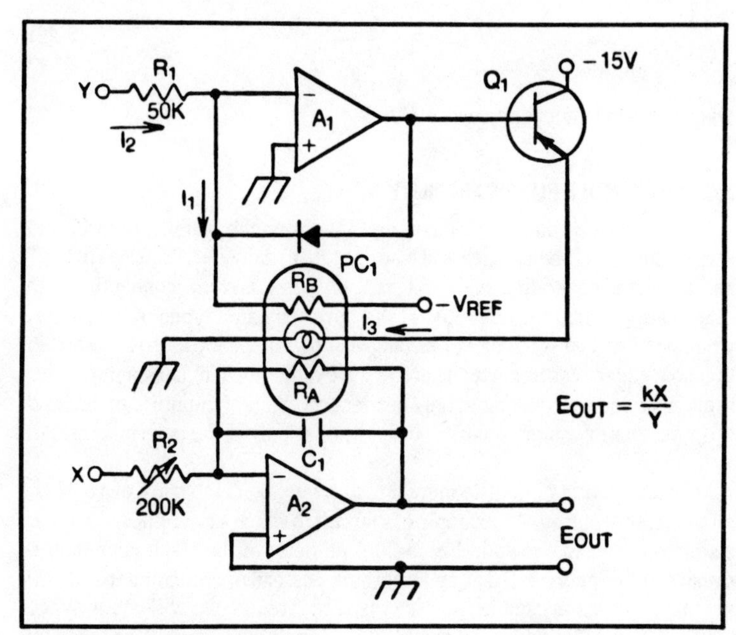

Fig. 5-29. Alternate analog divider.

The circuit in Fig. 5-28, therefore, can be called an analog multiplier with a scale factor of k. The precise value of k will depend upon the particular circuit design.

The *ratio* or *analog divider* circuit of Fig. 5-29 operates in a manner similar to the multiplier of the previous example. Indeed, we might expect such to be the case since division is only a special case of multiplication, in which $A/B = A(1/B)$. Once again, we have the input of an operational amplifier, A_1 in this example, held at a negative value by current I_1 through resistance R_B of the photocell. When voltage E_Y is applied to A_1, current I_2 will begin to flow. This causes the output of A_1 to go more negative, turning on transistor Q_1 and the photocell lamp. Resistance R_B then drops to a point where I_2 nulls I_1 to zero. In this circuit, though, R_A is in the feedback loop of amplifier A_2 rather than in the input circuit. If $R_A = k''R_B$ then the A_2 output voltage will be:

$$E_{OUT} = -\frac{E_X k'' R_B}{R_2} \tag{5-20}$$

Substituting Eq. 5-14 into Eq. 5-20;

$$E_{OUT} = -\frac{E_X k'' R_1 V_{REF}}{E_Y} \tag{5-21}$$

Clearly, then

$$E_{OUT} = -\frac{kE_X}{E_Y} \tag{5-22}$$

where the constant is in reality $k''R_1V_{REF}$.

EXTENDING MULTIPLIER CAPABILITIES

There are a number of analog multipliers on the market, both IC and special-function types, which will also operate as a divider, "square rooter," and so forth, depending upon external circuitry and pin connections. In other cases, which include most of the purely op-amp types of multiplier, we must resort to some clever circuit manipulation in order to accomplish division, square rooting, etc. There is little difficulty in making a multiplier think it's a squarer; one need only connect the X and Y inputs together and observe whatever sign (polarity) conventions apply to the particular circuit at hand.

Square rooting is a little more difficult, but it isn't too much of a bother, all things considered. An example of a circuit in which a multiplier is used as a square rooter is shown in Fig. 5-30. The heart of the stage is an operational amplifier connected as an integrator. Instead of grounding the noninverting input, as is usually the case for such circuits, we will use it as the input for a variable which we shall call Z (since both X and Y are taken by

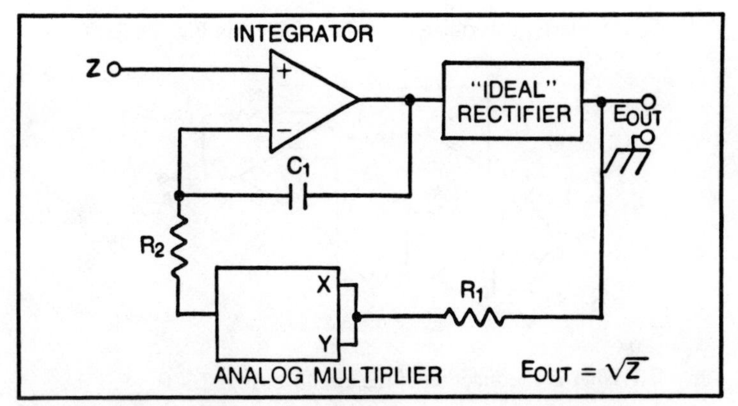

Fig. 5-30. Square rooter.

the multiplier). Following the integrator is a rectifier circuit. To use a simple silicon diode, a sample of E_{OUT} is fed back as a current via resistor R_1 to the input of the "squarer connected" multiplier.

This circuit is an example of using the feedback loop to good advantage by placing an easy-to-realize function in the negative feedback path in order to generate the opposite function, which might be difficult to realize without feedback. This idea will be seen again in a slightly different form in Chapter 7 on active filters. The circuit of Fig. 5-30 will deliver an output voltage equal to the square root of the input variable Z, or $E_{OUT} = \sqrt{Z}$.

A divider which solves for $E_{OUT} = Z/X$ is made by modifying the circuit to eliminate the ideal rectifier, and unstrapping the X and Y inputs to the analog multiplier. Negative feedback from E_{OUT} is applied to the Y input of the multiplier, while the X input is used to accept the denominator variable. Numerator variable Z is again applied to the noninverting input of the operational amplifier integrator. The output of this circuit will be approximately $E_{OUT} = Z/X$.

TEST QUESTIONS

5.1 What is the value of E_{OUT} in Fig. T5-1?

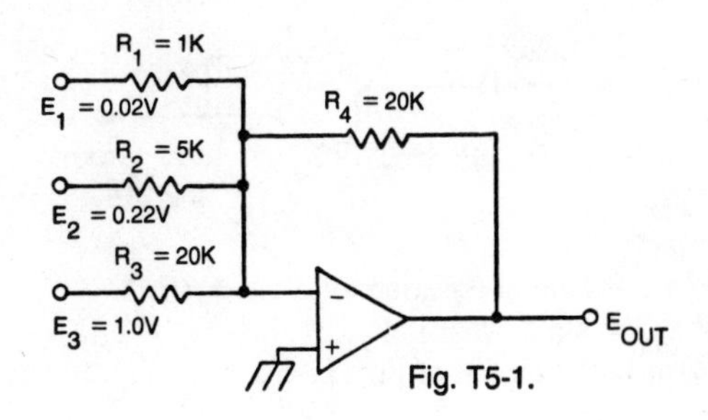

Fig. T5-1.

5.2 Similarly, determine the value of E_{OUT} in Fig. T5-2.

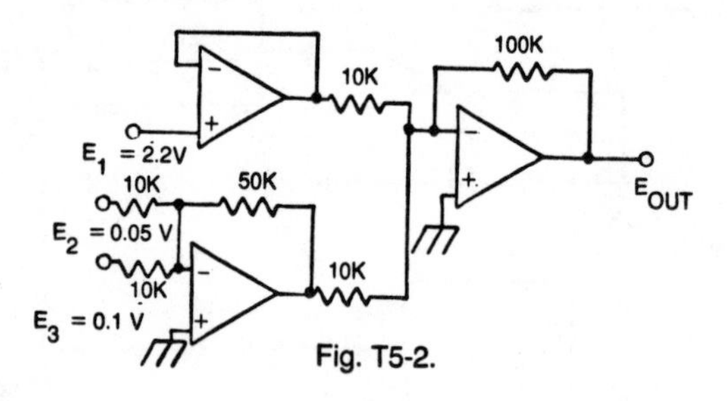

Fig. T5-2.

5.3 What is the function of the circuit in Fig. T5-3?

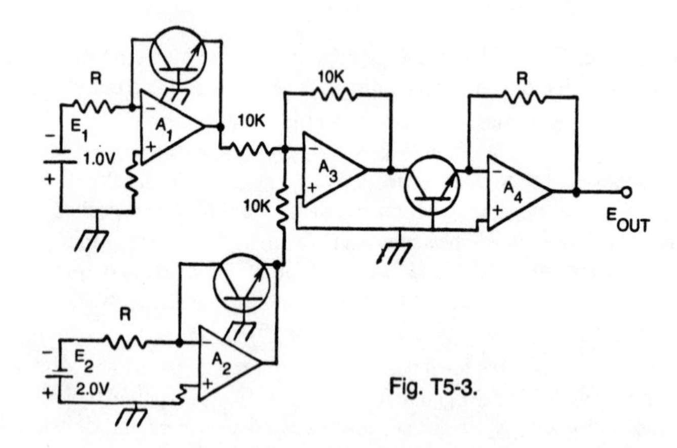

Fig. T5-3.

5.4 What is the value of E_{OUT} in Fig. T5-3?
5.5 What change would be required to have this circuit perform the operation E_1/E_2?
5.6 What type of circuit is shown in Fig. T5-4?

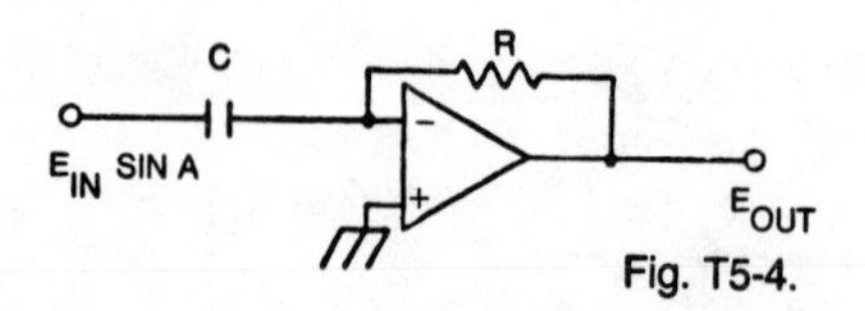

Fig. T5-4.

5.7 Write a general equation for $E_{OUT} = f(E_{IN})$.
5.8 If E_{IN} = sin A what is E_{OUT}?
5.9 What is the circuit of Fig. T5-5?

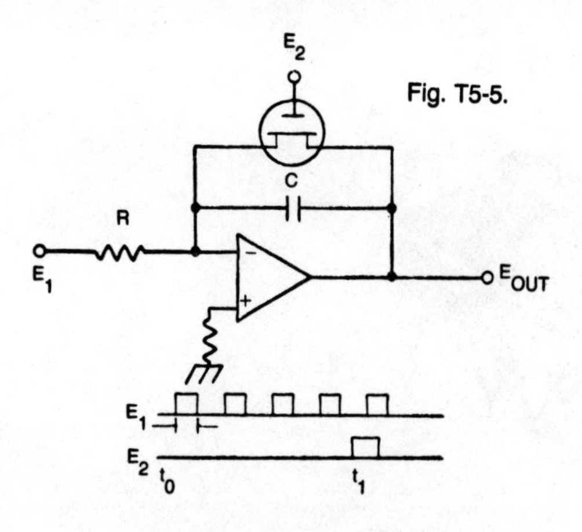

Fig. T5-5.

Answers to test questions are in the back of the book.

Chapter 6

Simple Op-Amp Instrument Design

Operational amplifiers have facilitated the design of instruments which would have been more difficult, more expensive, or even impossible using nonoperational techniques.

An example of a circuit function made better by the use of the operational amplifier is the precision or *precise* rectifier. Normally, a semiconductor rectifier will exhibit a degree of nonlinearity at low amplitudes. This occurs for signals too low in amplitude to overcome the fraction-of-a-volt junction potential normal to any semiconductor junction. An "ideal" rectifier will produce a characteristic with a straight-line slope and the "Y-intercept" at the origin (0, 0). This is illustrated in Fig. 6-1. This matter of poor linearity becomes especially important in circuits which call for good linearity in the low-amplitude region of operation.

PRECISE DIODE CIRCUITS

The poor linearity of regular semiconductor diodes means that many circuits must be operated with only an approximation of proper diode function. The "precise diode" is an op-amp circuit which can be used to overcome that nonlinearity and restore proper circuit function. Such circuits are possible because of the op amps high gain and the existence of the feedback loop. Anomalies such as temperature drift, junction potential, voltage drop, etc., can be removed by the combination of feedback and gain.

The circuit of Fig. 6-2 is an example of a precise diode circuit configuration. Although not the only precise diode circuit known, it may well be the most popular. If the input voltage applied to this circuit is negative, the voltage at the output terminal of the op amp will be positive. This will reverse bias diode D_1 and forward bias D_2. The current flowing in D_2 is then applied to the input; a negative voltage will want to appear at the output.

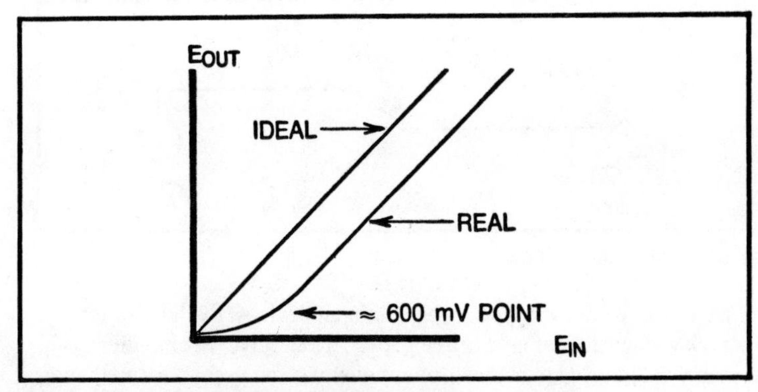

Fig. 6-1. Ideal and real diode response curves.

This will reverse bias D_2, causing zero current flow in the feedback network. At this same time, diode D_1 will be forward biased, effectively clamping the inverting input to virtual ground—a situation required by the grounding of the noninverting input. Since this circuit is both linear and unidirectional, it nicely satisfies the criterion for an *ideal* rectifier.

SIMPLE DC VOLTMETER

Figure 6-3 shows the schematic of a simple dc voltmeter driven by an operational amplifier. At first glance, there seems to be little use for this circuit, as we use a regular analog or digital voltmeter to read the output voltage of a unity-gain operational amplifier circuit. The real utility of this circuit is that it effectively raises the impedance of the voltmeter as seen by the circuit being tested. This can substantially reduce the loading effects on that circuit.

Recall, if you will, that the input impedance of the unity-gain noninverting follower is normally very high. If a Darlington or FET input device is selected for the op amp, then the input impedance is even higher than for

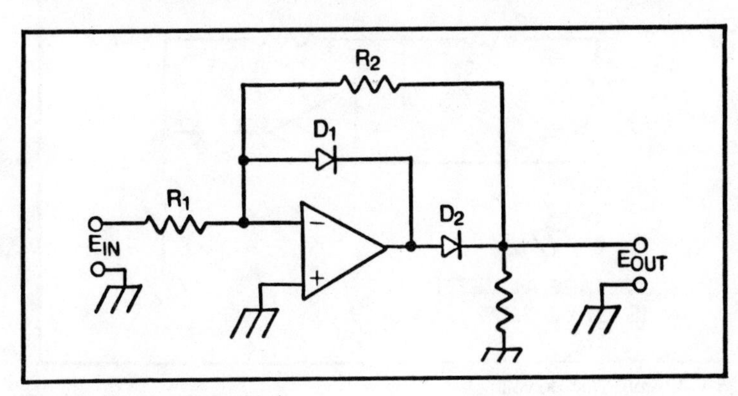

Fig. 6-2. Precise diode circuit.

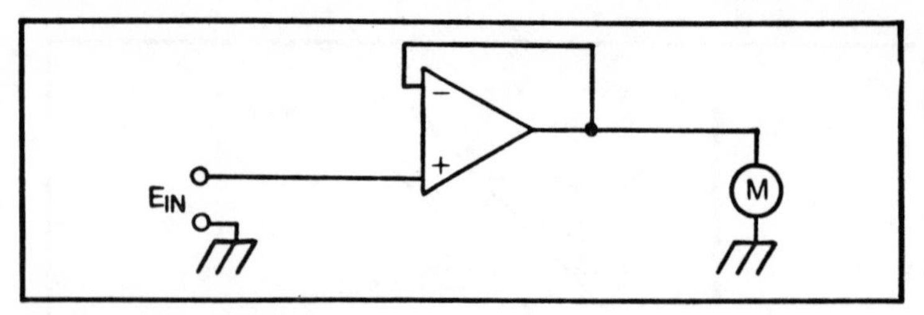

Fig. 6-3. Simple dc voltmeter.

the usual 741/5556/1456 types of bipolar input devices. By the addition of a feedback voltage divider network (Fig. 6-4), we can give the amplifier a gain greater than unity. Under these conditions, we can use a relatively high full-scale voltmeter range to measure very tiny potentials. It is best to make the ratio of the feedback voltage dividers some power of 10 so that the calibration of the voltmeter scale will retain some meaning; the user need only move a decimal point around to read the correct value.

It isn't always possible, or even desirable, to use a voltmeter as the output indicator for a measuring device. In fact, it is far more likely that a current meter will be used; milliammeters and microammeters are probably far more often used than are voltmeters, even when voltage is being measured. An example of the use of a current meter is shown in Fig. 6-5. You will note that this is essentially the same idea as for the voltmeter with just enough of a twist to allow the use of the current meter. The current passing through the meter will be equal to the input voltage divided by the sum of the resistances involved. For example, suppose we have a 200 μA meter movement with an internal resistance of 1000Ω. What value multiplier resistor is needed to provide a full-scale reading of 2.0V?

The problem is solved as follows:

$$I_M = E_{IN}/I_M = E_{IN}/(R_x + R_M)$$

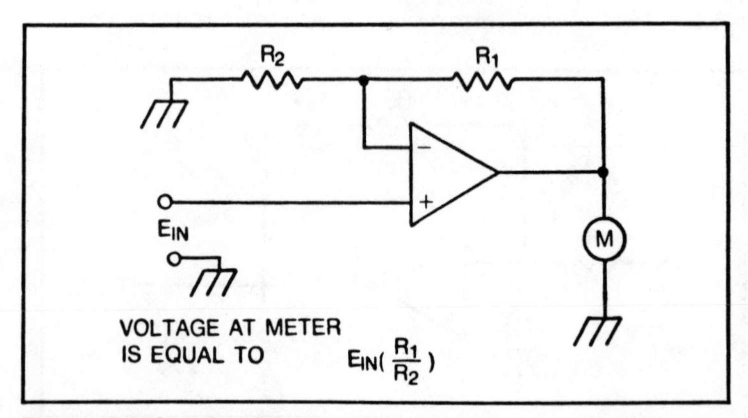

Fig. 6-4. Amplifying dc voltmeter.

where R_x is the multiplier resistance and R_M is the resistance of the meter. Therefore,

$$R_x = (E_{IN}/I_M) - R_M$$
$$= \left(\frac{(2 \times 10^0}{2 \times 10^{-4}}\right) - 1 \times 10^3$$
$$= 1 \times 10^4 - 1 \times 10^3$$
$$= 1 \times 10^4 - 0.1 \times 10^4$$
$$= 9 \times 10^4$$
$$= 9000\Omega$$

Of course, the resistor should be an adjustable type, say a 10K potentiometer, so that errors in op-amp gain, resistor value, and so forth, can be "tuned out." These and other errors are minimized by the use of an op amp with a high input impedance and low offset current.

The necessity of knowing and taking into consideration the internal resistance of the meter movement can be a bit of a bother, especially where different meters might be used in the same circuit at different times. These considerations can be totally negated if we take advantage of one of the prime virtues of the operational amplifier—*feedback*. This is illustrated in Fig. 6-6. In the circuit, slight variations in meter resistance from one unit to the other are made impotent by correction of the op-amp's voltage gain.

The current flowing in the meter movement is the feedback current, which has a magnitude of:

$$I = E_{IN}/R_x$$

Once again, the use of the noninverting voltage follower assures a high input impedance, consistent with the requirement for minimum circuit loading. The meter scale will have to be appropriately calibrated in voltage units rather than current units.

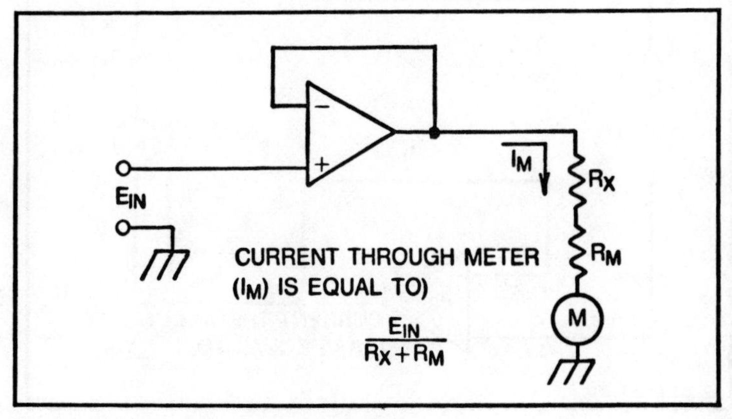

Fig. 6-5. Using ammeter to measure voltage.

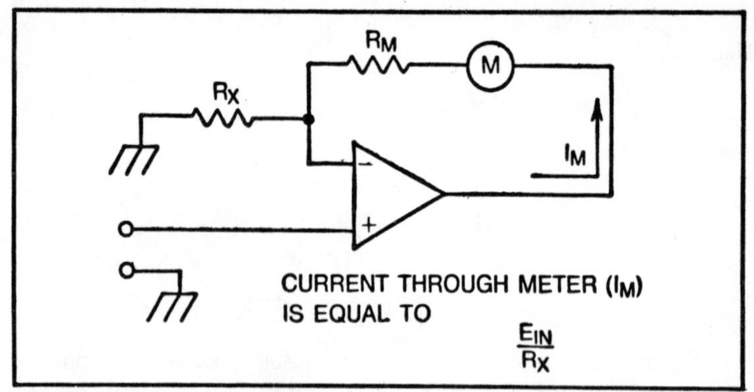

Fig. 6-6. Improved dc voltmeter.

SIMPLE DC DIFFERENTIAL VOLTMETER

Not every voltage measurement is referenced to a common ground point. Some are balanced with respect to ground—a situation requiring a differential voltmeter for measurement. Such instruments actually measure the difference between two voltages which are individually referenced to ground. Figure 6-7 is an example of a simplified dc differential voltmeter.

Amplifiers A_1 and A_2 are high-impedance types (e.g., FET or Darlington) connected in the noninverting unity-gain configuration.

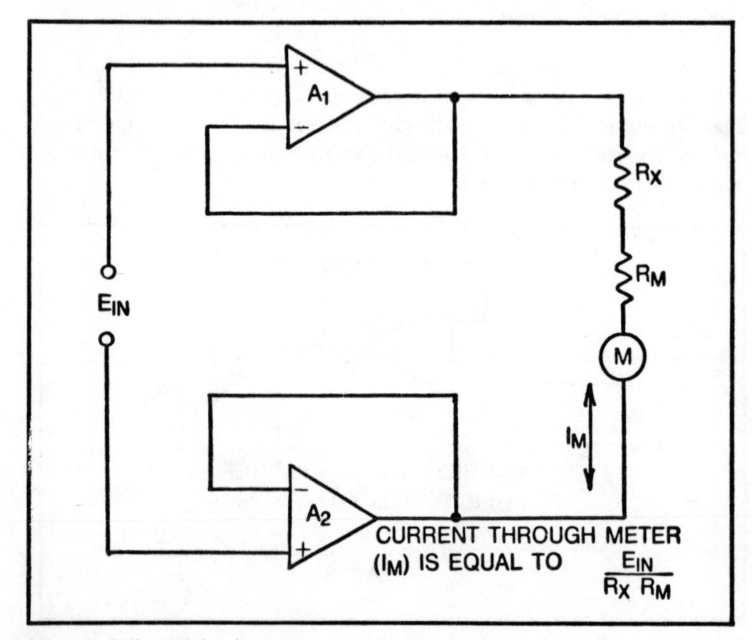

Fig. 6-7. Differential voltmeter.

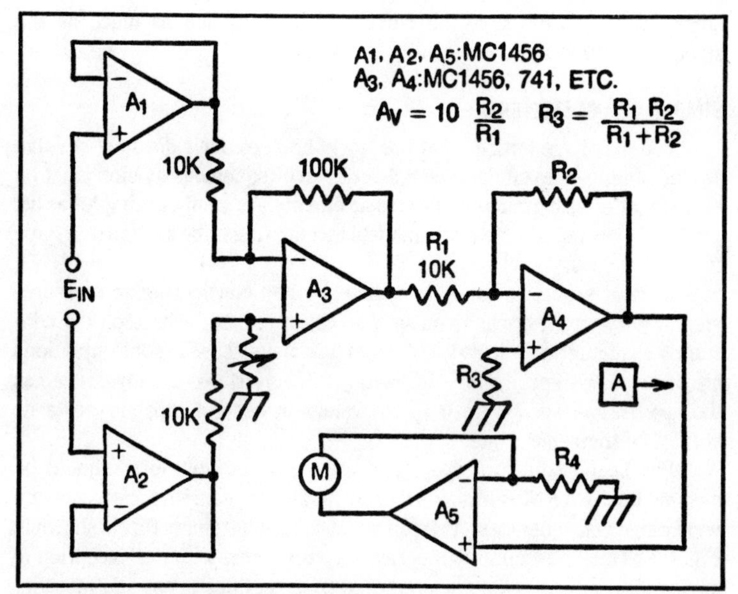

Fig. 6-8. Improved differential voltmeter.

The circuit shown in Fig. 6-7 represents what is merely a simple form of differential voltmeter. It does, of course, suffer from its own simplicity, a fact that is hard to escape in many electronic applications. For one thing, the deficiency in the circuit requires the calculation of meter accuracy by considering the internal resistance of the meter movement. It also suffers from another defect—it can only be used on one relatively high range. Figure 6-8 is an attempt to overcome this situation.

Basically, all we have done in the design of Fig. 6-8 is to cause the "marriage" of two operational amplifier circuits, which are individually useful, each in its own right. The front end of our new-style voltmeter is similar to the instrumentation amplifier of Fig. 3-13. Gain figures are selected which allow a minimum of effort in user interpretation of the readout (i.e., ×1, ×10, ×100, ×1000, etc.). The last stage (A_5) of our "second-generation" differential voltmeter is the single-ended feedback voltmeter of Fig. 6-6.

It is quite easy to connect the output of our Fig. 6-8 differential voltmeter to a digital panel meter to form a wide-range digital multimeter for little more than the cost of the digital panel meter. Addition of a means for varying the gain of the instrumentation amplifier can allow measurement of very low potentials, while an attenuator allows us to handle very high values. Caution must be observed when trying for very low potentials, because in most practical circuits there is a limit to the amount of gain that can be used. This becomes especially true where stability of the amplifier becomes a problem or where the signal being sought is really down in the noise. In the latter case, the noise will be amplified as much as the signal—resulting in no net gain.

SIMPLE AC VOLTMETERS

You may have noticed that the world of electronics does not revolve around simple or even quite complex dc circuits; some provision must be made for alternating current (ac) measurements. Ac is not as "simple" as dc; you can't even use simple mathematical terms to describe ac. You may have to use "imaginary" values.

Several problems arise immediately when considering ac measurements. For instance, when you say "ac volts," exactly where on the constantly changing ac cycle do you mean? Of occasional use in some situations are peak, peak-to-peak, and RMS voltages. This latter is usually defined as the *effective* voltage, since it is equivalent in heating capability to a dc voltage of the same value.

For best results in most applications, an ac voltmeter should be designed to read RMS volts. Further, it should maintain its accuracy over a wide range of frequencies. A circuit which at least attempts this is shown in Fig. 6-9. This is essentially the *feedback* voltmeter, with the exception of having the meter movement bracketed by a rectifier bridge. In most instances the bridge can be constructed from ordinary silicon diodes, unless more accuracy is required. Ready-made "instrumentation rectifiers" are listed in many electronic-parts catalogs.

RMS CONVERSION

As mentioned earlier, the most frequently made ac voltage measurement is the RMS (root mean square) value. This is usually defined as:

$$E_{\mathrm{RMS}} = 0.707E_{\mathrm{P}}$$

This is fine if, and only if, the ac signal has a perfect sine shape. Distorted sine waves, and waves never intended to be sine waves in the first place, require a somewhat more sophisticated technique.

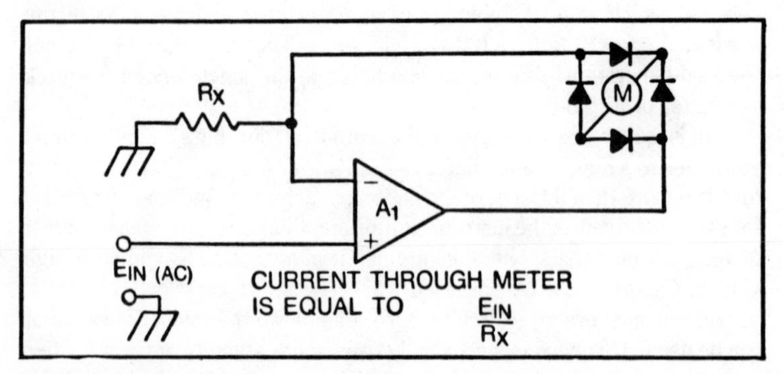

Fig. 6-9. An ac voltmeter.

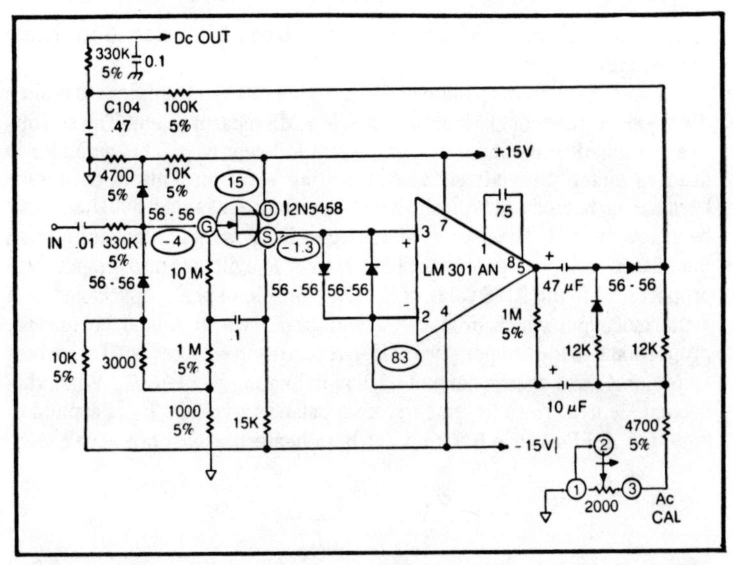

Fig. 6-10. RMS-to-dc converter (averaging type). (Courtesy the Heath Company).

One extraordinarily clumsy technique of RMS-to-dc conversion is to use a voltage divider that divides the peak voltage (as delivered to a capacitor after rectification) by the reciprocal of 0.707, or some power-of-10 submultiple of same. This only "works" if the input signal is nice and cooperative by assuming a pure, harmonicless, no-distortion shape—in short, the ideal sine wave. Better attempts use an averaging method to deliver the RMS from a complex waveform.

The RMS voltage of almost any complex waveform can be described mathematically with a tedious equation and there are a number of ready made circuit modules designed to solve this equation or a close approximation of it.

Figure 6-10 shows the circuit of a relatively low-cost averaging circuit which gives a good accounting of itself in finding the RMS value of an ac signal. Only a small investment in parts is required.

The "standard" (calibration lab) method for measuring the RMS value of an ac signal is to compare it with a direct current capable of producing the same amount of heating in a standard resistance. The resistor is first connected to the unknown ac voltage and allowed to heat up to a point where the temperature stabilizes and is no longer rising. The temperature is measured and noted, and then the resistor is allowed to cool to its initial (room) temperature. The resistor is then connected across a variable calibrated dc power supply. The dc voltage is increased until a point is reached where the resistor is at the same stable temperature as when the ac signal was applied to the resistor. The RMS value of the sine wave is equal to the value of the dc which raised that standard resistor to the same temperature.

Figure 6-11 shows a method that uses operational amplifiers to realize the "temperature comparison" method of RMS measurement. The ac voltage is applied to the input of a unity-gain follower (A_1). This amplifier is used to buffer the source and the heating element. This is necessary because the heater will typically have a resistance less than 500Ω, and may be as low as 10Ω. The source, on the other hand, wants to look into a high impedance, at least higher than 500Ω. Heater R_1 will take on a temperature proportional to the RMS value of E_{IN}. Heating element R_1 is packaged with a thermocouple which produces a voltage E_1 which should be linearly proportional to the temperature of R_1 over the range of interest. This drives amplifier A_2 and causes current to flow in heating element R_2. When this second element rises in temperature a balancing voltage E_2 is applied to amplifier A_2. Power is E^2/R so, for both heaters, which are equal:

$$\frac{E_{IN}^2}{R_1} = \frac{E_{OUT}^2}{R_2}$$

And

$$E_{OUT}^2 = \frac{R_2(E_{IN})^2}{R_1}$$

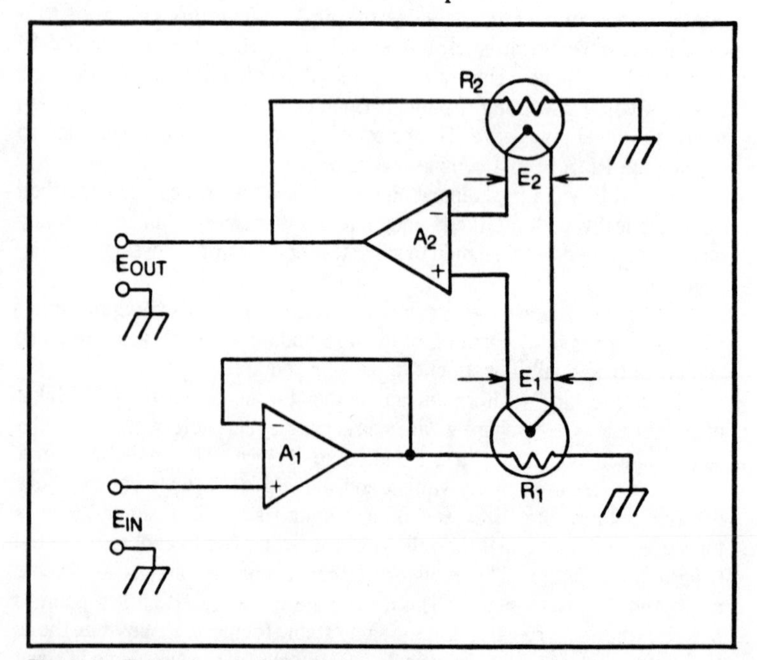

Fig. 6-11. Thermocouple RMS-to-dc converter.

$$E_{OUT} = \left(\frac{R_2}{R_1}\right)^{1/2} \cdot E_{IN}$$

If $R_1 = R_2$, then

$$E_{OUT} = E_{IN}$$

where E_{IN} is the RMS value of the applied ac voltage.

Accuracy of this type of circuit can be quite good if the integrity of selected components is high. Accuracies on the order of less than 0.5 percent are obtainable. The circuit works at frequencies up to 10 MHz. Limiting the accuracy, however, is the match of the thermocouple heater assemblies. For best accuracy, these units must have matched characteristics throughout the range of measurement. Both assemblies must also have the same thermal conductivity to the environment. In order to reduce interaction, it is necessary to thermally isolate the two assemblies from each other. Otherwise, we could expect an artifact voltage to appear in one thermocouple output generated by the heating element of the other assembly.

Another source of error is the low amplitude signal performance of amplifiers A_1 and A_2. A thermocouple will produce a tiny signal of less than 100 μV/C^0. Even modern solid-state silicon thermocouples produce signals which are only on the order of millivolts per Celsius degree. It is necessary to limit the input range for applied voltage to about 3:1 or 4:1. Keep in mind that power is proportional to the square of the input voltage, making a power dissipation ratio of 16:1 for a 4:1 voltage excursion. This could easily lead to the destruction of R_1.

For symmetrical waveforms, the RMS converter of Fig. 6-11 will be valid up to a point approaching the upper frequency limit of amplifier A_1 (in its noninverting unity-gain configuration), or where stray capacitances and inductances begin to attenuate E_{IN}. Where tight layouts are used, the circuit is generally bound only by the amplifier characteristics. A low-frequency limit is established by the time constant of the heater—thermocouple assemblies.

Computational methods for converting RMS to dc are shown in Figs. 6-12 and 6-13. In Fig. 6-12, we use two analog multipliers and a pair of operational amplifiers in a circuit which is actually a single-function analog computer permanently programmed to solve the RMS equation. The input stage is one of the analog multipliers connected with its X and Y inputs strapped together so that it functions as a *squarer*. A multiplier so connected delivers the value E_{IN}^2 at the output.

Following the squarer is an integrator using an operational amplifier as the active element. This integrator must have an RC time constant longer than the period of the lowest frequency ac signal which is expected to be measured.

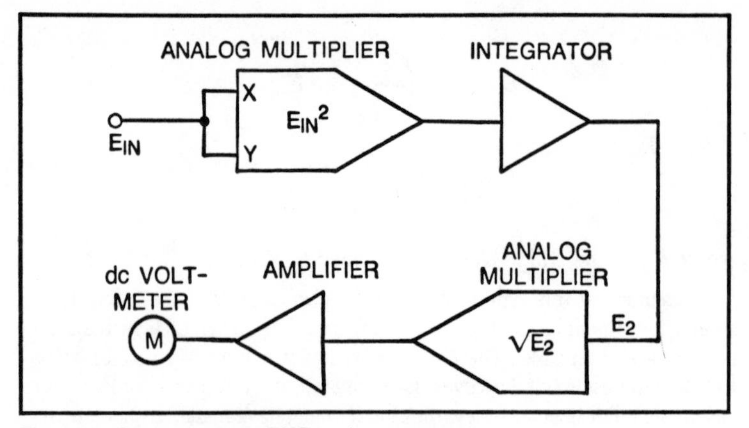

Fig. 6-12. Computing-type RMS-to-dc converter.

A second multiplier is used following integration which is connected as a square rooter. The output of this stage is proportional to the RMS value of the input voltage signal. The output amplifier serves three purposes: it drives the voltmeter, buffers the output of the last multiplier, and serves to scale the output as required. The frequency response of this type of RMS-to-dc converter is bound above by the parameters of the operational amplifiers, and below by the time constant of the integrator.

Most multipliers have a high enough frequency response to be able to

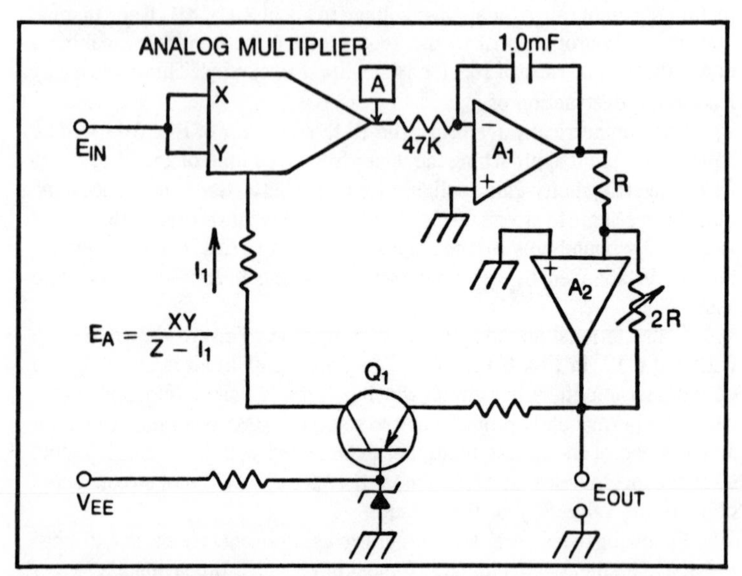

Fig. 6-13. Alternate RMS-to-dc converter.

follow the best operational amplifiers. Op amps from the 741 family cannot be expected to provide superior performance above 10 kHz. Use of a wideband type, however, allows decent operation of this circuit to 1 or 2 MHz. Expected accuracies can range below 1 percent if quality components, especially the multipliers, are selected. Fortunately, good monolithic IC multipliers are available at reasonable cost which will operate to frequencies well over a megahertz, with errors less than 1 percent.

The full range of inputs which this type of circuit can handle is on the order of several hundred millivolts to several volts. Ranges can be extended above and below these points by adding suitable input attenuators for the higher voltage ranges, and amplifiers for the lower voltage ranges. That input amplifier must, however, be a high-gain type and should have a frequency response at least as good as the rest of the circuit. Even if an input amplifier is not required for low signal amplification, it is wise to precede the first multiplier with a unity-gain noninverting follower—if only to provide isolation.

A simpler version of the RMS-to-dc converter is shown in Fig. 6-13. This circuit requires a multiplier which allows its scale factor to be manipulated by the user through programming of external current I_1. In this circuit, the analog multiplier functions as both a squarer and a square rooter, due to the action of current I_1 flowing in the system's feedback loop. Operational amplifier A_1 serves as an integrator—averager, while A_2 is a buffer amplifier and scaler. Transistor Q_1 is used as a voltage-to-current converter, which changes voltage variations to the proportional current needed to drive the I_1 input of the analog multiplier. Voltage E_{OUT} will be proportional to the RMS value of E_{IN}. Frequency limits are bound above by the operational amplifier frequency response and below by the integrator time constant. Of course, if a low-quality multiplier is used, expect it to bound the frequency response as well as deteriorate the overall accuracy of the circuit. As an alternative design, which may track better, a voltage-to-current converter using an operational amplifier may be substituted for Q_1.

OPERATIONAL CURRENT METERS

There are several ways to measure the flow of current using an assist from operational amplifiers. One method is to create a floating voltmeter (actually, it is a version of the differential voltmeter). We can insert a resistance in the path of the current being measured and complete the current flow from the voltage drop, as read on the floating voltmeter (see Fig. 6-14). The obvious disadvantage is the necessity of inserting a foreign resistance in the circuit being tested. The criterion for an ammeter is that it must have as low a resistance as possible in order to not distort the accuracy of the reading. Because of the extra resistance, the actual reading is somewhat lower than the current in the circuit without the meter. This error becomes a real problem both at low voltage levels and in low-

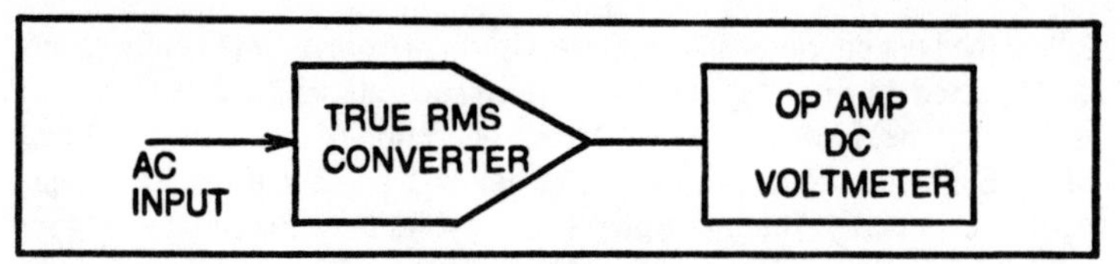

Fig. 6-14. Block diagram of a true RMS voltmeter.

resistance circuits. In both circumstances, the inserted resistance may well become a significant part of the whole.

An almost lossless measuring scheme for current is shown in Fig. 6-15. This method takes advantage of the fact that the inputs are at virtual ground. The voltage appearing across the op-amp output will be proportional to the input current and the multiplying resistance. This circuit works well for low currents, especially in the microampere range, where meter movements are hard to come by. Do not, however, try jamming an amp or so into the op amp; it might object violently!

A version of the op-amp current meter which uses a milliammeter as the output indicator is shown in Fig. 6-16. It is essentially similar to the former circuit, but the differences are worthy of note. Although the indicator is a milliammeter, it is capable of reading full-scale current levels down to microamperes. Let us assume that meter M has a full-scale current range of 1 mA and that the load resistance is 1000Ω. For a full-scale current of 10 μA:

$$R_x = \frac{R_L(I_M - I_N)}{I_{IN}}$$

$$\doteq \frac{10^3(10^{-3} - 10^{-5})}{10^{-5}}$$

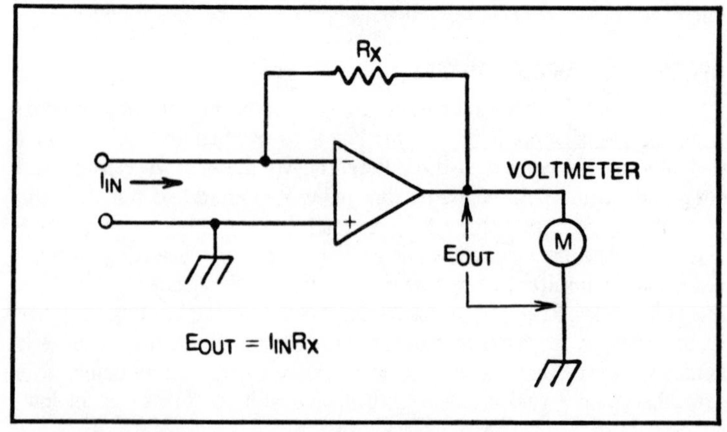

Fig. 6-15. "Lossless" (so-called) current meter.

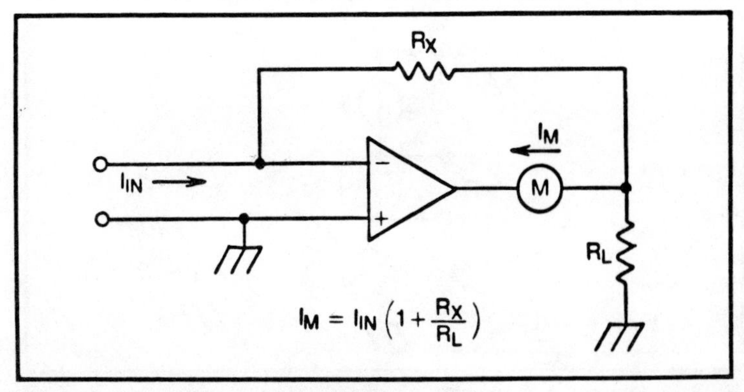

Fig. 6-16. Alternate form of current meter.

$$= \frac{10^3\,(99 \times 10^{-5})}{10^{-5}}$$

$$= \frac{99 \times 10^{-2}}{10^{-5}}$$

$$= 99 \times 10^3$$
$$= 99\text{K}$$

This circuit serves to demonstrate how the operational amplifier can be used to make a sensitive instrument, which would have been either difficult or extremely expensive without the op amp. Normally, meters that measure 10 μA full scale are hard to come by and are expensive when located. The op amp supplies the amplification and driving power needed to raise the low-level current to the 1 mA range, where instruments are available at lower cost.

OHMMETERS USING OP AMPS

The operational amplifier circuit of Fig. 6-17, called the Shaffer meter after, Dr. Michael J. Shaffer, has been used to measure resistance using a very low value of current flow. This is very useful in solid-state circuits where the usual ohmmeter, using a 1.5V battery, will either cause damage or an erroneous reading. The operational amplifier allows the use of microampere currents which are at voltage levels too low to forward bias any semiconductor junctions in the circuit.

The constant-current source (CCS) in Fig. 6-17 can be a properly biased FET or a 1.36V mercury cell fed into a high resistance. If a 1 μA CCS were desired, two resistors could be used, one in each leg, which total 1.36 megohms. The gain of the op amp is scaled so that a predetermined voltage will exist when a specified R_x is present across the terminals. Assume, in our next example, that a scale factor of 100 mV per 10K of resistance is used. At a CCS level of 1 μA, the differential input to the op amp is:

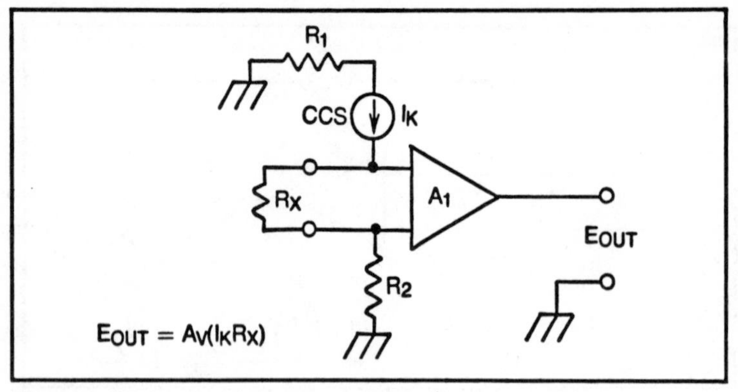

Fig. 6-17. Shaffer's ac ohmmeter.

$$E_{IN} = R_X I = R_X(1 \times 10^{-6})$$

For R_{IN} = 10K,

$$10^4 10^{-6} = 10^{-2}\ V = 0.01V = 10\ mV$$

Since the actual input is 0.01V and 0.1V is required, the amplifier voltage gain must be 10. You can use different voltage gains, scale factors, and CCS levels to accommodate different resistance ranges.

NULL VOLTMETERS

A large number of electronic instruments make use of the null voltmeter as an output indicator. An example of a null voltmeter is shown in Fig. 6-18. This instrument uses two different methods for detecting the null: a

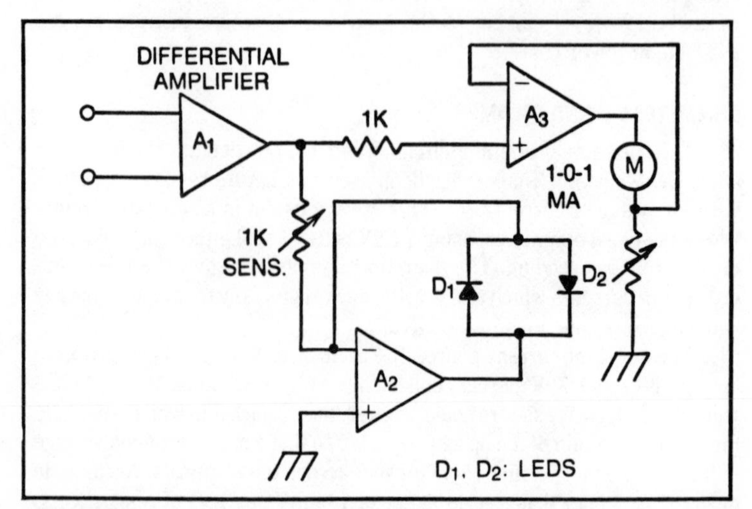

Fig. 6-18. Null voltmeter and detector.

galvanometer and a light-emitting diode (LED). One advantage in the galvanometer method is that the meter can be calibrated to show how much of a voltage difference exists between the inputs for any given off-null condition.

At null, the LEDs will glow dimly or not at all. Although extremely simple, the LED null indicator has been used on scientific and medical instruments where a factory- or operator-set null must be optimized. A value of differential voltage other than zero (which exists at null) will light up the appropriate diode and extinguish the alternate LED. Although one might reasonably expect this circuitry to suffer from its own simplicity, it gives a high degree of accuracy with good repeatability from one case to another.

DECIBEL METER

A decibel meter is nothing more than a logarithmic amplifier feeding an ac voltmeter. A special scale will be necessary for the meter face in most applications. In the example of Fig. 6-19, we use an op-amp logarithmic amplifier ahead of a standard voltmeter circuit. As is usual, amplifiers or attenuators can be used ahead of this circuit to provide various ranges and flexibility.

OTHER SPECIAL METERS

There are any number of special preamplifying conditioners which can

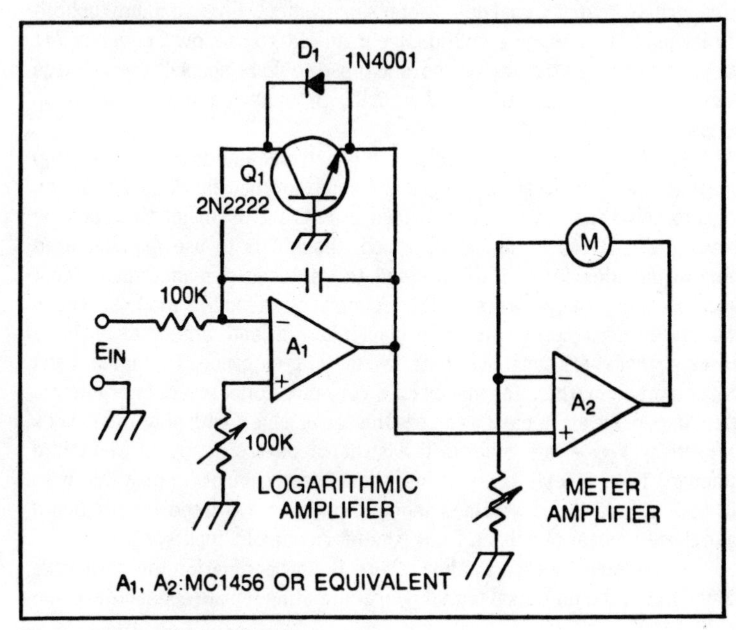

Fig. 6-19. Logarithmic voltmeter.

be used ahead of an op-amp current or voltage meter to provide any number of special measuring instruments. We have seen the use of RMS ac converters, logarithmic amplifiers, and differential amplifiers. Also seen occasionally are Miller integrators that form integrating voltmeters. In some special cases, you might want to precede the voltmeter with an *X-Y* multiplier or small-scale analog computer-like instrument designed to perform a single highly specialized task. The really nice thing about the use of operational circuitry is that imagination is one of the major factors in determining versatility!

UNIVERSAL INSTRUMENTS USING OP AMPS

Engineers, technicians, experimenters, workers in the various physical/biological sciences, and just about anybody else concerned with processing some sort of analog signal could probably find use for a modest collection of simple op-amp instruments which are easily adaptable to the present need.

One reasonable approach to production of such instruments is the *op-amp manifold*. Such devices contain from one to 10 op amps and a power supply. Only the inputs and outputs of the respective amplifiers are available at the user's front panel. Inside the manifold, we find V_{CC} and V_{EE} power supplies, and the required compensation (dc and signal) and protection circuitry. Users need only worry about such things as voltage gain (R_F/R_{IN}), dc shift, and so forth. This frees him from having to really design the circuitry surrounding the op amp, or from having to mess around with the nitty-gritty constructional details of his instrument. For maximum flexibility it might be wise, on a multidevice manifold, to use low frequency 741 family types for all but one or two, and those could be special types such as high-frequency, high-voltage, low-drift, or superlow-input-current op amps.

Another approach is to actually build instrumentation circuits using op amps in boxes which can be plugged into some sort of mainframe. Of course, any box could be used for the individual circuits and the mainframe could be bench built. A more elegant approach, though, is to use manufactured plug-in modules for the circuits and the associated mainframes. Most oscilloscope manufacturers in this country offer plug-in models. These manufacturers generally also offer blank plug-ins, and sometimes portable cases so that users can make their own units. If elegance is paramount and cost no problem, then this makes for a very nice collection of instruments. Less expensive and almost as nice is the "strut cage," with plug-in modules offered by *Vector* and others. The strut cages are designed to fit into standard 19-inch relay racks or into those many cabinets compatible with 19-inch panels. Each shielded module contains a printed circuit board (purchased extra) and has a front panel for controls, inputs, etc.

At the rear of each module, there is an opening for the card-edge connector of the universal circuit board. A mating female connector on the rear panel of the strut cage accepts this edge connector so that power supply and other desired connections are made automatically when the module is inserted into the cage.

Modules typically accept standard cards with lengths up to 9 inches. Cards are available with a printed, foil pattern on one side suitable for mounting resistors, ICs, capacitors, and so forth. It might be desired that a simple op-amp manifold be in any given module. This allows a certain flexibility at the expense of a messy front panel. It might be appropriate to build active filters, amplifiers with programmable or continuously variable gain, or integrators and differentiators with variable time constants for wide range of input signals. Also found in such a system might be a number of function generator modules for many different purposes.

Imagination is a prerequisite for making the optimum use of op-amp instruments, to be sure, but the approaches described here allow those whose sophistication lies in nonelectronic areas to be almost as good as would be a top-notch designer.

LIMITERS AND BOUND VALUE AMPLIFIERS

Unless some nonlinear device is incorporated into the circuit, an operational amplifier will produce an output which is a linear function of the input voltage. Linear functions, you should recall from elementary algebra, have the form $Y = MX + b$ in the rectangular coordinate system. For a noninverting follower this function, graphed in Fig. 6-20A, will be:

$$E_{OUT} = A_V E_{IN} + E_O$$

E_O is any offset voltage which might exist (it might also be zero) and determines the Y intercept. In cases where the offset voltage is nulled to zero or low enough to be of negligible importance, the curve will pass through the origin. The slope of the curve, the M term in the standard form, is given by the voltage gain which is set by R_F/R_{IN}. If the amplifier has unity gain, the curve will have a slope of one. If the slope is negative, we know the amplifier is an inverting follower.

In the usual operational amplifier application, we want E_{OUT} to be able to vary as far as possible between limits imposed by the power-supply voltages. Otherwise, signal clipping may occur on strong inputs. In other instances, though, it might be desirable to set bounds on the maximum allowable excursions of E_{OUT}. Some of the specific circuits in other chapters used some kind of output limiting to keep the value of E_{OUT} below some level. Figure 6-20B shows the output voltage vs input voltage graph of such an amplifier. In the example shown here, the positive and negative bounds are not equal, but in most cases they will be.

There are three basic methods for limiting the output voltage swing in an operational amplifier circuit: series, shunt, and feedback. In the series limiting circuit, illustrated in Fig. 6-21A, a zener diode is used to set the

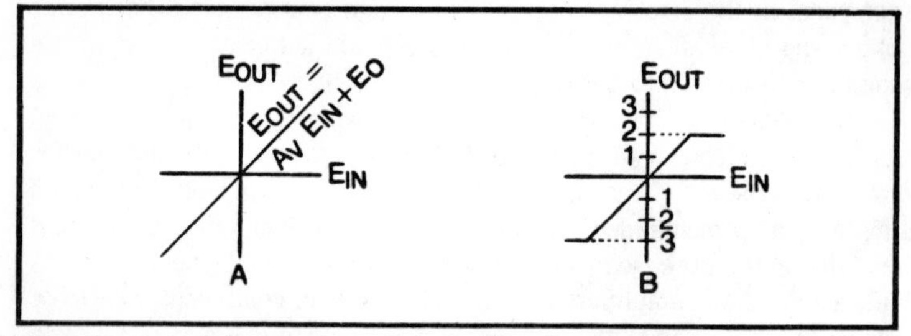

Fig. 6-20. Bounded and unbounded amplifier characteristics.

limiting point. The graph of such a circuit, (Fig. 6-21B) shows that the output voltage will be zero until the input voltage rises to a value greater than or equal to the sum of the zener voltage and the voltage drop across D_A. This latter voltage will be about 0.7V for silicon diodes. Diode D_A is needed to block the flow of current when E_{IN} is negative. E_{OUT} will be zero until the critical voltage is reached. Then it will increase in a manner which is almost linear. Should a negative-going output function be required, diodes D_A and D_Z are reversed. A dual breakpoint results from parallel operation of the positive- and negative-going versions of this circuit. The output function will be symmetrical if identical diodes are used for D_A, and zeners which are identical (with the same value of V_Z) are used for D_Z. If these conditions are not met, the output will be asymmetrical.

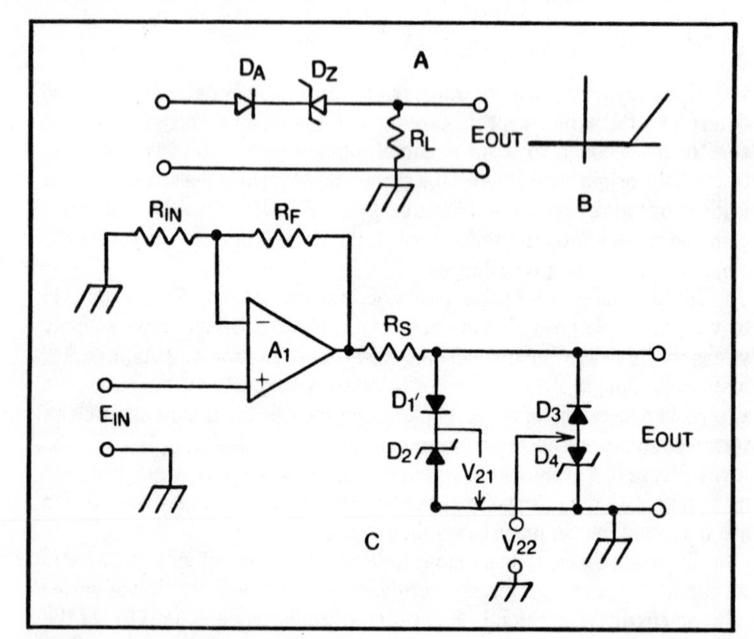

Fig. 6-21. Simple zener amplifier.

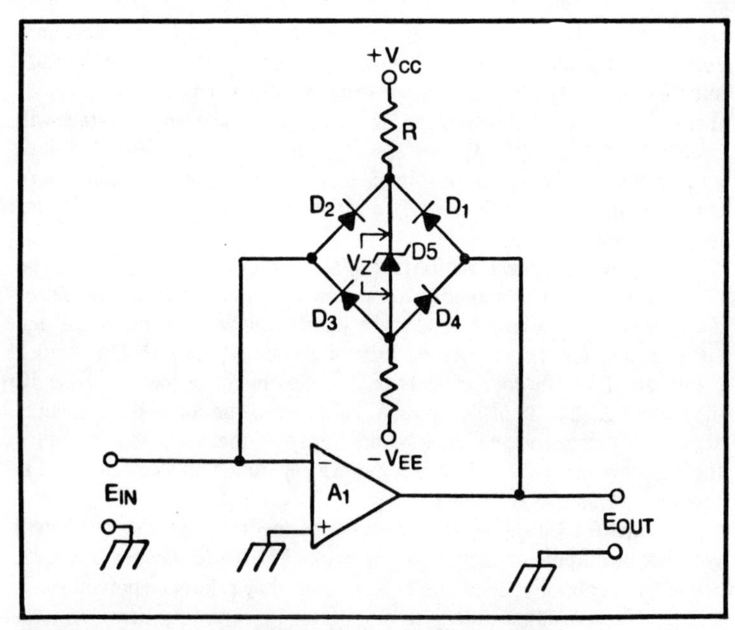

Fig. 6-22. One type of feedback bounded limiting amplifier.

Shunt limiting is shown in Fig. 6-21C. Here we have a noninverting follower with a gain of R_F/R_{IN}. This configuration's output voltage function agrees with Fig. 6-20B. In the real world, we could just as easily use an inverting follower and obtain the output function simply by viewing Fig. 6-20B in a mirror! The shunt limiter uses the same sort of diode arrangement as the series circuits, but they are connected across the output rather than in series with the signal line. If a positive E_{OUT} voltage tries to rise above a critical point, defined as $(V_{D1} + V_{Z1})$, diodes D_1 and D_2 will clamp it from any further increase. On negative excursions of E_{OUT}, diodes D_3 and D_4 perform a similar function. Symmetry of the output function is determined by the relationship of $(V_{D1} + V_{Z1})$ and $(V_{D3} + V_{Z2})$. Series resistor R_S is needed to limit the current through the diodes to a nondestructive level.

One example of a feedback limiter is an operational amplifier with a circuit such as Fig. 6-21A in the negative feedback path. In that case, the output voltage function will simply be the inverse of Fig. 6-21B. Another example, which is a bit more sophisticated, is shown in Fig. 6-22. In this circuit, we use a small-current bridge rectifier excited by E_{OUT}, E_{IN}, a reference potential V_Z. When a voltage is applied to the input, current will flow in the feedback loop. If the input voltage is positive, then E_{OUT} is negative (the circuit is an inverting follower). E_{OUT} will continue to increase in the negative direction until it is high enough to overcome the reverse biasing effect of V_Z on diodes D_2 and D_4. When that point is reached, diodes D_2 and D_4 will be forward biased and will begin to conduct. Current will then be able to flow through diodes D_2, D_4 and D_5 to the input, completing the feedback loop. When E_{IN} is negative, exactly the opposite situation occurs because the output voltage will be positive-going. Under those circumstances, diodes D_1 and D_3 will conduct. The output voltage will be bound at two points: $-(V_Z + V_{D2} + V_{D4})$ and $+(V_Z + V_{D1} + V_{D3})$. Values for resistors labeled simply as R in the figure can be computed using Ohm's law. Use either voltage, V_{CC} or V_{EE}, and current I_Z (zener current of D_5) for this calculation.

Temperature compensation is crucial in this circuit if precision is to be maintained. All diodes should have a common thermal environment. Zener diode D_5 should have a temperature coefficient which cancels out and compensates for the cumulative drift of diodes D_1 through D_4. A good combination for the four conventional diodes might be one of those IC diodes packs such as made by RCA and others. The diode pack, though, should be thermally coupled with the zener so that they have identical thermal environments. A few centimeters separation on a circuit board is too far for effective tracking.

Figure 6-23A shows another form of feedback limiter which will generate an output voltage which graphs like Fig. 6-23B. Diodes D_1 and D_2 are in the feedback path but are reverse biased by reference potentials E_1 and E_2. These voltages are generated from V_{CC} and V_{EE}, using resistor voltage dividers. If E_{IN} is positive, then E_{OUT} will go negative until it reaches a point approximately 0.3V greater than E_1. At that point, diode D_1

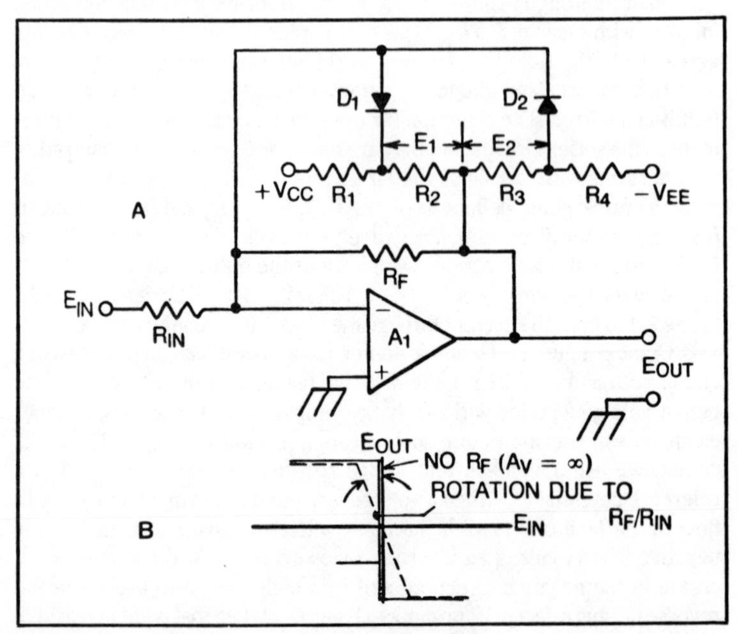

Fig. 6-23. Another feedback loop bounded amplifier.

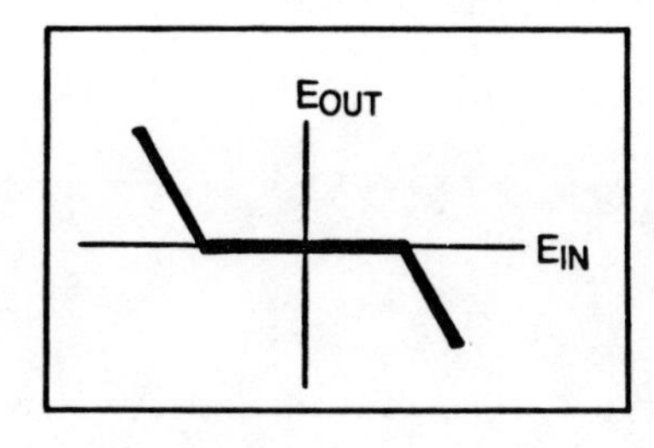

Fig. 6-24. Dead band amplifier.

will begin to conduct and feedback current will flow to the inverting input. When the input voltage is negative, on the other hand, the output will go positive until it is about 0.3V above E_2, at which point diode D_2 begins to conduct. If no feedback resistor (R_F) is used, the circuit will make a good bipolar switch, and will have an output voltage slope close to infinity. This is represented by the plot along the E_{OUT} axis in Fig. 6-23B. If a feedback resistor is used, however, the slope will reduce to a value which is somewhat less. This situation is represented by the rotated plot in the same figure.

DEAD-ZONE AMPLIFIERS

Bound amplifiers or *limiters* permit output voltages to be a function of the input voltage only up to a critical point, after which any further increase is clamped. A dead zone amplifier is just the opposite in that they produce no output voltage for all values of E_{IN} within certain bounds. Although almost all dead-zone amplifiers are symmetrical with respect to zero, the limits could actually be set just about any place within reason on the output curve.

One method for making a dead-zone amplifier is to design two series limiters which produce the output function of Fig. 6-21B, and its inverse (Fig. 6-24). E_{IN} would than be fed to the inputs of both limiters in parallel while the outputs would be fed to alternate inputs of a summing amplifier. Use of reference grade zener diodes and "ideal" operational amplifier rectifiers for the regular diodes will result in a precision dead-zone amplifier.

Chapter 7

Active Filter Circuits

A filter is an electronic circuit designed to pass certain frequencies and reject all others, or vice versa. Although it can be convincingly argued that this is too simplistic a definition, it is workable on the practical applications which this book treats.

FILTERING WITH OP AMPS

Traditional frequency selective filters have been made using passive devices such as resistors, capacitors, and inductors. Although the techniques worked, they had several problems. One is the fact that passive filters inherently attenuate the desirable frequencies. Any filter that cannot supply power will dissipate some of the signal, causing a loss of signal amplitude. This insertion loss is usually expressed as so many decibels at a specified frequency within the passband.

Another problem is obtaining the precise inductance values often required. It is very rare that a filter inductor value will be nice enough to come out to a figure deemed decent by inductor manufacturers.

The last problem, which is by far the most serious one, is the fact that inductors are bulky. This becomes especially true as operating frequency decreases with the corresponding increase of required inductance. Even at relatively high frequencies, though, modern IC techniques reduce the size of other components so much that even small inductances take up a lot of room.

Using a gain block with the properties of an operational amplifier to simulate inductance allows us to construct filter circuits using RC networks. This approach allows us to minimize unwieldy inductors and the practical problems associated with cross coupling via the magnetic field.

There are several ways to use an operational amplifier in an active filter circuit. One method, which is admittedly not too awfully elegant, is to follow a passive filter circuit, usually an RC network, with a gain stage (Fig. 7-1A). In that case the high input impedance of the op amp keeps the problems of changing load conditions from interfering with filter performance. The gain of the operational amplifier is used to overcome the loss of the network.

In other circuits, it is possible to make use of that most endearing property of the op amp (feedback) to create a reasonably low-cost filter circuit. It seems that it is possible to create an amplifier with a given transfer characteristic by inserting a network with the opposite characteristic in the negative feedback loop (Fig. 7-1B).

The amplitude—frequency (that is, the frequency response) graph for different types of filters are shown in Fig. 7-2. Although there are several different classifications within each of these groups, we need not worry too much about them at this point in our overview treatment. The subject of filters, active or otherwise, is an entire subspecialty within electrical engineering. Those intending to pursue the study of filters in more depth will find a lot of suggested reading in the bibliography at the end of this chapter.

A perfect passband filter will have a response such as that in Fig. 7-2A. In this rather ideal case, the filter passes only those signals within the passband. Above and below the two critical points, the response is sharply and abruptly truncated. This is a nice filter to have especially if phase shifts and other parameters are as perfect as the passband (which we have no reason to assume is the case). Of course, this is the real world and real filters are used here. Real filters usually do not meet the ideal criteria (although some approach it where money is no object). In fact, real filters will exhibit some phase shift, which we can live with if the shift is within reasonable bounds. Filters also do not have the ideal frequency response

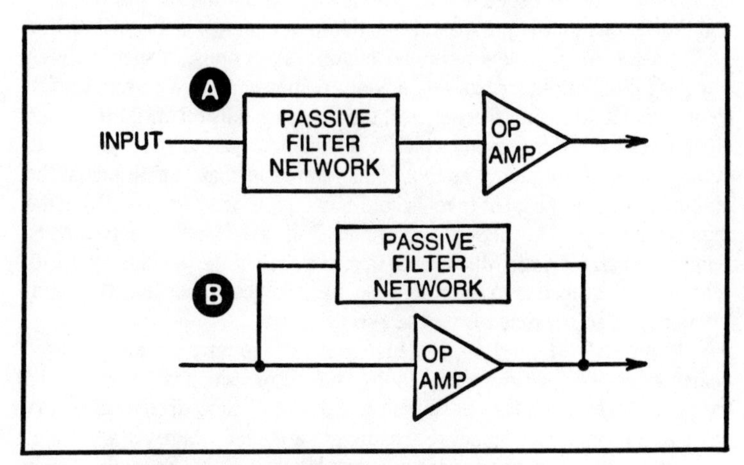

Fig. 7-1. Block diagrams of alternate active filter circuits.

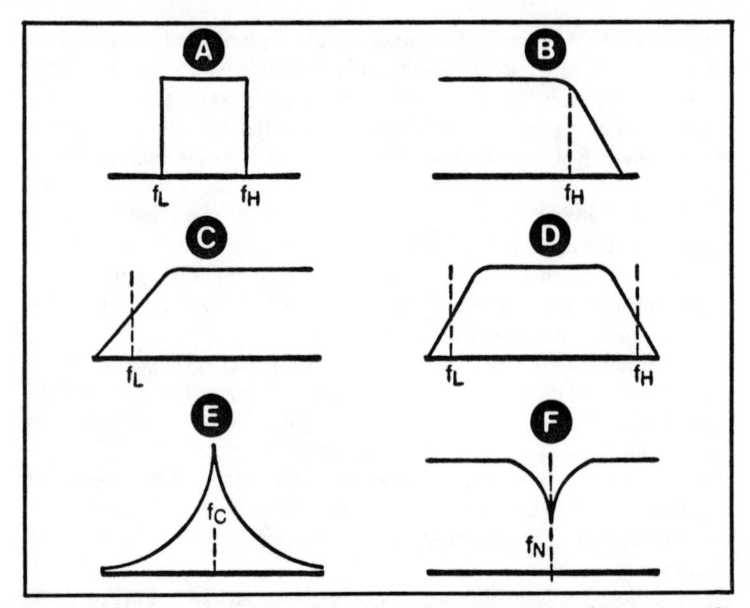

Fig. 7-2. Filter frequency response curves: (A) ideal passband, (B) low-pass, (C) high-pass, (D) real bandpass, (E) peaking, and (F) notch.

characteristic. In general, a passband filter will possess a characteristic such as that of Fig. 7-2D.

Real filters have a frequency response which, instead of sharply truncating, falls off at a certain number of decibels per octave above and below the critical frequencies. The high and low cutoff points are usually defined as the points where the response has fallen off a set number of decibels relative to a certain specified test frequency within the passband.

Variations on the passband filter theme are shown in Figs. 7-2B and 7-2C, in the form of low-pass and high-pass versions, respectively. A low-pass filter offers a relatively smooth response up to a certain critical frequency. At all higher frequencies, the response falls off until little or no signal is passed. For reasons which will become apparent shortly, we will define the cutoff frequency as that point where the signal amplitude at the output, assuming the input level is held constant, is one half (—6 dB) of the input amplitude. The high-pass version (Fig. 7-2C) offers a frequency response characteristic which is the mirror image of the low-pass type. Its reason for existence is to pass signals of frequencies higher than the cutoff frequency (also reckoned from the —6 dB point).

Figures 7-2E and 7-2F illustrate two reciprocal and related characteristics—*peak* and *notch*. In the peak filter, which is a very special case of the passband filter, the circuit will pass only those frequencies very close to the center frequency. Such circuits are used wherever a "single" frequency must be separated from a complex waveform. Examples are in separating the 19 kHz pilot subcarrier from the composite signal in FM stereo receivers, or in making "audio selectivity" adapters for CW communications receivers. The opposite situation obtains in Fig. 7-2F. This is a notch filter used primarily to rid a signal of an unwanted frequency. Fixed, or more likely, tunable filters are often used in CW communications receivers to suppress unwanted signals whose frequency is close to desired signals. For example, the signal desired might, when heterodyned with the beat-frequency oscillator (BFO) needed for CW reception, produce a 500 Hz tone. An interfering signal, though, might produce a tone of 850 Hz. By using a notch filter tuned to 850 Hz, we can rid the passband of that offending signal at a much lower cost than using filters normally possessing sufficient selectivity at the i-f of the receiver.

Another very common use for the notch filter is the elimination of 60 Hz signals in scientific instruments, audio equipment, or just about any other place where even small hum components would prove particularly troublesome. Although these two types of filters seem opposites (which they are), they can actually be implemented by the same techniques because they are really different circuit configurations of the same basic network: the twin-tee notch filter.

FILTER CHARACTERISTICS

One of the more popular methods for classifying filters is by examining the properties of the frequency-amplitude response. A *Butterworth* filter exhibits flatness throughout the passband. A good Butterworth, in fact, is considered maximally flat up to the beginning of the rolloff knee. Two other types of filter, called Chebishev and elliptical, offer substantially better rolloff properties at the expense of amplitude ripples in the response curve. The Chebishev has ripples only within the passband, while the elliptical has variations both in and outside the passband.

The order of a filter, at least in the naive sense, is a measure of the rolloff rate. In all filters, amplitude response falls off at a hopefully linear rate as frequency departs from the knee frequency, f_0, until a point at which there is essentially little improvement with further changes in frequency—where the rolloff becomes asymptomatic. The order of the filter determines how rapidly the rolloff approaches that point. A simple passive RC filter is said to be first order, since its natural rolloff is 6 dB/octave (an octave is a frequency interval where the high frequency is twice the low frequency). A single operational amplifier properly configured can operate as a second order filter (12 dB/octave) or a third order filter (18 dB/octave). Use of two operational amplifiers allows fourth order (24 dB/octave) or even higher orders.

It might seem that cascading active filter circuits would result in the creation of an order which is merely the sum of the orders of the individual circuits. This is not true. To make higher order filters, it is the usual practice to factor the polynomial (to be discussed in a subsequent section) which describes the filter's transfer property. Order can be predicted from this polynomial because the degree of the equation is the order of the filter. A second order filter, for example, is described by a quadratic equation. By factoring the polynomial into two or more lower degree polynomials, we can generate the transfer functions for the lower order filter stages to be cascaded.

The sensitivity of an active filter is an expression of the circuit's toleration of changes in component values. Both resistors and capacitors, principle elements in active filters, change value with age and temperature. The designer must be aware of this when making his selections of filter circuitry and component types.

Damping factor, usually represented by ζ, the Greek letter zeta, controls the shape of the response curve in the immediate vicinity of the rolloff knee. For LC filters, damping is a function of the LC ratio. In active filters, on the other hand, it is the ratio of certain capacitors or resistances which sets the damping factor. Generally, a low damping factor results in a longer rolloff knee, which takes a larger change in frequency to reach its natural rolloff rate.

Filters which have both upper and lower frequency limits have another characteristic not found in high- and low-pass types: *(quality factor)* is defined as:

$$Q = \frac{f_0}{\beta} \tag{7-1}$$

where f_0 is the center of the passband, and β is the bandwidth. Frequency can be expressed in either hertz or radians per second as long as the same units are used for both f_0 and β. Q is affected by bandpass, as can be seen from Eq. 7-1. *Apparent* Q can be considerably affected by the point on the response curve where bandwidth is measured. If the 3 dB response points are selected, for example, Q can be made to appear extremely high. At the 6 or 60 dB points (and both are used at times!) the bandwidth is greater making the Q less. Q is a measure of selectivity; the higher the value for Q the narrower the selectivity. Since damping factor controls how rapidly the filter response breaks at the knee, we might suspect that it is arithmetically related to Q; in most cases:

$$Q = \frac{1}{2\ (\text{damping factor}} \tag{7-2}$$

ACTIVE INDUCTORS

The operational amplifier can be made to simulate the action of an inductor. Although this simulation is not total, we can recreate the function of inductance in a filter circuit by simulating the energy storage property of inductors. The op amp pumps energy from the power supply into an RC network at a point and in amounts suitable for the inductance desired. For inverting amplifiers with $R_{IN} = 0$:

$$L \cong \frac{1}{A_{VOL}\omega} \tag{7-3}$$

This expression will hold true only within certain limits on maximum frequency, which is a function of the type of op amp selected.

NAIVE HIGH- AND LOW-PASS FILTERS

It has been noted that integrator and differentiator circuits effectively form low- and high-pass filters. They are not, however, the *be all* and *end all* of simple filters. Other techniques include following the simple RC rolloff network with an operational amplifier, with gain set to exactly overcome insertion losses. This tactic improves the loss situation, but will not affect the first order roll-off characteristic of the RC filter.

Another simple approach to the formation of low-pass filter circuits is shown in Fig. 7-3. The cutoff frequency is given by:

$$f_0 = \frac{1}{2\pi RC} \tag{7-4}$$

where:

f_0 is frequency in hertz
R_S resistance in ohms
C is capacitance in farads

Equation 7-4 is well worth memorizing as it will continue to reappear, in this text and others.

The filter circuit of Fig. 7-3 depends upon two applications of the same phenomenon to beat down unwanted high frequencies: capacitive reactance goes up as frequency is lowered and goes down as frequency is raised. That is to say it is inversely proportional to frequency, as shown by:

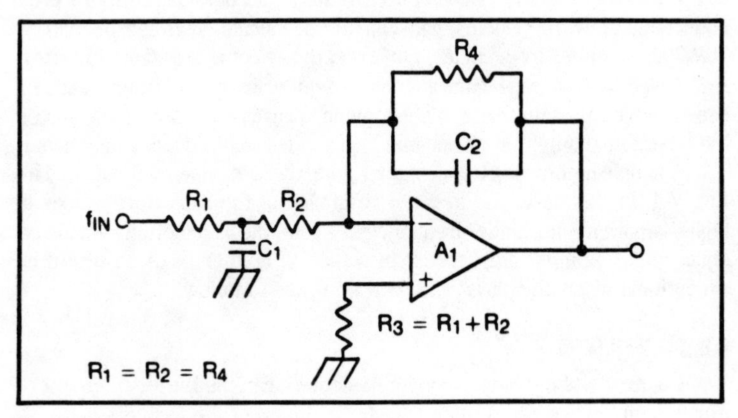

Fig. 7-3. Simple low-pass filter.

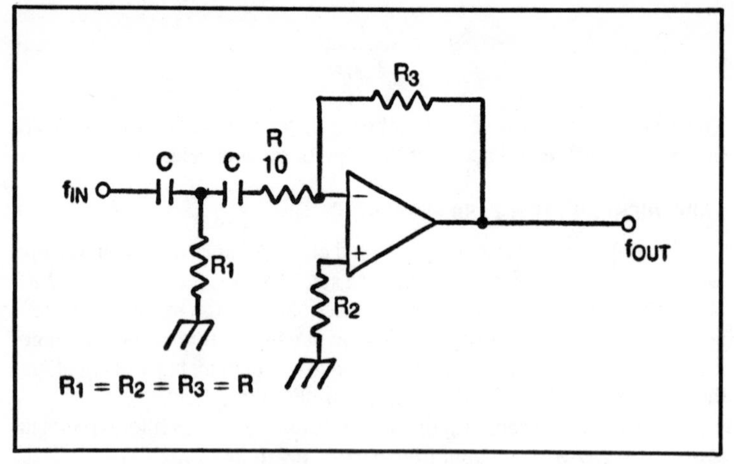

Fig. 7-4. Simple high-pass filter.

$$X_C = \frac{1}{2\pi FC} \tag{7-5}$$

This means that capacitor C_1 in Fig. 7-3, which has a value twice that of the C term in Eq. 7-4, will tend to roll off higher frequencies more than lower frequencies. Therefore, assuming they both have the same amplitude to start, the lower frequencies will have a higher amplitude at the input terminal of the operational amplifier. That in itself is quite sufficient to make the circuit performance mimmick that of the low-pass filter. The low-frequency response is further enhanced by a little tactic which must seem to the high frequencies a case of adding insult to injury. Note that the voltage gain of the op amp is given by $10R/2R$ at dc since $R = R_1 = R_2 = R_4$ in the figure. As frequency is increased, however, the effect of the capacitive reactance shunting the feedback resistor becomes even more pronounced. At low frequencies, gain can still be calculated as approximately $10R/2R$; at higher frequencies, however, the effect is substantial making the closed-loop voltage gain at those frequencies considerably less. In essence, we can state that this phenomenon causes the closed-loop gain of the operational amplifier to become less and less as frequency increases.

A simple high-pass filter designed along the same lines is illustrated in Fig. 7-4. In this case, the lowered reactance of the capacitors causes a higher amplitude for higher frequencies. Again, the assumption is made of equal initial or input amplitudes. In actuality, neither of these filters is exceptional when compared with certain types to follow.

COMPLEX FILTERS

Figure 7-5 shows an op amp implementation of the Butterworth filter. For this circuit we can write a transfer equation of the form:

$$\frac{E_{OUT}}{E_{IN}} = \frac{k}{S^2 + aS + b} \tag{7-6}$$

The gain of the circuit is the gain when S goes to zero, which is k/b. The operational amplifier is said to operate as a voltage-controlled (E_{IN}) voltage source (E_{OUT}). The values of R_1, R_2, C_1, C_2 are chosen such that the constants a and b in Eq. 7-6 are obtained. The remaining constant k is given by:

$$k = \frac{A_V}{R_1R_2C_1C_2} \tag{7-7}$$

where A_V is a function of the ratio R_F/R_{IN}. The circuit of Fig. 7-5 is popular because of its high-grade second-order performance, and yet relative simplicity of design. For example, resistors R_1 and R_2 will be equal in the low-pass design, and $R_1 = 2R_2$ in the high-pass design. The damping factor of the op amp Butterworth is

$$\zeta = \frac{\sqrt{2}}{2}$$

This allows a sharply falling cutoff slope without too much mind-boggling arithmetic.

Figure 7-6 has a cutoff frequency which follows Eq. 7-4 but with a special twist: the capacitance in the equation is equal to the square root of

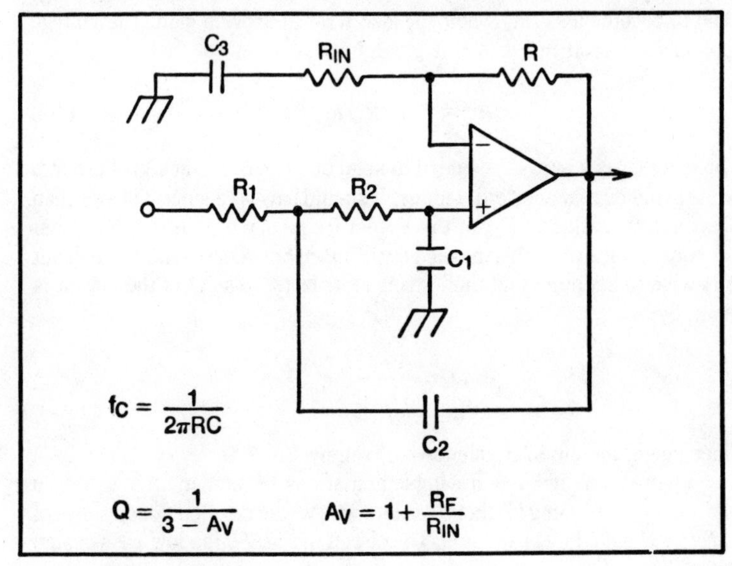

Fig. 7-5. Butterworth filter.

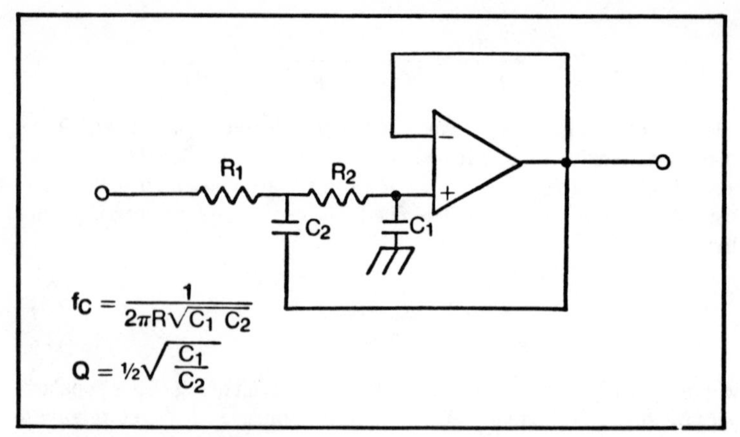

Fig. 7-6. Alternate Butterworth.

the product of C_1 and C_2. Of course, Eq. 7-4 can be applied literally if the capacitors are equal to value, but this twist does allow a little measure of design flexibility.

The Q of the circuit can be taken to be a measure of the filter's sharpness. In this case the value of Q is given as one-half the square root of the quotient of C_1/C_2. Again, if the two capacitors are equal, a special situation results and the Q is half the square root of one or, simply, one-half. The gain of this filter is unity at dc and low frequencies, but will fall off to a level equal to the value of Q at the cutoff frequency.

As is the usual case when you might want something for nothing, things tend to become less tidy when you also want to provide gain. The voltage gain of the circuit in Fig. 7-5 is given by:

$$A_V = 1 + (R_F/R_{IN}) \tag{7-8}$$

Capacitor C_3 is a bypass designed to keep one end of R_{IN} at signal ground, while avoiding that possibility for dc. It should have a reactance of less than one tenth the value of R_{IN} at the lowest frequency of interest. For most common applications, this means a capacitance between 10 and 100 μF; but it is wise to keep in mind that "cases alter facts." The Q of the circuit is given by:

$$Q = \frac{1}{3 - A_V} \tag{7-9}$$

Once again, the cutoff frequency is given by Eq. 7-4.

Figures 7-7 and 7-8 are implementations of similar filter schemes offered only in passing for those readers who would develop a deep sense of injustice should they be deleted. The circuit of Fig. 7-7 is a low-pass design while that of Fig. 7-8 is a high-pass type.

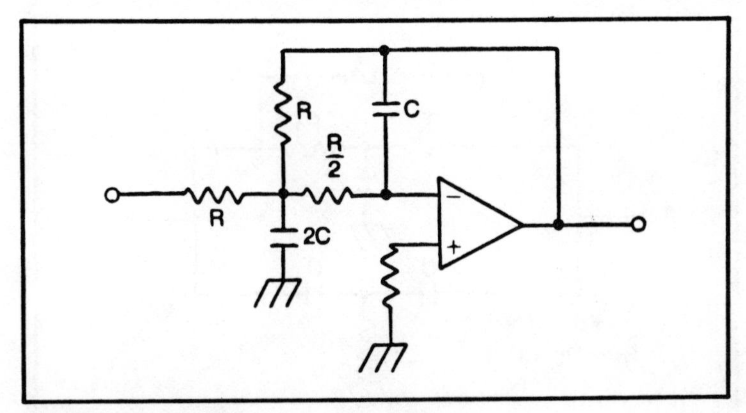

Fig. 7-7. Low-pass filter.

TWIN-TEE RC NOTCH FILTER NETWORKS

There is a special RC network called the twin-tee which will attenuate frequencies at the point satisfied by Eq. 7-1, but not frequencies removed from that point. An example of the twin-tee is shown in Fig. 7-9. The frequency of the twin-tee is shown in Fig. 7-10. The dotted line resistor in Fig. 7-9 represents the added component needed to make a closely related version sometimes called the "bridged tee." The depth of the notch and the steepness of the sides are functions of the component tolerances. In really crucial applications where the best characteristics are desired, it will prove wise to either purchase precision components or select from less costly types using a Wheatstone bridge to find those close to the correct values.

One method for using the twin-tee in an active filter is shown in Fig. 7-11. In this case, which is really too simple, the voltage gain is used to merely overcome the insertion losses of the filter network and to place a limit on output loading that is within livable bounds; a factor which might

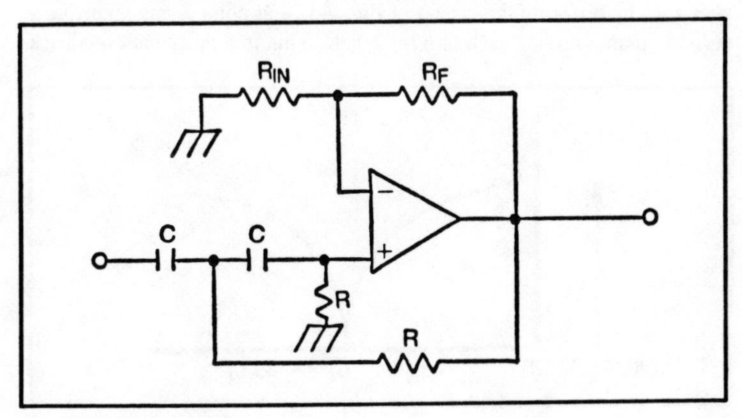

Fig. 7-8. High-pass filter.

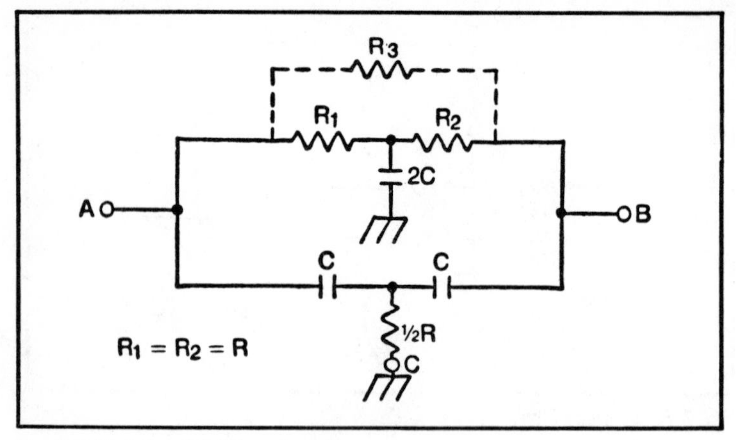

Fig. 7-9. Twin-tee RC filter network.

otherwise tend to deteriorate performance under the correct set of circumstances.

The use of an operational amplifier can deepen the notch and dramatically increase the Q of the notch filter. An example is shown in Fig. 7-12A. Normally, the Q of the RC notch filter without the op amp to dump energy into the circuit is low—typically less than unity. By narrowing the bandwidth we can increase Q. In the op-amp circuit shown in Fig. 7-12A, bandwidth is 1-M times the bandwidth of the RC network taken alone where M is a constant. Q approaches its maximum value as M approaches unity. An op amp simulates an inductor when it can supply in-phase energy to the network. This places the circuit dangerously close to oscillation; a condition which will, in fact, occur if M is allowed to be equal to or greater than unity.

Q can be varied between the maximum when M is unity and a value near zero by breaking the circuit of Fig. 7-12A at point X and inserting a second op-amp circuit such as Fig. 7-12B. This is a unity-gain feedback

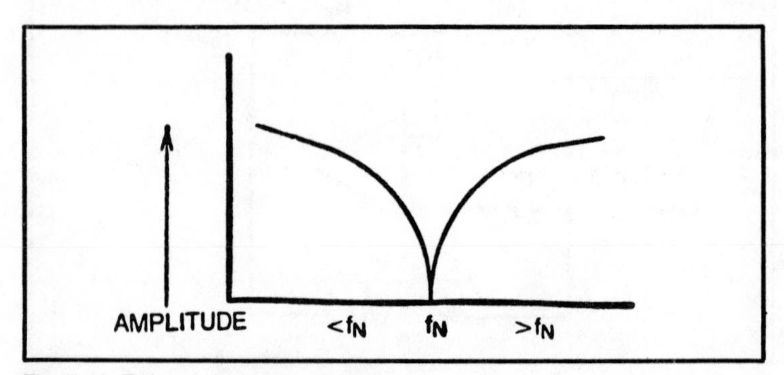

Fig. 7-10. Twin-tee frequency response.

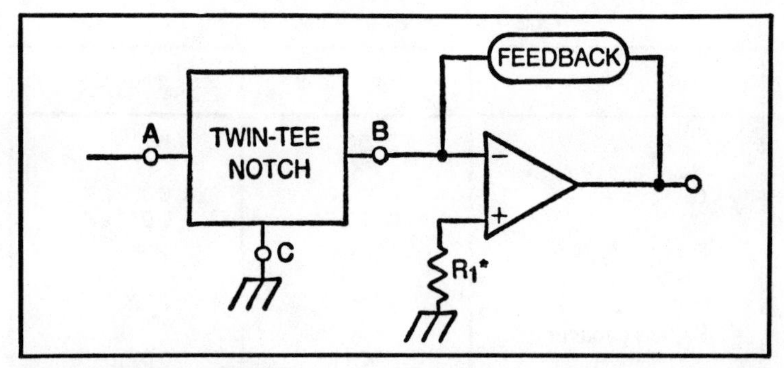

Fig. 7-11. Simple notch filter.

amplifier driven by the A_1 output voltage through a level control potentiometer. Q is maximum when the potentiometer is set to maximum.

60 HZ SUPPRESSION

Power lines in the U.S. are the source of 60 Hz interference which plagues a large variety of electronic equipment. In many cases, the use of good shielding techniques and the maintenance of a high common-mode rejection ratio with differential inputs can solve the problem. In other cases, especially where low-level signals are involved, we must resort to techniques such as filtering to rid the equipment of the unwanted 60 Hz

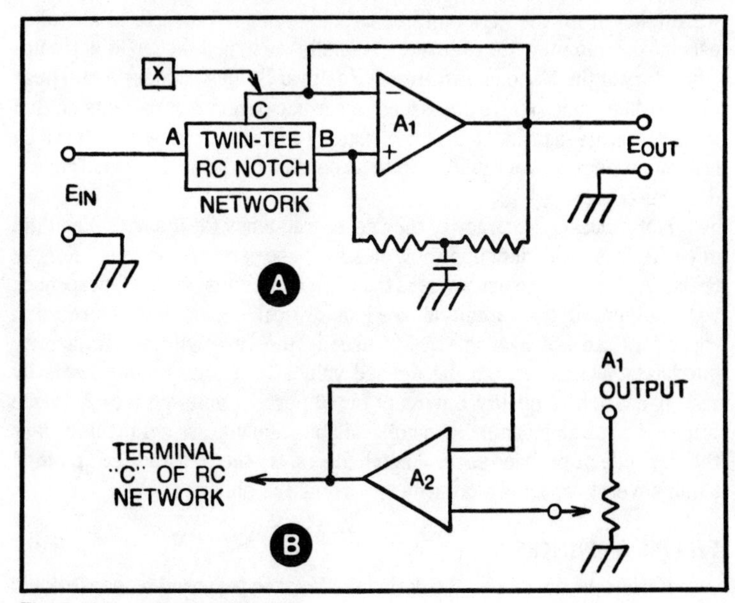

Fig. 7-12. Improved notch filter.

Table 7-1. Filter Network Components.

	Moderate Q	High Q
R_1, R_2	267K	68.1K
R/2	133K	34.05K
C	0.01 μF	0.039 μF
2C	0.02 μF	0.078 μF
Feedback resistors (Fig. 7-12A)	1.0M	270K
Bypass capacitors (Fig. 7-12A)	0.005 μF	0.02 μF

interference signals. The ubiquitous nature of this interference justifies our calculating the values for notch filter components at that frequency.

One main requirement demanded of 60 Hz notch filters used in medical and scientific instruments is that they have a *Q* figure high enough that the circuit will have only a very narrow bandwidth, so that only a tiny offending portion of the original waveform is lost. Even signals with very low fundamental frequencies are often composed of many harmonics, some of which may fall close to the notch frequency. If the filter wipes out too many of these harmonics, then the shape of the waveform will be altered.

We have calculated the values for the components used in the filter at Fig. 7-9. This network can be incorporated into the circuit of Fig. 7-12A. Table 7-1 lists the values for moderate *Q* and high *Q* designs. These values were taken from the various filter circuits designed for use in a cardiac pacemaker monitor transmitter, originally designed by an electronics laboratory at the National Institute of Health at Bethesda, Maryland. These modem-like transmitters are issued to cardiac pacemaker patients so that their heart rate, a prime indicator of battery condition, can be monitored by telephone once a week without the necessity of the patient visiting his doctor's office.

Note that the accuracy of the center frequency (at the notch) and the effective *Q* is dependent upon how closely these parts are selected. For the resistors, it is best to use not less than 1 percent units, with 0.5 percent or 0.01 percent if the circuit is used in critical equipment. If precision capacitors are not available, as is usually the case with small quantity purchases, we can match the needed values to design requirements by testing a batch of quality 5 percent or 10 percent units on a capacitance bridge. If such an instrument is not available, and you are not making more than a single or perhaps several notch filters, try the "cut and see" method using several capacitors until the best notch is obtained.

PEAKING AMPLIFIERS

Earlier we developed the notion that a given passband response could be obtained by placing a passive network with the opposite properties in an op-amp feedback loop. We can generate a peaking filter by using the tee-notch network in that manner. A peaking amplifier may be used for any number of purposes requiring enhancement of a certain frequency, or it might be used in a unique form of notch filter called the summation filter.

Figure 7-13 shows a summation-type notch filter. Amplifier A_1 is a peaking amplifier with a center frequency f_0 at the frequency which we ultimately hope to reject. This amplifier must possess two properties: high Q and a 180° phase inversion between input and output. The second op amp is used merely to compensate for the time delay caused by A_1. It should have a gain equal to that of A_1. The output signals from A_1 and A_2 are summed in amplifier A_3. Since the phase of A_1 is reversed, the net output from A_3 for those frequencies enhanced by A_1 will be close to zero—resulting in a high rejection of those frequencies.

GYRATOR FILTER CIRCUITS

The gyrator gets its name from the fact that there are certain valid analogies between its behavior and the behavior of a mechanical gyroscope. The gyrator can be made to perform as an inductor and therefore, as an active filter.

An inductance presents an impedance of:

$$Z_L = j2\pi fL \qquad (7\text{-}10)$$

where:

Z_L is impedance in ohms
f is frequency in hertz
L is inductance in henrys

j is the imaginary operator $\sqrt{-1}$ necessitated by the fact that a phase shift takes place in which the current is caused to lag the voltage.

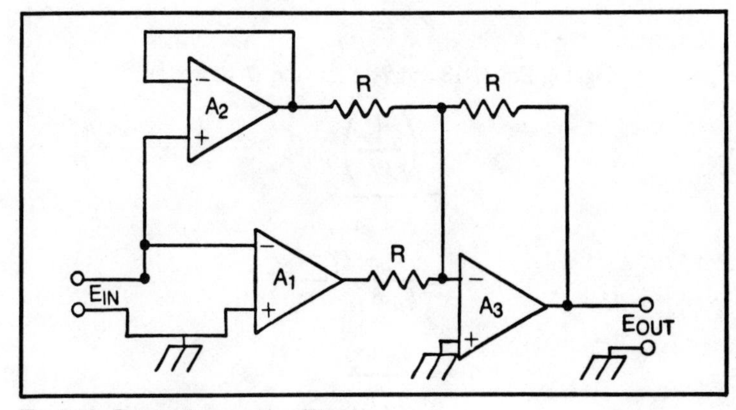

Fig. 7-13. Summation peaking filter.

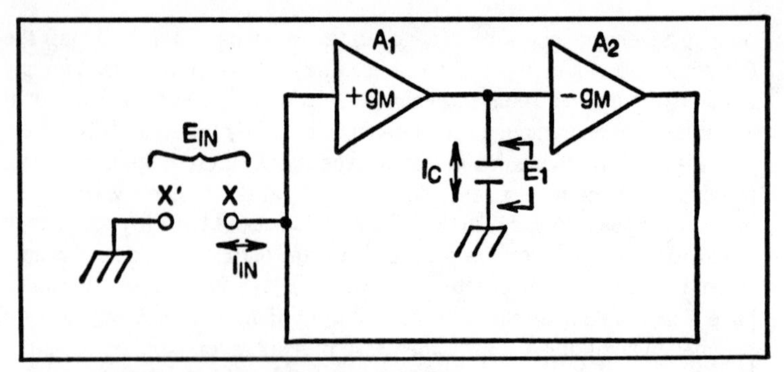

Fig. 7-14. Block diagram of the "gyrator" filter.

In order to simulate inductance, we require a circuit which will satisfy Eq. 7-10. Figure 7-14 shows the block diagram of such a circuit. Amplifiers A_1 and A_2 are transconductance amplifiers (which can be made from operational amplifiers as described in Chapter 5). They are identical except that A_2 inverts the signal 180° while A_1 does not. To simplify matters it is further stipulated that:

$$|g_{M1}| = |g_{M2}| \tag{7-11}$$

A_2 is effectively connected into the negative feedback loop of A_1. The input impedance of this (and any) circuit is given by:

$$Z_{IN} = \frac{E_{IN}}{I_{IN}} \tag{7-12}$$

More specifically for the circuit of Fig. 7-14:

$$I_{IN} = g_M E_1 \tag{7-13}$$

$$E_{IN} = \frac{-I_C}{g_M} \tag{7-14}$$

By plugging Eqs. 7-13 and 7-14 into Eq. 7-12 we get:

$$Z_{IN} = \frac{\left(\frac{-I_C}{g_M}\right)}{g_M E_1}$$

$$= \frac{1}{g_M E_1} \cdot \frac{-I_C}{g_M}$$

$$= \frac{-IC}{g_M{}^2 E_1} \tag{7-15}$$

But since I_C:

$$Ic = \frac{E_1}{X_C}$$

$$= \frac{E_1}{\frac{1}{j2\pi fC}} \tag{7-16}$$

$$= -j(2\pi fC)\, E_1$$

Substituting Eq. 7-16 for $-I_C$ in Eq. 7-15 yields:

$$Z_{IN} = \frac{-(-j2\pi fC)\, E_1}{g_M{}^2 E_1} \tag{7-17}$$

$E_1/E_1 = 1$, so:

$$Z_{IN} = \frac{-(-j2\pi fC)}{g_M{}^2}$$

$$= \frac{j2\pi fC}{g_M{}^2} \tag{7-18}$$

Equation 7-18 will begin to look a lot more like Eq. 7-10 (which is our goal) if we allow:

$$L = \frac{C}{g_M{}^2} \tag{7-19}$$

To keep things nice and tidy, let us rearrange 7-18 using Eq. 7-19 as L:

$$Z_{IN} = X_L = 2\pi f(C/g^2_m) \tag{7-20}$$

Presto! An inductorless inductor!

HIGH FIDELITY TONE CONTROLS

Hi-fi amplifiers usually provide the user some means of varying the frequency response of the system in order to compensate for poor quality program material and to cater to the individual tonal preferences of a wide spectrum of listeners. Circuits which accomplish this are essentially active filters.

In inexpensive equipment (which may barely deserve the name *high fidelity*), it is common to find simple treble-rolloff tone controls. These are nothing more than a series network consisting of a capacitor and a rheostat-connected potentiometer shunted across the signal path. At the treble setting there is little attenuation of the high frequencies because the shunt impedance is equal to the impedance of the capacitor added to the entire resistance of the potentiometer.

At the bass setting, however, the shunt impedance is equal to the impedance of the capacitor alone—a figure which is lowered as frequency is increased. At that setting, most of the high frequency signal is shunted to ground. Such circuits do not really provide good control over the tonal qualities of the reproduced signal. They must also suffer the loss of amplitude due to loss of the high frequency component.

A better configuration is one of the *Baxandall* circuits, in which a frequency-sensitive network is placed in the negative (degenerative) feedback loop of an amplifier. In Fig. 7-15A, we see a method of using an operational amplifier in such a circuit. This example shows a standard inverting follower configuration less R_F and R_{IN}. These will be added when the frequency selective feedback is added.

In Fig. 7-15B, we have an old fashioned bass/treble boost network which is still popular despite the fact that its application can be dated back to vacuum-tube circuitry. In this network, we actually have two parallel substitutes for the R_F/R_{IN} arrangement. For the treble ranges, the frequency-selective network consists of R_1, R_4, and C_3. Capacitor C_3 in conjunction with the total resistance of R_4 and a portion of the resistance of R_1 forms a frequency-selective RC network which acts as a high-pass filter. The gain of the circuit for passed frequencies is determined by the ratio of the resistance on either side of the potentiometer wiper arm.

The bass boost circuit consists of R_2, R_3, R_5, C_1 and C_2. At low frequencies the reactance of C_1 and C_2 is extremely high. By the standard parallel impedances formula, we can see that their shunting effect on the potentiometer is almost neglible. At those frequencies, A_1 simply acts as an amplifier with controllable gain. At higher frequencies, however, the capacitors have much lower reactances resulting in a much larger shunting effect at those frequencies. Since this is a feedback circuit, the result is suppression of those frequencies and enhancement (relatively speaking) of the bass. This technique produces a control amplifier suitable for high fidelity service with a boost factor of ±20 dB; this is a value consistant with standard hi-fi practice.

For high fidelity application, an operational amplifier for A_1 should be selected which has a sufficient high-frequency capacity. Some unconditionally stable types (i.e., internally frequency compensated) get that way by dropping A_{VOL} to unity at a ridiculously low frequency that is well within the range considered proper for a high fidelity preamplifier/control amplifier circuit.

An alternative tone control circuit is shown in Fig. 7-15C. The operation is functionally equivalent to that of the previous example. What makes this circuit so inviting, despite its dependency on inductors, is the fact that several overlapping networks can be paralleled. This results in a finer degree of control over the tone color of the reproduced audio. These circuits have been popularized under the heading *tone equalizers* for several years. Capacitor C_4 and inductor L_1 form a series-resonant tank circuit shunting signal currents in the feedback loop to ground.

Such tanks offer a very low impedance to frequencies close to resonance and a very high impedance at frequencies removed from resonance. The bandwidth of the response is broadened by addition of resistor R_6; effectively lowering Q. The exact shape of the passband contour can be tailored to individual preference by varying the value of this resistance.

The depth of the notch created by shunting a series resonant circuit across the line is controlled by the setting of the potentiometer. Since this network is essentially a notch filter placed in the negative feedback loop of an operational amplifier, the system response will be that of a peaked

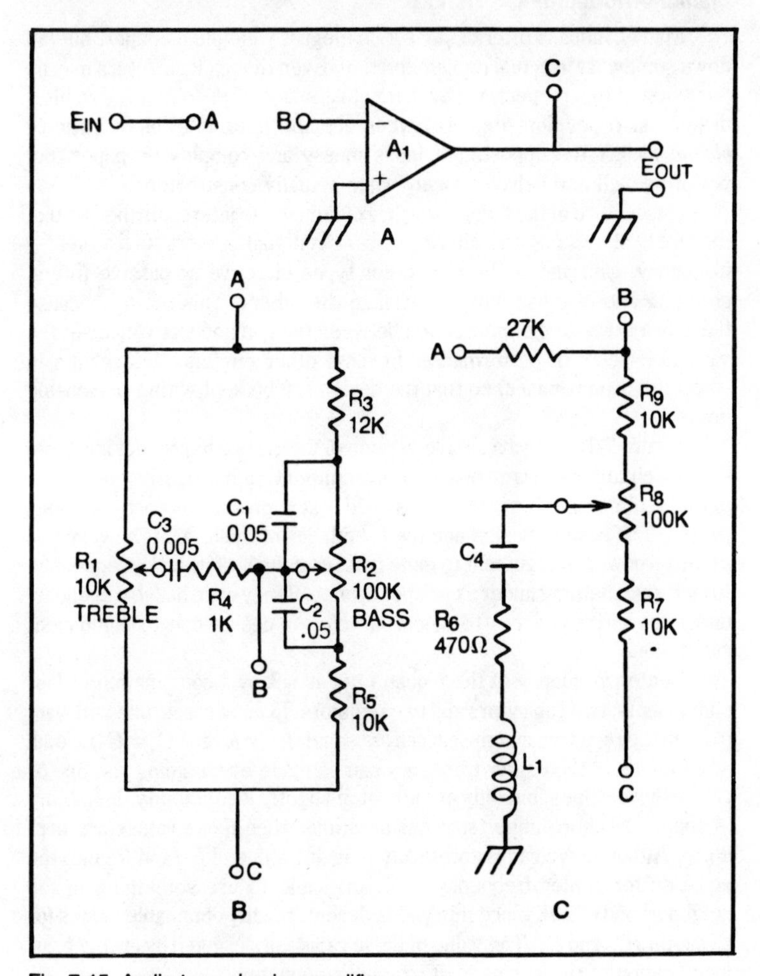

Fig. 7-15. Audio tone shaping amplifier.

amplifier. The frequency of any given tank should be the center of the desired passband and is determined by:

$$f = \frac{1}{2\pi LC} \qquad (7\text{-}21)$$

Where:

f is frequency in hertz
L is inductance in henrys
C is capacitance in farads

The series resistor, R_6, can be a value between 0 and 5K.

BIQUADRATIC BANDPASS FILTERS

Many bandpass filter designs look elegantly simple on paper, but fall down somewhat in actual implementation. Even though RLC filters may be the worst in this respect, we even find that many much-touted active filter designs also develop problems when actually built. The biquadratic or *biquad* is just the opposite; it looks messy and complex on paper, but performs well and behaves nicely when actually constructed.

One feature of the biquad which is of immediate interest is the fact that the circuit allows custom tailoring of key circuit parameters such as center frequency, gain and Q. In most other types of active or passive filters, changing one of these will also change the others. This occurs because there is a great deal of interaction between the components which set the various aspects of performance. In most other circuits, this results in tradeoffs (compromises) so that the design can be kept within reasonable limits.

Figure 7-16 shows a simple version of the classic biquad design. Note that the circuit uses three operational amplifiers, rather than just one. It is, perhaps, this single fact that creates a bad first impression in cost-conscious people. The ease of design and the usefulness of this circuit, however, is usually a powerful argument to mute most criticisms of its lack of economy. In fact, at something under a buck per op amp, it may even be false economy under the circumstances to select an inferior design due to component count alone!

Center frequency of the biquad filter is set by a combination of four components, two capacitors and two resistors. In most cases, one will want to keep the resistors and the capacitors equal ($R_A = R_5$ and $C_1 = C_2$). Small adjustments in the center frequency can be made by trimming just one or two of these values, but only at the cost of slightly less stability. If stability is one of the more important considerations, then those values are kept equal. Although we can theoretically plug any value of R_A and R_5 into the equation for center frequency, it is advisable to use something in the neighborhood of 10K since this yields decent, readily obtainable values for capacitors C_1 and C_2. The value of these capacitors is given by an algebraic modification of the standard RC frequency equation:

$$C = \frac{1}{2\pi Rf}$$

$$= 1/10^4 (2\pi f))$$

$$= \frac{1}{\omega \times 10^4} \quad (7\text{-}22)$$

where $\omega = 2\pi f$.
This equation is valid, though, only for filters in which $R_A = R_5$ and $C_1 = C_2$.

Amplifiers A_1, A_2, and A_3 can be economical 741-family devices if the range of center frequencies can be kept below 5 to 10 kHz. Use of a premium operational amplifier type, however, will extend the range to well into the ultrasonic region.

Circuit Q can be varied by adjusting the value of resistor R_1. Q can take on values ranging over three decades from about 0.5 to 500. A ballpark expression for Q as a function of R_1 is:

$$Q = \frac{R_1}{1 \times 10^4} \quad (7\text{-}23)$$

For values of Q less than 60, this expression is reasonably accurate, but error increases rapidly at greater values. Gain is given, albeit approximately, by another expression:

$$A_V = \frac{Q\ (10^4}{R_2} \quad (7\text{-}24)$$

This equation is reasonably accurate for values of R_2 between 100Ω and 100K.

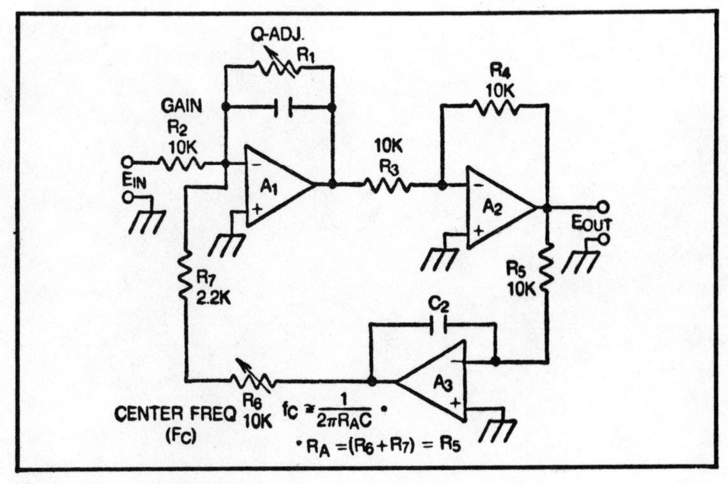

Fig. 7-16. Biquadratic filter.

The one limiting factor in biquad filter design is the fact that supply voltages must be kept high, on the order of one-half maximum values for V_{CC} and V_{EE}, or problems will develop. Among these is destruction of the usefulness of our formulas! Although they purport to describe the behavior of certain aspects of filter performance, this is true only if the voltage criteria are met. Also, we find that stability deteriorates at low supply voltage levels, and the circuit will ring, or even oscillate, if an attempt at obtaining a high Q is made. This limitation isn't really too great, because most op amps are used at voltages closer to maximum than minimum anyway. The biquadratic filter is a fine one to keep on file until a filter requirement presents itself.

Chapter 8

Regulated Power Supplies

There are numerous good reasons, sound and just, for going to the trouble and expense of building a well-regulated power supply. Indeed, many electronic circuits will operate marginally or not at all with nonregulated supplies. One of the reasons why a regulated supply is considered superior to a nonregulated supply is the fact that it will hold the output voltage at a precisely controlled, steady value, regardless of input voltage excursions. Another good reason for their use in audio equipment and scientific instruments is that power supply ripple is reduced almost to nothing by the regulation process. This is the basis for the claim by some power-supply manufacturers that they have an effective filter capacitance of 1 farad or more, "by using a transistor as a capacitor." Actually, the transistor acts like a regulator capable of following voltage variations created by the ripple component.

VOLTAGE REGULATION

In a theoretically perfect power-supply there is no need for regulation. Such supplies are represented by a voltage source feeding a load resistor. The load resistor, of course, is a representation of the resistance for the sum total of electronic circuitry fed by the supply. In a perfect supply, we find that the output impedance is zero ohms. This allows a maximum output current close to infinity. Actual output current is controlled solely by the value of the load resistor and source voltage E. The typical practical power supply, however, has an output impedance greater than zero ohms. These supplies can be graphically represented by a voltage source (defined as perfect), a load resistance, and a series source resistance (R_S in Fig. 8-1) equal to the internal impedance of the power supply. In this type of supply, the output current is:

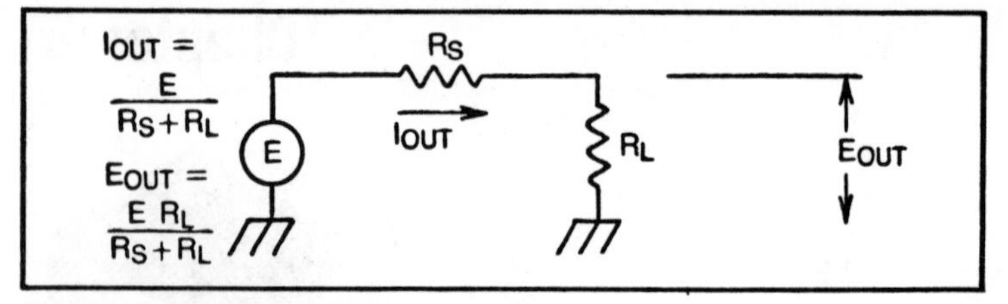

Fig. 8-1. Unregulated power supply model.

$$I_{OUT} = \frac{E}{R_S + R_L} \tag{8-1}$$

Since some of the source voltage is dropped across the source resistor R_S, the available output voltage is only a fraction of the source voltage:

$$E_{OUT} = \frac{ER_L}{R_S + R_L} \tag{8-2}$$

In most cases, we can assume R_S to be a constant. Regulation problems come from two sources: variation in E and changing load conditions.

As for the first of these, we must recognize that any given power supply will derive its original current from any of a number of sources which generally prove to be none too stable; power mains, vehicle alternators, and so forth. Even a battery will drop in voltage after use. The second source of trouble, changing load conditions, results because the circuitry fed by a supply may have different current requirements at different times. These may vary slowly or abruptly. Regardless, though, the supply is expected to track the changes. By Eq. 8-2, we can see that variation in R_L can cause changes in E_{OUT}; that is something we wish to avoid.

IMPROVING REGULATION

Regulation can be improved by designing a circuit to vary the effective value of R_S or R_L in accordance with changes in load. The methods to implement these are based on the use of *series* or *parallel shunt* regulators. An example of the shunt regulator is the zener diode of Fig. 8-2A. A zener diode has a unique property which allows its use in voltage regulator service. In the forward direction, it behaves much like any ordinary semiconductor diode. The output current will remain at zero until the applied voltage exceeds the junction potential (typically around 0.7V). At this point, current will start to flow and the diode looks like any well-behaved diode. In the reverse direction, though, a peculiar and useful phenomenon occurs. The diode current will remain zero, as it should on any reverse biased diode, until a certain voltage (V_Z in Fig. 8-2B), called variously *avalanche, breakdown*, or *zener point*, is reached. At this point, the diode will break down and pass a large current (which is the reason for the

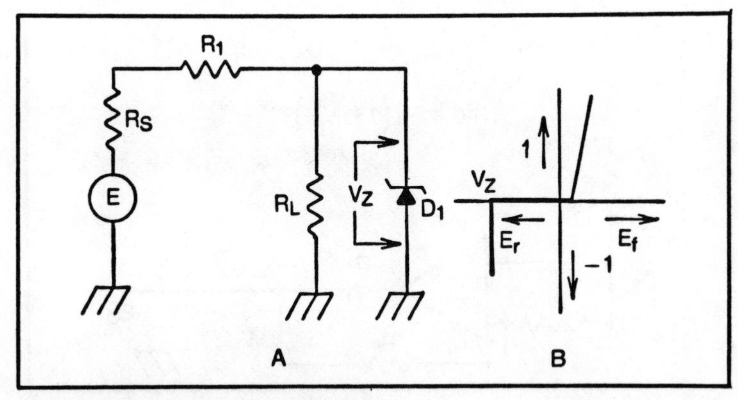

Fig. 8-2. Regulated power supply model.

series resistor added in Fig. 8-2A). Further increases in reverse bias potential will have little affect on the output; the impedance of the zener is already too low for that. The value of V_Z remains relatively constant over wide ranges of applied voltage. A typical FM car radio power supply, for example, drops an input voltage (which can vary from 11.5V to 15.0V as the vehicle is accelerated) to a steady 8.2V. If the voltage were not regulated the vhf local oscillator in the FM radio would drift all over the band as the car pulled away from a traffic light. The zener is not the total answer, however, since zener potential tends to drift with changes in temperature. It also has a relatively low power handling capability unless one is prepared to pay a much higher cost.

Figure 8-3 shows how we can boost power capability by using the *series pass* transistor. This is a series regulator that allows us to trim the effective value of R_S by varying the collector—emitter resistance of Q_1. The regulation results when the value of the base voltage applied to Q_1 is kept constant. When load current requirements drop, the output voltage will

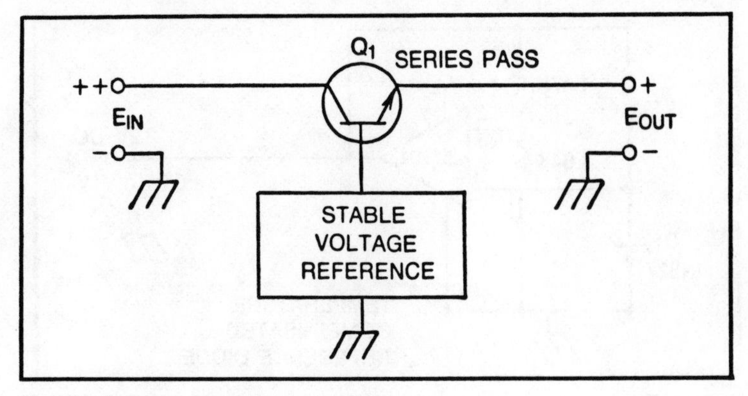

Fig. 8-3. Series pass regulator transistor.

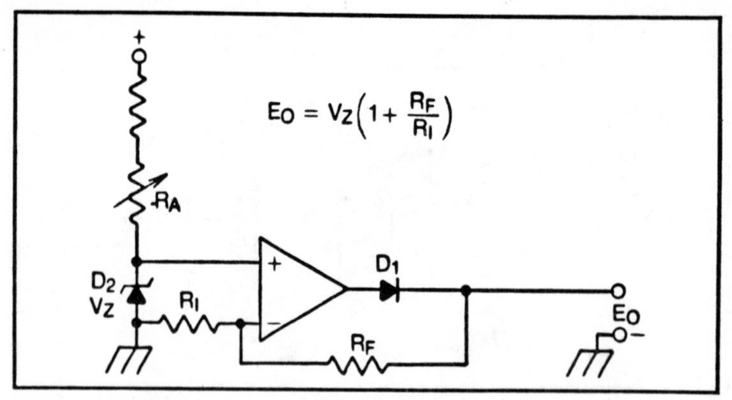

Fig. 8-4. Voltage reference source.

tend to rise. In a transistor regulated power supply, this will reduce the voltage between the emitter and the controlled base of the series-pass transistor. This will tend to force the transistor toward cutoff—reducing the output voltage. For most cases:

$$E_{OUT} = k(E_{REF} + E_{BE}) \tag{8-3}$$

where:

E_{OUT} is the output voltage
E_{REF} is the reference voltage
E_{BE} is the voltage drop between base and emitter of the transistor
k is a constant applicable to the specific power supply

The stable reference voltage can be supplied by a simple zener diode. There are, however, certain problems when using nothing more than this simple arrangement. An operational amplifier, with its feedback loop, can be used to overcome these defects. Figures 8-4 and 8-5 are examples of

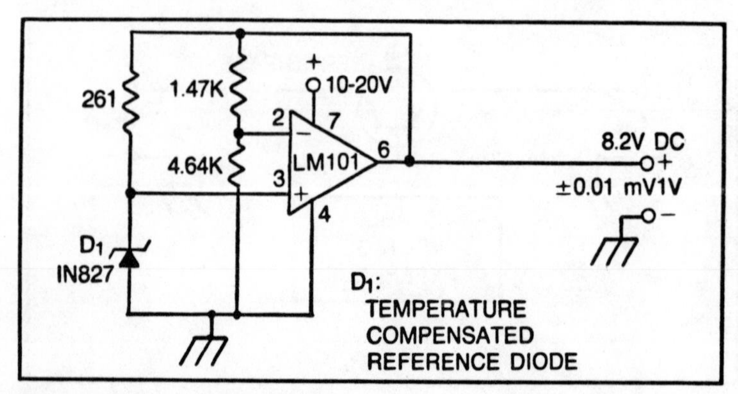

Fig. 8-5. Precision reference source.

reference sources which use zener diodes to set the operating point of an op amp, but the op amp is the device which actually controls the series-pass transistor. In most cases, the actual zener chosen should be a temperature-compensated reference type. These, although more costly, have superior stability and precision of the zener voltage.

PRACTICAL REGULATED SUPPLIES

Figures 8-6 and 8-7 illustrate two regulated power supplies using different techniques for stabilizing the op-amp reference. In Fig. 8-6, we use a 741 operational amplifier as a reference voltage source to control the base of the series-pass transistor. It, in turn, is established by a zener diode. The transistor used can be any silicon type with a medium to high beta, and the ability to sustain expected collector currents and power dissipation (one does *not* imply the other—the specs must be consulted). The reference voltage fed to the + input of the op amp is generated by the 12K resistor and zener diode D_1. A better degree of control will be realized if a better quality op amp and zener reference diode are used. This latter item is a close tolerance zener with superior temperature characteristics and a calibrated V_Z. In any event, a sample of the output voltage is fed to the minus input of the amplifier. It is developed by divider R_1-R_2-R_3. Although this supply offers only a single output voltage, we can calibrate (or optimize if you prefer) the value by trimming R_2. A 10-turn pot for R_2 should be used.

The power supply in Fig. 8-6 uses a voltage regulator as a reference for the operational amplifier. In Fig. 8-7, on the other hand, we use a current

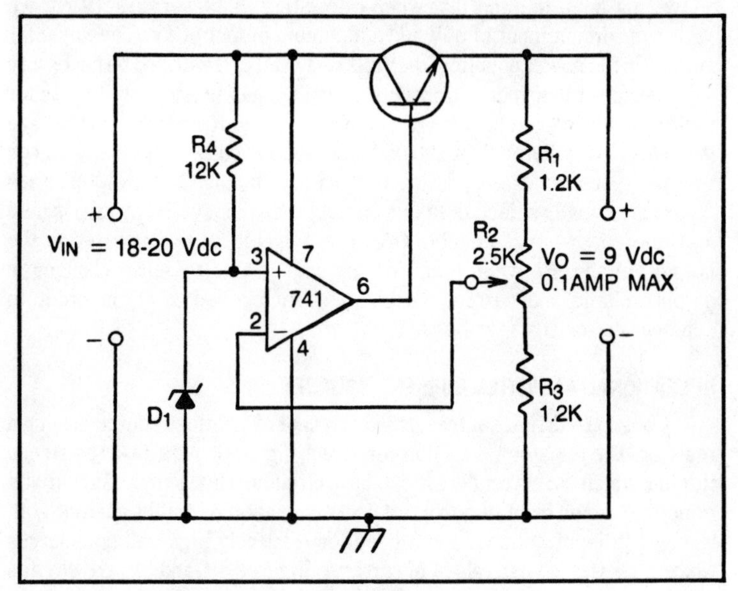

Fig. 8-6. Regulated 9V, 100 mA dc power supply.

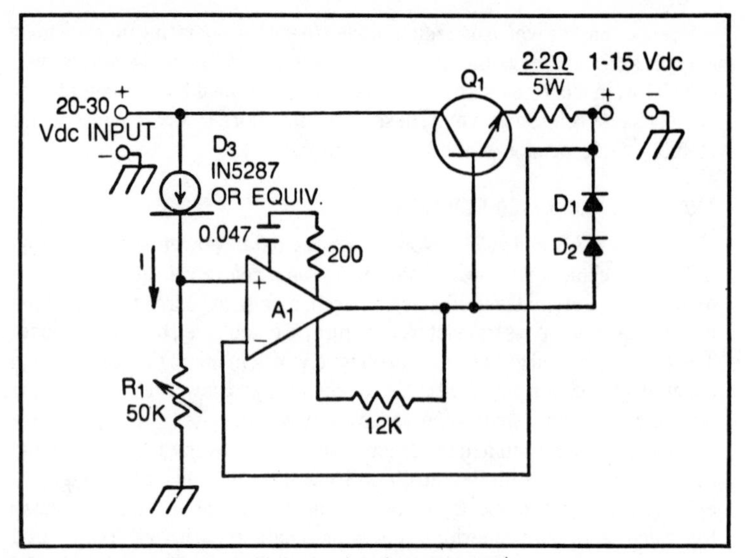

Fig. 8-7. Adjustable 1–15V dc regulated power supply.

regulator diode to perform this function. Diode D_3 in Fig. 8-7 is a constant current type. It will hold the value of I to a value close to its spec set by the manufacturer. This particular design is competent to offer output voltages between 1 and 15 Vdc. Q_1 is selected according to the rules developed above, but keep in mind that when calculating its power dissipation, we have a maximum input of 30V and a minimum output of 1V. The value for voltage in the power equation, then is $30 - 1 = 29$V. It will also be necessary to make sure the selected transistor doesn't object to a V_{CE} of 30V. As for the op amp, it should be a fairly wideband type with an open-loop voltage gain (A_{VOL}) of greater than 100,000. Diodes D_1 and D_2 can be any silicon rectifier types capable of passing 1.0A without failing. The 1N4000 series diodes are usually selected. In this circuit the + input of the op amp is held at a referencs voltage equal to IR_1. The minus input is connected to the output voltage. Between them, the op amp is able to sense changes in output voltage and correct the bias current applied to Q_1 in order to compensate for any variations.

OPERATIONAL AMPLIFIER CURRENT SOURCES

Constant-current sources usually consist of a voltage source driving a resistor. The resistor has a value very much higher than the load resistance through which the current is to flow. Such circuits, while simple and initially tempting, suffer from two major defects: variation of output current with changes in input voltage, and a need for relatively high voltage sources (except for the lowest values of current). Figures 8-8 and 8-9 are circuits which use the feedback loop of an operational amplifier to cancel these

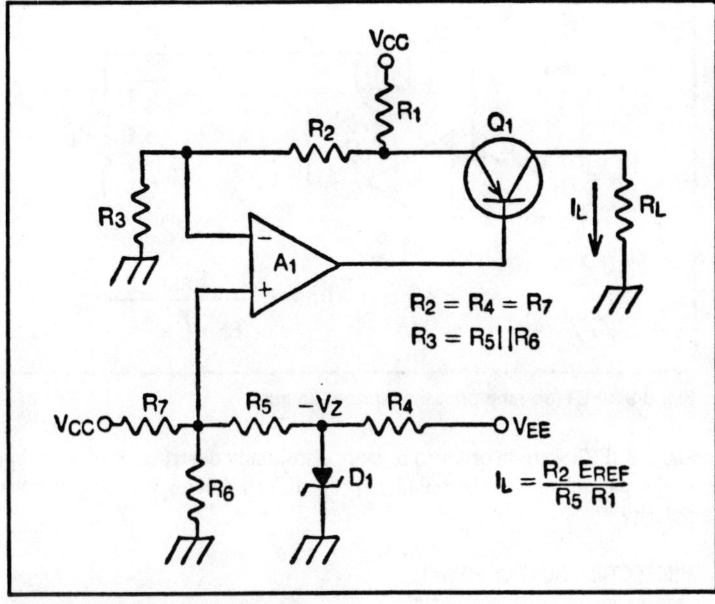

Fig. 8-8. Constant current source.

defects. These circuits operate with manageable supply voltages, and offer extremely high output impedances. This is, after all, one of the requirements of a constant-current source!

In the circuit of Fig. 8-8, we have a bipolar transistor controlled by the operational amplifier. The reference level, which is stabilized by a zener diode, is set by a complex voltage divider network consisting of R_4, R_5, R_6, R_7 and D_1. Reference voltage E_{REF} is found from a set of simultaneous loop equations solved to find I_{R6}. When this is known, the reference voltage will be equal to $I_{R6}R_6$. To form the loop equations, the first loop is made with V_Z, R_5, and R_6. The other loop is made from V_{CC}, R_7, and R_6. R_6 is the common element in this set of loops, so it is a simple matter to find the current through it.

Assuming that $R_2 = R_4 = R_7$, and that R_3 is set equal to the parallel combination of R_5 and R_6, the output current will be:

$$I_L = \frac{R_2 E_{REF}}{R_1 R_5} \qquad (8\text{-}4)$$

An improved output impedance figure is obtained by replacing the bipolar transistor with a JFET biased well into its pinchoff region. This is done in Fig. 8-9. Once again, we use a voltage divider to set the op-amp reference level. The output of the amplifier will be negative enough to pinch off the JFET (Q_1). A diode is used in the line between the op-amp terminal

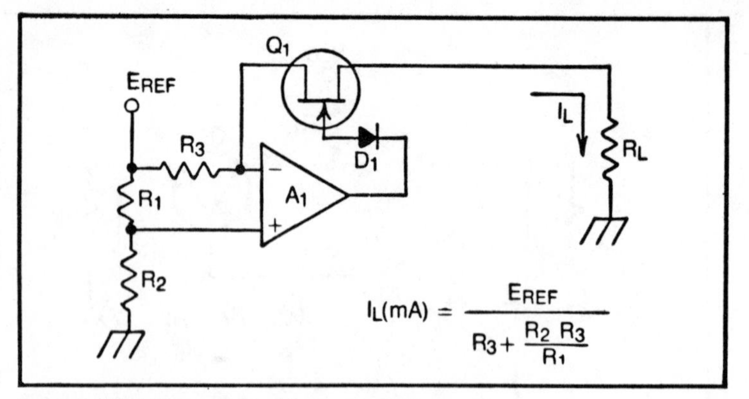

Fig. 8-9. JFET/op-amp precision current source.

and the JFET gate in order to prevent potentially destructive reverse bias of the gate-channel. The op amp, after all, can deliver voltages of either polarity.

PROTECTION SUPPLY POWER

Most electronic circuits can be seriously damaged by the application of excessive voltage. Since the input to a regulated power supply is usually much higher than the output, it is mandatory that we supply some means for protecting the equipment from a shorted series-pass transistor or from a loss of control over the reference voltage. In either case, a large dc voltage will be applied to the equipment.

A circuit such as Fig. 8-10 offers the needed degree of protection. The variable resistor is adjusted to trip the gate of the SCR whenever the output voltage rises above the critical value. When the SCR is gated on, the

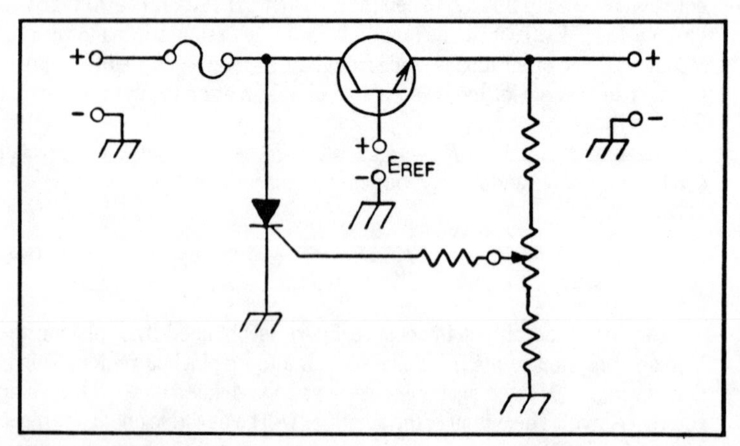

Fig. 8-10. SCR crowbar protection.

resistance from anode to cathode drops drastically, producing what is essentially a short circuit across the power supply input line. This will cause the fuse to blow (or a circuit breaker to trip), protecting the other circuits from overvoltage. Although this may result in damage to rectifiers or transformers in the power supply, it is still preferred over the loss of a major piece of equipment. The technique presented here is not too awfully sophisticated, and it works. Since it is something like whacking the supply with a heavy, blunt object, one can readily see why the nickname *crowbar* is popular.

DUAL-POLARITY POWER SUPPLIES

Almost all operational amplifier circuits, and quite a few transistor circuits, require dual-polarity power supplies for proper operation. The circuit shown in Fig. 8-11 will deliver equal regulated voltages of opposite polarity. This type of circuit is an example of the technique where one supply is regulated by a fixed reference source (in this case zener diode D_1), while the other supply is referenced to the output voltage of the first supply.

Transistor Q_1 is an npn series-pass element for the positive voltage side of the circuit. Its base current is controlled by operational amplifier A_1. A fixed reference voltage V_Z is set by the action of resistor R_1 and the zener diode. This voltage is applied to the noninverting input of operational amplifier A_1. The positive output voltage is sampled by voltage *divider* R_2/R_3 to produce voltage E_1, which is applied to the amplifier's inverting input. As long as E_1 is equal to V_Z, the amplifier will remain in a stable condition. Should E_1, which is proportional to the output voltage, rise or

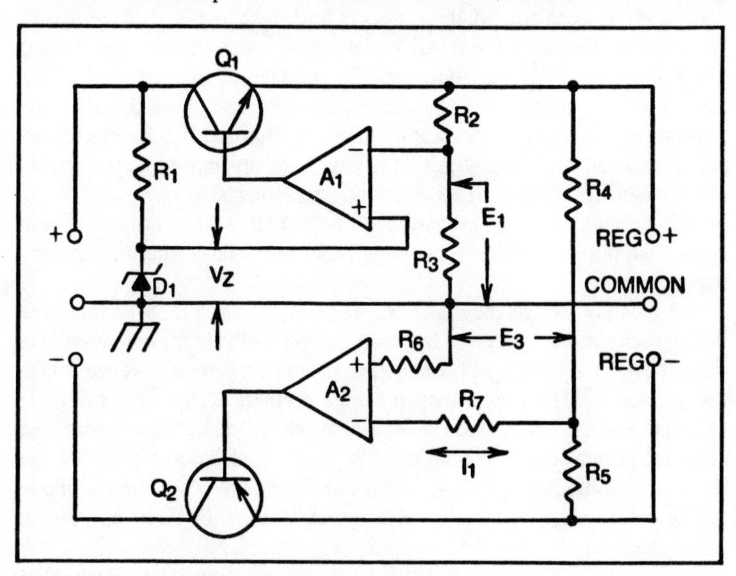

Fig. 8-11. Dual-polarity regulated power supply.

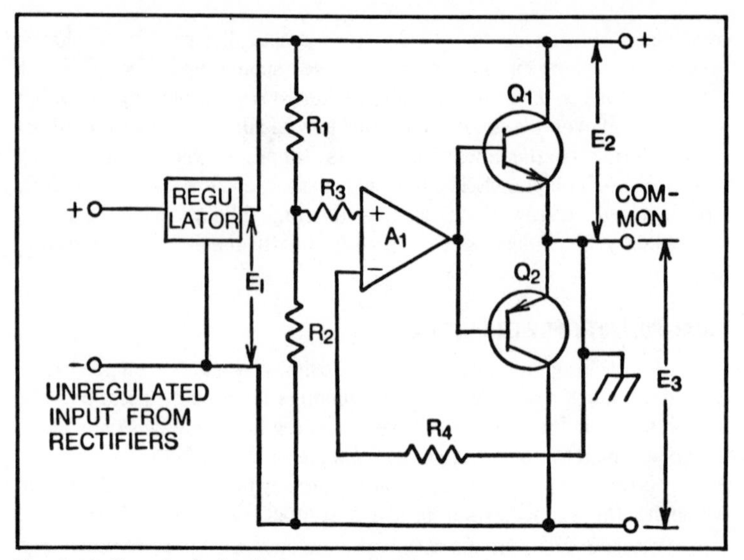

Fig. 8-12. Pseudo dual-polarity power supply.

fall, the amplifier output will be driven in a direction which causes transistor Q_1 to cancel the change.

Transistor Q_2 is the pnp negative voltage series-pass element. Note that a change in output polarity has occasioned a switch in transistor polarity, npn to pnp. Resistor R_6 references the noninverting input of the control amplifier to ground. If resistors R_4 and R_5 are equal, then voltage E_3 will be zero whenever the positive and negative output voltages are also equal. If those voltages are not equal, E_3 will take on a nonzero amplitude and polarity proportional to the amount and direction of the change. This will create a current I_1 in resistor R_7, which is used to drive the operational amplifier input. This causes current to flow in the op-amp output to the base of transistor Q_2. That current causes Q_2 to either shut down or turn on harder, depending upon the nature of the output voltage change. These power supplies are of a type generally called dual-polarity *tracking* supplies.

Appealing though they may be, supplies such as Fig. 8-11 require a dual-polarity input voltage to begin with. One method for obtaining these voltages is to use a single, center-tapped transformer—delivering twice the voltage needed—and a pair of bridge rectifier stacks. One bridge is connected across one-half the secondary winding, and the other connected across the remaining half of the secondary. The center tap is grounded and is common to both supplies. We shall ground the positive terminal of one bridge and the negative terminal of the other. With a little filtering, we have a dual supply power supply.

The polarity converter of Fig. 8-12 uses a pair of complementary shunt regulator transistors to create an artificial or counterpoise ground or common point. Complementary transistors, common in audio power amplifier design, have identical electrical characteristics except for polarity—one is pnp and the other is npn. A pnp will conduct as the base becomes more negative than the emitter, while in the npn exactly the opposite situation occurs. Resistors R_4, connected between the common point and the inverting input of the operational amplifier, senses the situation at the common junction. If the other op-amp input is held fixed at a reference point by voltage divider R_1/R_2. If $R_1 = R_2$ and $R_3 = R_4$, then the two output voltages will also be equal ($E_2 = E_3$). We can change the ratio almost at will by varying the ratio $R_1 : R_2$. Unfortunately, reality imposes a couple of restraints on our enthusiasm:

1. The input power supply *must* be floating (neither side of the output grounded).
2. The input power supply must also be regulated.
3. Transistors Q_1 and Q_2 must be able to dissipate a fair amount of power.

If the second restriction is not met, disastrous results can be expected. The regulated power supply could be a standard bench supply, or possibly an integral part of the circuit. In the former case we would then use the circuit as an outboard converter. Nevertheless, there is no reason why the input supply cannot be the simple three-terminal, fixed-output-voltage type used so frequently these days.

Chapter 9

Miscellaneous Op-Amp Circuits

In this chapter, we will consider a number of interesting applications of operational amplifiers which do not really fit too well into any of the other chapters. Some of these circuits are just plain fun even though they are outside the organized structure; even the most stodgy technical books should have at least one "fun" chapter.

AGC AMPLIFIERS

An amplifier such as that shown in Fig. 9-1 offers the capability of using a dc voltage level to control the gain of an operational amplifier. It can be used as either a manual or an automatic gain control (AGC), depending upon the specific application.

Some AGC amplifier designs place the control element, usually a junction field effect transistor (JFET), directly in the feedback loop of the op amp. After all, a JFET can, over a limited range, operate as a voltage controlled resistor. The problem with this is that the allowable output voltage is only a fraction of the pinchoff voltage of the JFET. In the circuit of Fig. 9-1, this is partially overcome by placing the JFET at the junction of a resistor feedback network, causing the voltage across the drain and source (E_{DS}) to be only a fraction of the output voltage. While the distortion still rises drastically when E_{DS} gets too high, the value of E_{OUT} can increase manageable levels before this occurs. E_{DS} will only be equal to:

$$E_{DS} = \frac{E_{OUT} R_1}{R_1 + R_2} \qquad (9\text{-}1)$$

when Q_1 is pinched off.

When Q_1 is turned on, R_{DS} drops to a low value at saturation. It is the

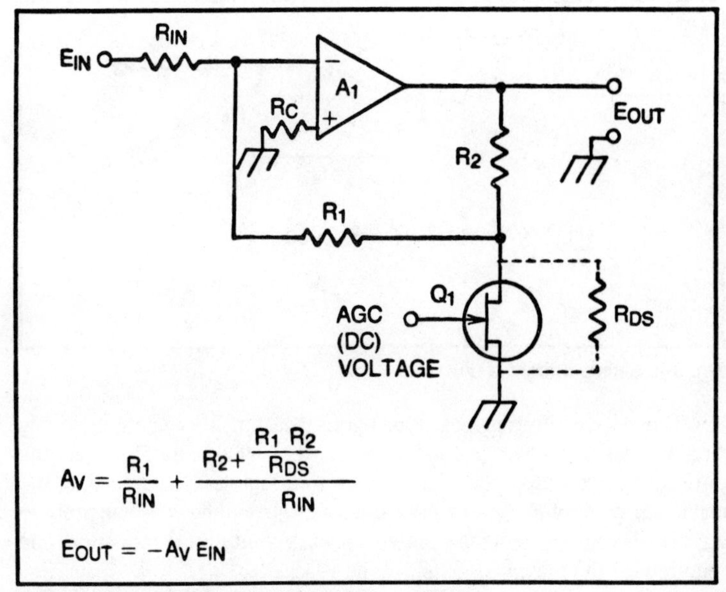

Fig. 9-1. Gain controlled (AGC or MGC) amplifier.

values of R_{DS} between these extremes that are voltage-controlled and are responsible for the change in voltage gain of the op amp. The equation for voltage gain is:

$$A_V = \frac{R_1 + R_2 + \dfrac{R_1 R_2}{R_{DS}}}{R_{IN}} \tag{9-2}$$

If R_{DS} goes down, as it will when the dc control voltage is applied, the ratio $(R_1 R_2)/R_{DS}$ begins to rise, thereby raising the total value for the numerator in Eq. 9-2. When this happens, of course, the value of A_V goes up. The limits on A_V are determined by R_{DS} at both pinchoff and saturation.

THRESHOLD DETECTORS

A limit or threshold detector provides an output every time the input voltage exceeds a certain value, which is preset by the designer.

Figure 9-2 shows one of the simpler types of threshold detectors which allows the use of relatively modest operational amplifiers. The reference voltage, which sets the threshold point, is set according to:

$$E_{REF} = \frac{V_{CC} R_1}{R_1 + R_2} \tag{9-3}$$

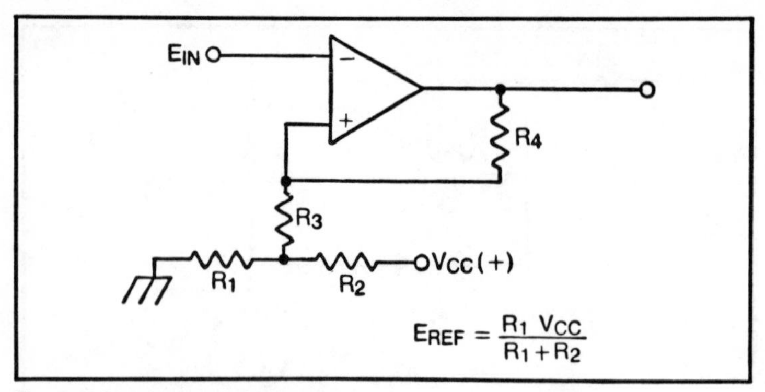

Fig. 9-2. Simple threshold detector.

One reason why a modest-type operational amplifier is usable in this circuit is due to the positive feedback provided by resistor R_4. When the threshold is exceeded, the output snaps to a high level approaching the maximum value of E_{OUT}. For most devices, this will be approximately ⅔ V_{CC}. The regeneration of the positive feedback shortens the transition time required for the maximum output to be reached.

A variation on the theme is shown as another threshold detector in Fig. 9-3. It is essentially the same as the previous design except for the removal of the regenerative feedback. Fast rise times can still be achieved, however, if a high slew-rate op amp is used with its compensation components (lead and lag) excluded. A fully compensated type, such as the 741, will probably not be appropriate in all but those applications where rise time can

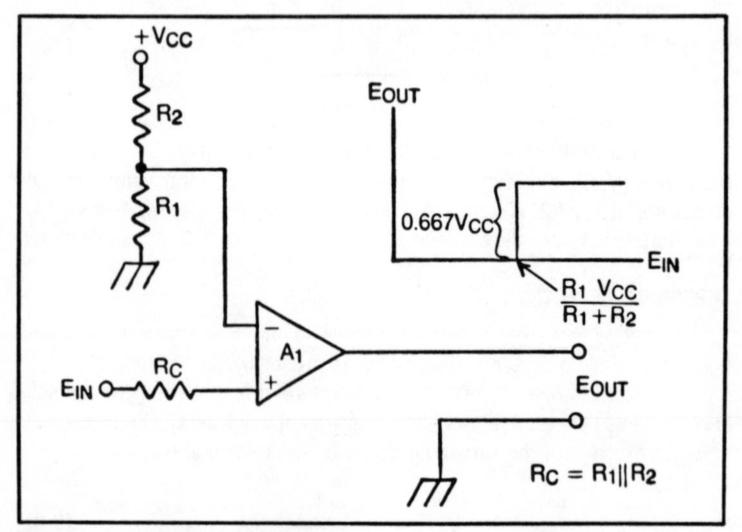

Fig. 9-3. Alternate threshold detector.

be a little slow. Resistor R_C is a compensating resistor equal to the parallel combination of the other two resistors. It possibly can be eliminated by the use of a low input current operational amplifier.

ZERO-CROSSING DETECTOR

At times, such as when making frequency or phase determinations, it is advisable to have a circuit that can produce a sharp (fast rise time) pulse precisely at the instant when the input waveform crosses the zero axis (see Fig. 9-4A). Ideally, the circuit will generate two pulses, each of which has a polarity indicating in which direction (positive or negative going) the input waveform crossed the axis. If pulses of only one amplitude are desired, such as the crossing of the zero axis in the positive going direction, it is a simple matter to design a precision rectifier to follow the zero-crossing detector. This circuit will pass only the pulses of the desired polarity.

Figure 9-4B shows the circuit implementation of the idea discussed above. Although an initial introduction to this circuit often leads to petulant shaking of the head and a bemoaning that it can't work (the connection of diodes D_1 and D_2 appears to render them useless), we soon find that the circuit does work nicely as a zero-crossing detector.

The diodes are connected to form the feedback path of amplifier A_1 making this op amp a noninverting follower (which of course means that the preceding stages see a very high input impedance). The voltage drop of the

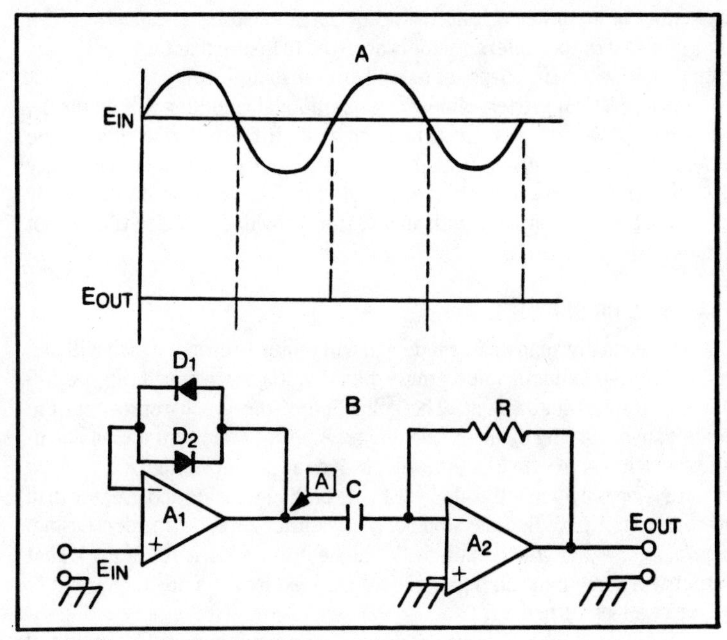

Fig. 9-4. Zero-crossing detector.

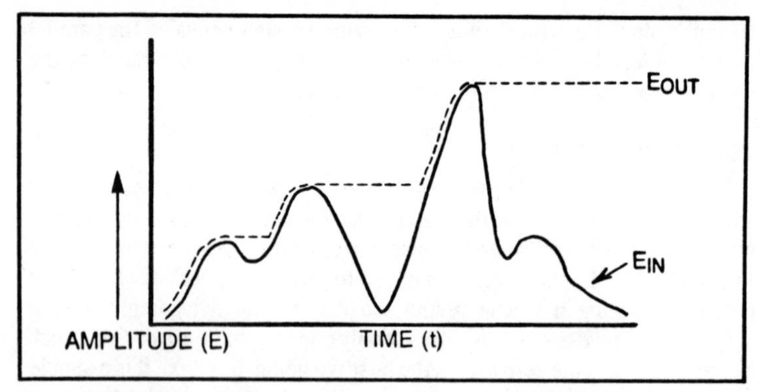

Fig. 9-5. Output and input voltage curves of a peak holding circuit.

diodes is servoed out by the action of the feedback, making A_1 act as a unity-gain noninverting follower. You will see that the voltage appearing at point A is approximately equal to E_{IN}. Note that with a single polarity at the input, only one diode is operable. This is the situation on one-half of an ac input signal. On the alternate half-cycle, the other diode takes over and the former diode becomes reverse biased. For that brief instant when $E_{IN} = E_A$ = close to zero, neither diode is effective and the voltage at point A makes an abrupt jump.

The signal at A is also fed to the input of a differentiator circuit consisting of amplifier A_2 and the associated resistor and capacitor. The time constant of this differentiator is adjusted to insure that there will be an output only when E_A snaps up to its zero-crossing level.

As a practical matter, almost any operational amplifier will do for A_1, but a high slew-rate type must be used at A_2 if the fast rise time of the differentiated E_A is to be preserved. The output pulses have a polarity opposite the direction of the zero crossing. This can be corrected by following the differentiator with an inverter, provided that rise time is not compromised.

PEAK HOLDING CIRCUITS

Occasionally an instrument design will require a circuit which will find and hold the maximum value attained by a voltage waveform. Figure 9-5 illustrates this requirement. The solid line of the graph represents the continuously varying input signal voltage. A peak-holding circuit, an example of which is shown in Fig. 9-6, will produce an output voltage E_{OUT} which is increasing only when the slope of E_{IN} is both increasing and greater than any previous E_{IN}. When the slope of E_{IN} is either zero, or it is decreasing, the value of E_{OUT} will remain at the highest previous level of E_{IN}. That output will remain at the highest level attained by E_{IN} until the circuit is either reset or turned off.

Amplifier A_1 shown in Fig. 9-6, acts as an input buffer. The output of

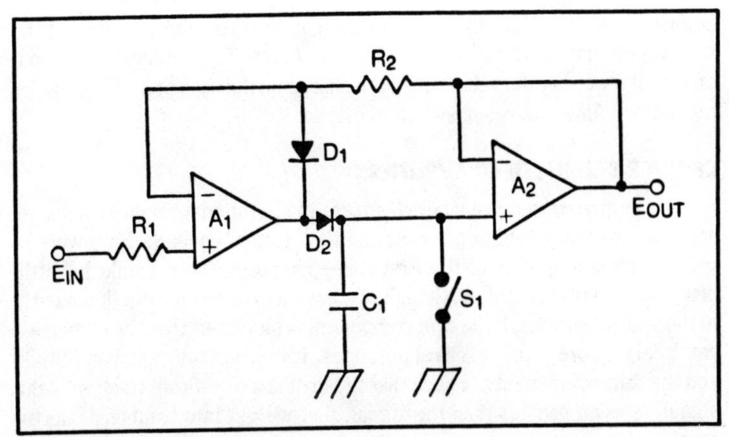

Fig. 9-6. Peak holding circuit.

this stage is equal to the input voltage and is used to charge capacitor C_1. High-back-resistance silicon diodes ("too high" doesn't exist!) prevent the low-impedance output of the op amp from discharging the capacitor.

In more critical applications, other techniques must also be used to maintain the charge on C_1: polystyrene or polyfilm capacitor is used for C_1 and an FET input op amp for A_2. A switch can be used to reset C_1 at any proper time. That switch can be either a mechanical type (pushbutton or set of relay contacts) or a field-effect transistor.

SAMPLE-AND-HOLD CIRCUITS

A closely related cousin of the peak holder is the sample-and-hold circuit of Fig. 9-7. In this circuit transistor Q_1 is a series-connected MOS-FET electronic switch used to control the charging of capacitor C_1. When a pulse appears at the sample input, the switch is closed and the capacitor

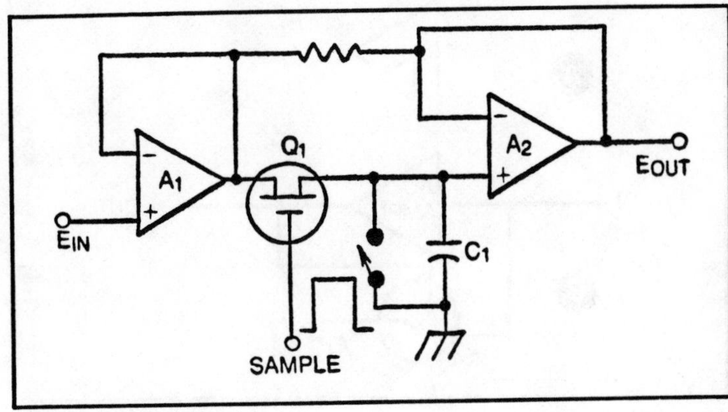

Fig. 9-7. Sample and hold.

begins to charge. Note that the capacitor only takes a charge during the interval when the switch is closed. After the finish of the interval, the output of A_2 will remain at the value set by the charge on the capacitor. This level is maintained until the reset switch is closed.

CHOPPER-STABILIZED DC AMPLIFIERS

As demonstrated in earlier chapters, an operational amplifier behaves admirably as a dc amplifier or as an amplifier of signals near dc. If we were to use the ideal amplifier of the first three chapters, there would be little problem. In a real amplifier, though, we have a drift component due mostly to thermal conditions. If the drift component is much less than the signal, we can safely ignore it for practical purposes. It is when the signal amplitude and the drift component are such that the drift is a significant fraction of the signal, or even greater than the signal, that we get into trouble. Unfortunately, a lot of naturally occurring signals are small enough that the 5 or 10 μV/C° drift looks like an awfully big error! Chopper-stabilized dc amplifiers offer drift improvement sufficient to handle such signals.

A chopper amplifier is one which converts the low-level dc or near-dc signal into a ac signal that can be processed using a feedback stabilized ac amplifier. The symbol for a chopper amplifier is shown in Fig. 9-8A.

Basic chopper technique, shown schematically in Fig. 9-8B, uses a switch (S_1) to alternately ground the input then the output of the ac amplifier. This converts the low frequency input into a series of amplitude modulated pulses that can be processed using an ac amplifier. This sort of tactic improves the drift figure by 50 to 100 times, resulting in drift specs between 0.05 and 0.1 μV/C°. Of course, SPDT switch S_1 is not just any simple switch but is, rather, either an electronic type, or a vibrator driven mechanical type.

Many existing low-level preamplifiers use the electro-mechanical

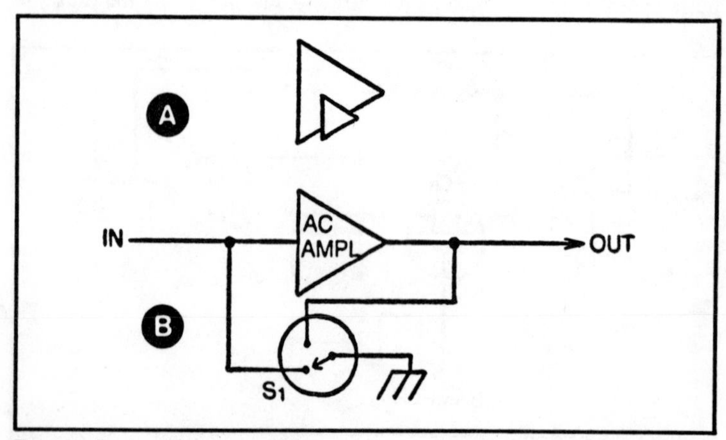

Fig. 9-8. Basic chopper amplifier.

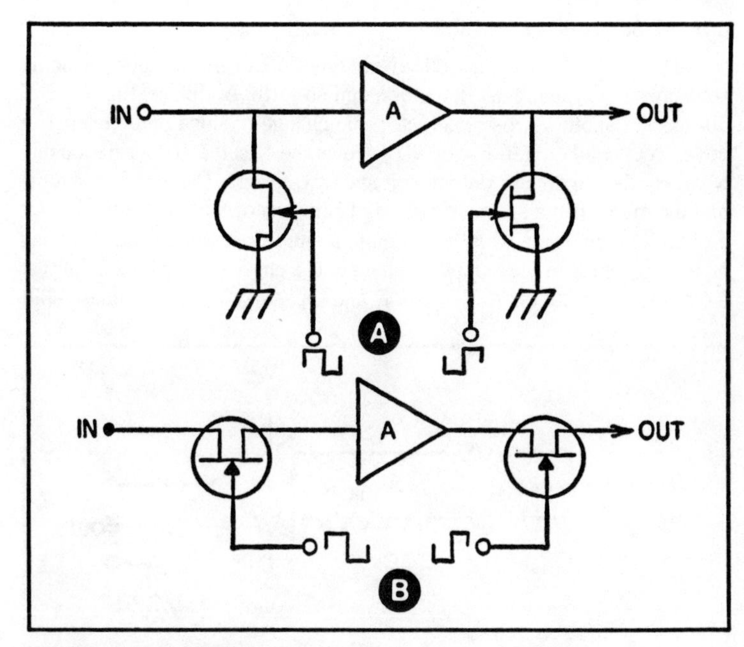

Fig. 9-9. Typical JFET chopper circuits.

type of switch. These are vibrators that drive a set of SPDT contacts at a rate of either 60 or 400 Hz with the latter being most common. Vibrator frequency (or electronic switch drive speed) is chosen to be a frequency at least twice the highest frequency component anticipated in the input waveform. Most authorities raise this even further to "...several times..."

Figure 9-9 shows two methods for implementing the electronic chopper. In these circuits the switch (S_1 of Fig. 9-8B) is a pair of JFETs. These can be operated as switches because they have an R_{DS} that is extremely high when the device is cut off, and relatively low when turned on. The required SPDT action is obtained by driving the gates of the respective transistors on alternate halves of an input square-wave. The first circuit, Fig. 9-9A is the shunt chopper variety much the same as the electromechanical vibrator. A series chopper amplifier is shown as Fig. 9-9B.

The action of the chopper on the output is analogous to that of a mechanical rectifier much like the old-fashioned synchronous vibrators in car radios. If the action is perfect (and it is not), no high frequency chopping signal components will appear in the output. In order to correct for a lack of perfection, it is necessary to depend on either the normal frequency response rolloff of succeeding stages, or a low-pass filter to eliminate that interference. Since most of these amplifiers process signals with components less than 50 to 100 Hz, the chopper drive frequency can be of the order of 400 to 1000 Hz, and the latter techniques used to suppress residual chopper noise.

CHANGE-OF-SLOPE DETECTORS

Thus far we have discussed several types of event detectors, including zero-crossing types, peak detectors, and so forth. In this section we will discuss yet another type of detector: the change-of-slope detector. It is a novel, yet useful circuit. Figure 9-10 shows the circuit and the relationship between the input and output voltage waveforms. The basic circuit is nothing more than a simple differential comparator with a modified input circuit. The input signal is fed through a single resistor to the inverting input. The signal to the noninverting input is a phase shifted version of that fed to the inverting input. Resistor R and capacitor C form the phase shift

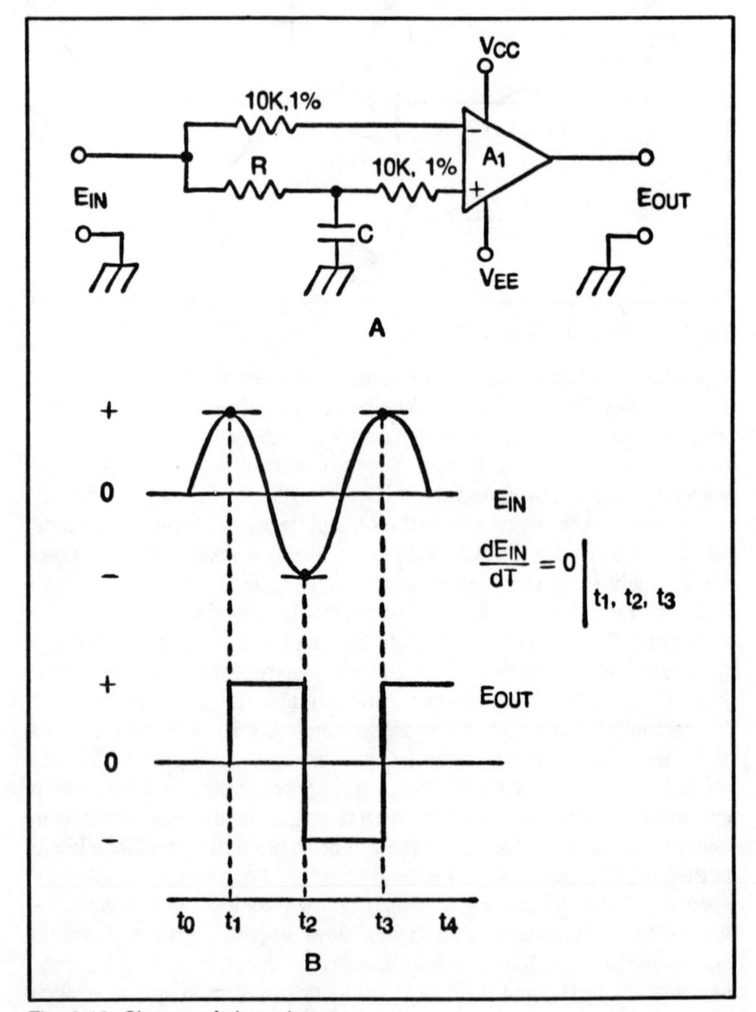

Fig. 9-10. Change-of-slope detector.

network. Values for these components will range between 10K to 500K, and 0.1 to 1.0 μF.

Examine the sine wave designated E_{IN} in Fig. 9-10B. Between times t_0 and t_1 the slope of the waveform has a positive value, since E_{IN} is increasing. At t_1 the slope reverses and takes on a negative value, because E_{IN} is then decreasing. For a brief instant at the time of reversal the slope will be zero ($dE/dt = 0$). At that point the output of the comparator snaps to a value equal to V_{CC} minus the internal op-amp voltage drop between the output terminal and V_{CC} terminal. The output will remain at that level until time t_2, when the slope of E_{IN} once again goes through a reversal, causing another $dE/dt = 0$ condition. Here, we will find that the output slews to a high negative level equal to V_{EE} plus the internal drop.

The change-of-slope detector will thus continue producing output excursions every time the slope of E_{IN} goes through zero indicating a reversal. Precision of detection is dependent upon three factors. One is the hysteresis of the op amp under conditions where it is acting as a comparator. Secondly, the match of the 10K resistors is important. Resistors with tolerances of 1 percent or less should be used here unless accuracy is of no real concern when compared to economy. The third factor affecting precision are false outputs generated by severe harmonic distortion. Low percentages of total harmonic distortion have little effect, because they do not usually cause slope reversals of the fundamental sine wave. Severe distortion, on the other hand, may well cause such reversals—resulting in a change of output.

WAVEFORM GENERATION

Operational amplifiers can be used to generate various useful waveforms. The criterion for oscillation is that some energy from the output must be fed back in phase (regeneratively) with the signal at the input. Furthermore, the overall gain must be greater than unity. We cannot use the noninverting input for this even though it appears on the surface to be desirable, considering the fact that the output is in phase with the input. The problem is that the op amp will oscillate at some unwanted frequency determined by its own characteristics.

Sine-Wave Oscillators

To pick a specific oscillation frequency for sine-wave generation (one that is usable by the specified application rather than a miscellaneous type), we need to introduce a frequency selective element in the feedback network which will, unfortunately, introduce some phase shift. The best bet is to use feedback to the inverting input through a network which offers an additional 180° phase shift at the frequency of oscillation. The op amp will oscillate only at that single frequency, because all other frequencies experience some other phase shift that will be essentially degenerative, rather than regenerative.

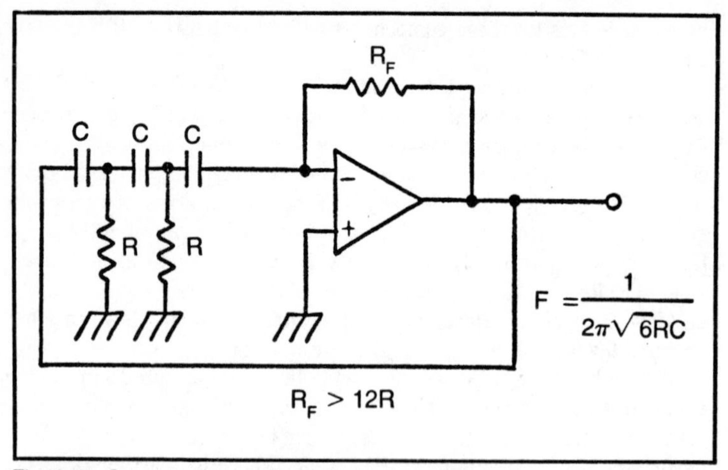

Fig. 9-11. Op amp phase-shift oscillator.

Figure 9-11 is a simple op-amp version of the classic RC phase-shift oscillator. Part of the feedback network consists of three RC phase-shift combinations, each of which provides a 60° phase shift at the design frequency.

In an earlier section, we considered the sort of peaking active filter which uses a twin-tee RC notch network in the feedback path of an operational amplifier (also see Fig. 9-12). One of the principal objections to that design is its tendency to oscillate at a frequency close to the notch frequency. Indeed, it is the regenerative action which tends to cause the peak—a fact not lost by some amateur radio operators who design active audio filters for selecting desired CW stations in their receivers. If the gain of the circuit is sufficient to sustain oscillation, that circuit will oscillate at a frequency approximated by Eq. 7-4.

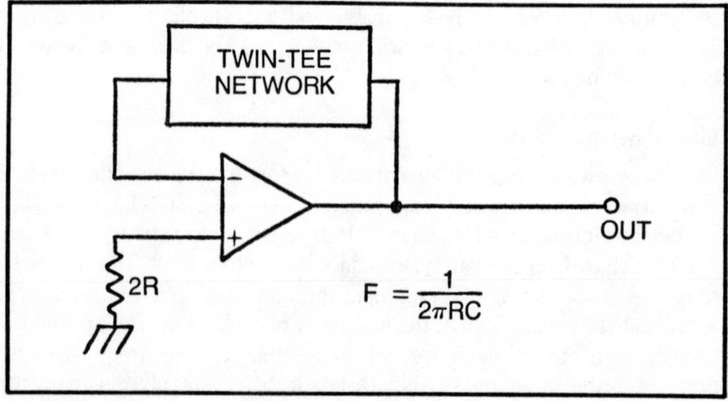

Fig. 9-12. Op amp with twin-tee network feedback.

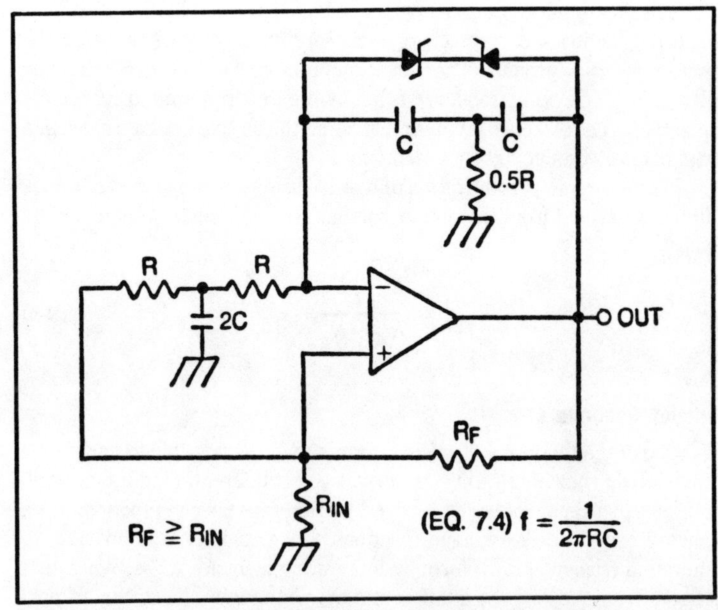

Fig. 9-13. Alternative method of feedback via a twin-tee network.

An alternate method of feedback via the twin-tee network is shown in the circuit of Fig. 9-13. Note that the tee sections of the RC network appear to be separated relative to their respective positions in the circuit as usually drawn. Perhaps that this accounts for the practice of some authors who call this the *double-tee* or *split-tee* configuration (rather than *twin-tee*.) In this circuit, a pair of back-to-back zener diodes are used to clamp the output amplitude to a certain maximum excursion. Although this generates a small amount of harmonic distortion, it does accomplish a desired purpose at the expense of one added low-pass filter, which is needed to remove the spurious harmonics from the waveform.

One of the best oscillator circuits using op amps (or any other amplifying device) is the Wien bridge configuration of Fig. 9-14. The principal advantages of this circuit are reasonably automatic control over gain and some measure of control over distortion. The stability of the circuit is due in large measure to the use of the low-current lamp and to the use of the variable resistance in the dc feedback network. This latter control is adjusted to yield the best tradeoff between amplitude, stability, and distortion. Once again, Eq. 7-4 determines the frequency of oscillation.

Square-Wave Oscillators

There are several methods for making a square-wave generator. One, although not the most elegant, is to follow a sine wave generator with either a Schmitt trigger or some other form of threshold detector. In another type of circuit, one input of the op amp is connected to a feedback network, in which the feedback current charges a capacitor connected between the minus input and ground. The other input is connected to a reference voltage. The operating frequency is set by the time required to charge the capacitor to the reference level. At that point, the op amp behaves much like a comparator, producing a stepped output.

Figure 9-15 is a modification of that basic idea in which the reference voltage is derived from the output voltage. The reference voltage will be equal to:

$$E_{REF} = \frac{E_{OUT} R_2}{R_1 + R_2} \quad (9\text{-}4)$$

Function Generators

One of the theorems of calculus states that it is possible to generate a function by either integrating its derivative or differentiating its integral. Both of these techniques can be used to generate special functions from standard easy-to-make voltage functions. For example, it is possible to generate a triangular waveform by integrating a square wave. When that triangle is passed through a differentiator, on the other hand, the original square wave will be produced. A quadrature oscillator produces two output signals which are both sine shaped. At one output, we will have the regular sine wave, while at the other we will have a cosine wave (sine shifted 90°).

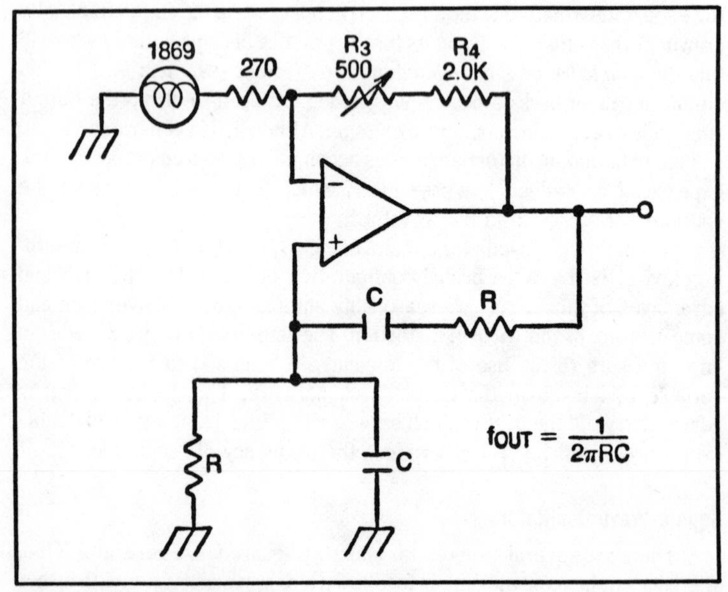

Fig. 9-14. Wien bridge oscillator.

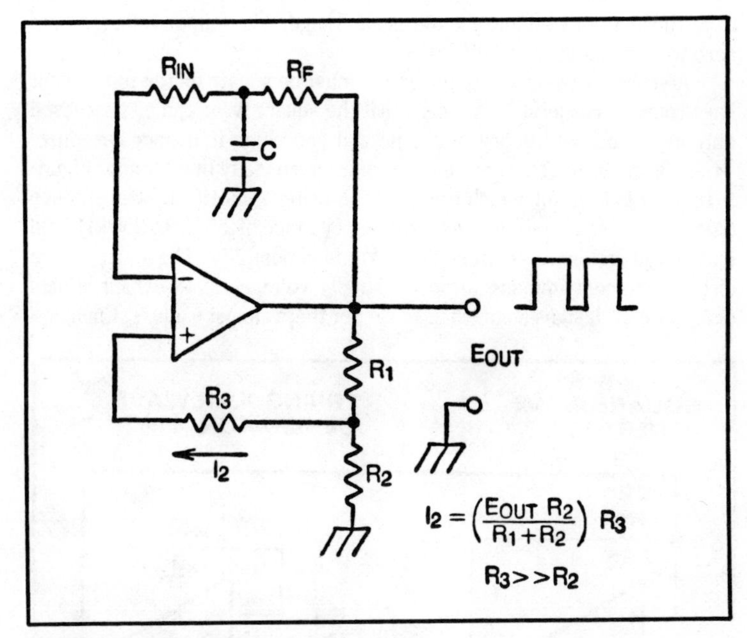

Fig. 9-15. Square-wave generator.

One easy method for implementing this idea is to build a sine wave oscillator using either bridge or phase-shift techniques, then either integrate or differentiate the output.

There are no less than three different approaches to designing a basic, three-function (sine, square, and triangle waveforms) generator. One is to start with a sine wave oscillator followed by a comparator. The output of the sine oscillator provides the sine wave while the output of the comparator provides the needed square wave. An integrator following the comparator output will create the triangle. The second technique has a square-wave generator as the prime circuit. Its output, of course, supplies the square wave to the generator output. It will also drive, in parallel, a filter section and an integrator will be the desired triangular waveform. The filter is designed to pass only the fundamental frequency of the square wave. All nonsine waveforms are made up by summing a fundamental and a number of harmonics. By filtering out all harmonics, we can regenerate a sine wave (it is the only waveform totally devoid of harmonics). The third and simplest way to make a triple-function generator is to buy one of those newer three-function IC devices. These combine in one IC package (using but a single timing RC network) all circuitry needed to generate all three basic functions.

A function generator which can supply both square waves and triangle waves is a very useful tool in any laboratory or service shop. For most applications, such a generator will be required to offer a frequency range from subaudio to well into the ultrasonic range, with output voltages from zero to something over 10V RMS.

A square wave from the generator must be square on the top and not have rounded corners. This means that the square wave can be processed only in circuits with a fast rise time and good high-frequency response. Triangle waves, on the other hand, require a perfectly linear ramp. Figure 9-16 shows a circuit which meets these criteria nicely. It will produce triangles and squarewaves over a frequency range of 2.5 Hz to 250 kHz and output voltage levels between 200 mV and almost 20V. The square-wave circuit is almost immune to power supply voltage ripple, which afflicts certain other designs so much as to render them almost useless. Changing

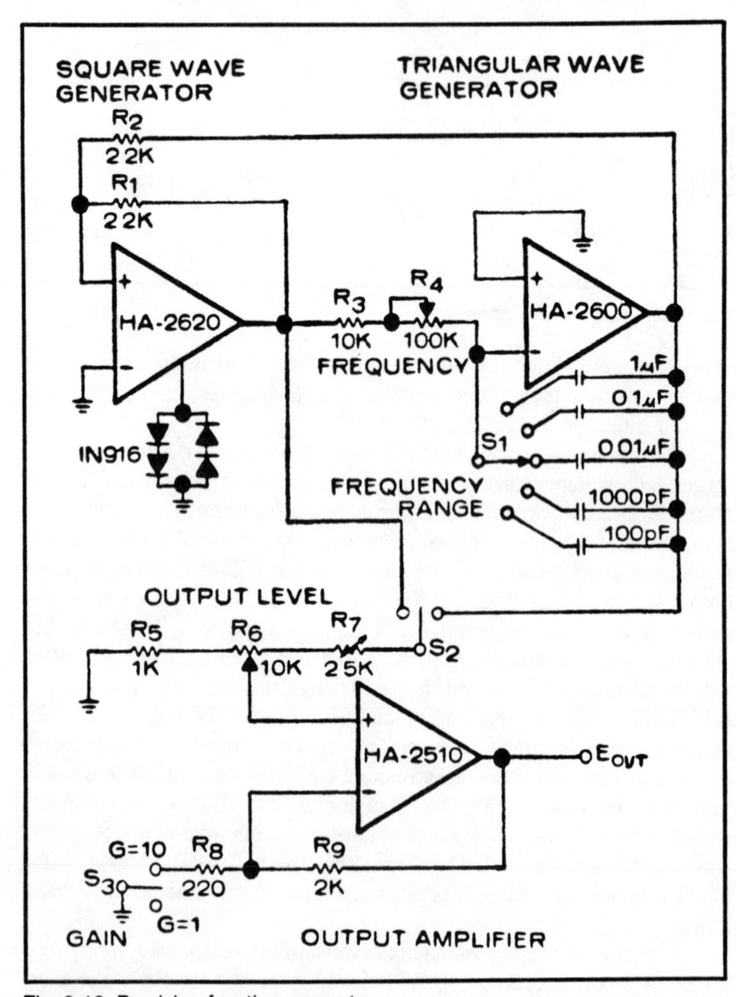

Fig. 9-16. Precision function generator.

the dc power supply voltage from 10 to 20V produces only minor shifts in the key operating parameters, including frequency.

Square-wave generation is accomplished by an operational amplifier used as a hysteresis trigger circuit synchronized to the output of a triangle integrator. The HA-2620 op amp (Harris Semiconductor) output is clamped to ±2.0V peak-to-peak by four 1N916 silicon diodes shunted between ground and the amplifier's bandwidth rolloff terminal. The amplitude of the square wave will be higher than that of the triangle by a factor of R_1/R_2.

The triangle wave is generated by integrating the output of the op amp hysteresis circuit. The slope of the integrator output and the trip points of the hysteresis amplifier set the frequency of oscillation. This is a function of the integrator time constant and is given by:

$$f = \frac{1}{4R_2(R_3 + R_4) \times C}$$

where C is the capacitance (in farads) selected by switch S_1.

Each capacitor selected controls a different decade range of frequencies. Best accuracy is realized if all of these capacitors are high-grade, close-tolerance types that won't drift with changes in temperature—1-2 percent error-tolerance types are advised.

Variable frequency control is achieved through the use of potentiometer R_4. This must also be a higher grade type that is panel-mounted. A large panel-mountable, multiturn potentiometer with a turns counting dial would certainly be in place at this point.

The overall frequency range can be modified by changing the value of the $R_3 + R_4$ combination. The values of the capacitors might be changed to adjust the frequency, but this might prove a bit difficult since precision units in either high or low extremes of value are a little hard to find.

When designing circuits such as this, we must pay close attention to the slew rate of the operational amplifiers processing the square waves as well as the bias and offset currents of amplifiers acting as integrators. The amplifier used as an integrator in Fig. 9-16 has an input bias current of only 1 pA, so it shows superior accuracy of integration.

The output impedance of the function generator described here is 600Ω. In order to reduce the output to zero, one could feed the output of this circuit to a 600Ω constant-impedance variable attenuator. The output tap of the attenuator could be used to feed signal to the outside world. The internal gain controls of the generator would be set to whatever value is appropriate to drive the attenuator. The attenuator dial could be calibrated in either voltage or dBm units. Alternatively, an ac voltmeter could be used to measure the output.

MONOSTABLE MULTIVIBRATORS

A monostable multivibrator or *one-shot* is a circuit which produces a single output pulse of fixed amplitude and duration every time a trigger input pulse is received, unless a second pulse is received prior to the completion of the first output pulse. One might be forgiven for asking, "What use is a circuit which delivers but one output pulse for every input pulse?" After all, a resistor, amplifier, or piece of wire will do that trick!

The key answer to this is the "fixed amplitude and duration" specification—and, of course, the trigger can be any of a number of input signals. This could prove highly advantageous. For instance, it could be a sloppy square wave which has been deteriorated (with high-frequency attenuation, for example) by passing over a long coaxial cable. The one-shot may be used to reconstitute the square wave.

In other instances, we might find the input is the differentiated spike delivered by the playback head of a digital or analog FM tape recorder. Again, we can use the one-shot to reconstruct a square wave.

One will also frequently see these circuits used in "bounceless" pushbutton circuits. Regular pushbuttons use mechanical spring leaves which don't actually produce a nice clean step function on closure. They actually produce a series of spikes caused by the bouncing of the contacts. Such spikes can really foul up some circuits rather badly. Digital counters, too, can be incremented a couple dozen counts by the reset-to-zero switch! The first spike out of the mechanical pushbutton can be used to trigger the monostable multivibrator, which then delivers the needed step voltage and ignores the rest of the spikes.

Figure 9-17 is an operational amplifier version of the monostable multivibrator. Under rest conditions, when the output is in its stable state, voltage E_{OUT} will be at $+V_{CC}$ or, if zener diodes D_4 and D_5 are used, at a positive voltage, V_Z. Capacitor C_2 will begin to charge as current driven by E_{OUT} flows in resistor R_4 and the resistor—diode combination R_5D_3. Voltage across capacitor C_2 will rise until it reaches a value in the neighborhood of 600—700 mV, at which point diode D_2 will begin to conduct heavily, effectively clamping any further rise in voltage. A trigger pulse at the input having a value greater than $0.5\,E_{OUT}$ causes the output to toggle to the minus zener potential, or to V_{EE} if no zener diodes are used. Since E_{OUT} is now negative instead of positive, capacitor C_2 will begin to discharge and will then recharge with the opposite polarity. When C_2 has charged to a level of $0.5E_{OUT}$ will toggle back to its initial stable condition—where E_{OUT} is a positive voltage of V_Z or V_{CC}. The one-shot will remain in its single stable state unable to retrigger until capacitor C_2 has had time to recharge to its positive value of about 9.7V. During this rest or refractory period, as well as during the time when an output pulse is actually being produced, the circuit will ignore any further input trigger pulses. During the reset time, current generated in the output can charge C_2 by flowing through both R_4 and the R_5D_3 path. During output pulse transitions, however, E_{OUT} is negative and therefore reverse biases diode D_3. C_2 can then be charged only through the R_4 path. This means that the monostable multivibrator has a *reset* (RC) time constant considerably faster than the *duration* RC time

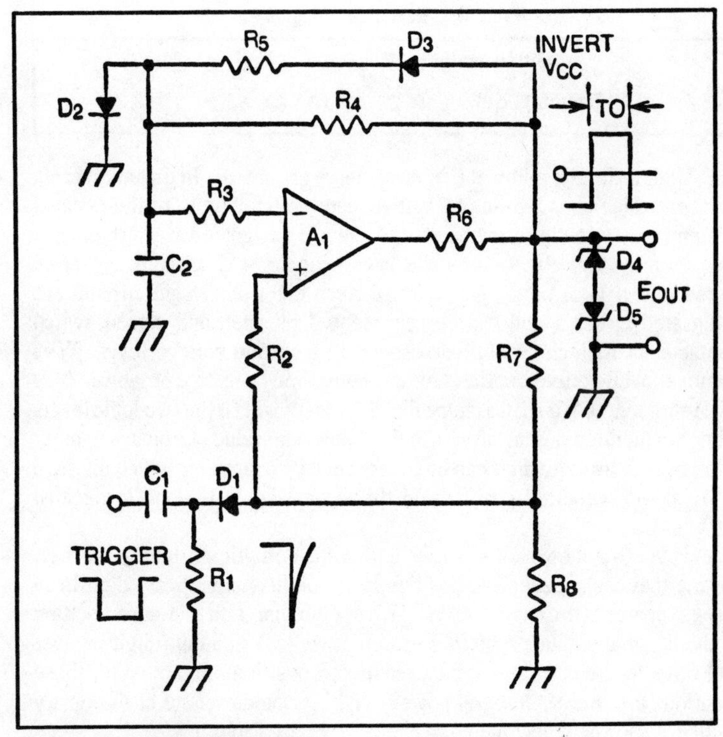

Fig. 9-17. Monostable multivibrator.

constant, because the R in the former consists of the parallel combination of R_4 and R_5, while the latter only has R_4.

In this case, we are using a step voltage applied to an input differentiator consisting of capacitor C_1 and resistor R_1 as an input trigger. The amplifier selected for use in a monostable multivibrator circuit must be capable of operating at the V_{CC} and V_{EE} extremes without latching up. Time period t_0 greater than 10 msec pulse duration is given approximately by:

$$t_0 \simeq R_4C_2/(1.414) \simeq 0.707R_4C_2$$

DIGITAL-TO-ANALOG CONVERTERS

It is sometimes desirable to create an analog voltage from a digital representation of that voltage. We might, for instance, want to read the voltage on an analog panel meter, view it on an oscilloscope, write it out on a strip chart recorder, or use it in some other electronic circuit to control some process. If we use certain switching arrangements, we can also use the analog-to-digital converter to make a programmable output dc voltage source. Before getting into the nitty-gritty of typical A/D converter circuits, however, let us first review a few basics of digital electronics.

Table 9-1. Numerical Weighting.

Binary weight	2^n	2^5	2^4	2^3	2^2	2^1	2^0
Decimal Equivalent	2^n	32	16	8	4	2	1

Digital circuits follow the rules of binary arithmetic. In that numbering system, which uses a base of 2 rather than the familiar 10 of the decimal system, only two digits are needed; these are designated 1 and 0. Since a two-state system also follows the laws of logic, such circuits are often called *digital logic* or simply *logic*. Modern electronic logic circuits are integrated circuits, and can be represented by open and closed switch contacts. In IC logic, 1 will correspond to a certain voltage level (5V is common) while either another voltage, sometimes negative or *ground* (0V) will represent 0. We shall assume that 5V and 0V will be the two logic levels when we mention digital circuits in this book. The value of a binary number of more than a single digit can be determined by examining which digits (0 or 1) are in weighted positions in the same way as is done in decimal arithmetic.

Table 9-1 shows standard weighting for a multidigit binary number. Notice that each successive position from the least significant digit is an integer power of the base or *radix* 2. We are familiar with this same notation in the decimal number system. Recall that we look at a multidigit number and refer to the units, tens, hundreds, etc., positions. In actuality, these positions are merely integral powers of 10. Consider some of the binary numbers and their decimal equivalents given in Table 9-2.

Let's look at the decimal number 35. It has as a binary equivalent 100011. Conversion from binary to decimal form is done by adding up the products of the digits and their equivalent weights:

Table 9-2. Numerical Equivalents.

Decimal	Binary
1	000001
2	000010
3	000011
4	000100
5	000101
6	000110
7	000111
8	001000
9	001001
10	001010
25	011001
32	100000
35	100011

$(1)(2^5) + (0)(2^4) + (0)(2^3) + (0)(2^2) + (1)(2^1) + (1)(2^0)$
$= 32 + 0 + 0 + 0 + 2 + 1$
$= 35$

The binary-coded decimal is an alternate form of binary expression. It uses four binary digits or *bits* to represent the decimal digits 0 through 9. Although several weightings are used, the most common is 1, 2, 4, and 8—written from left to right in the fashion *8, 4, 2, 1.*

Figure 9-18 shows use of an operational amplifier to convert a binary-coded decimal (BCD) word to an analog voltage. The reader should recognize this as the addition or *summation* circuit from Fig. 1-8. In this case, however, resistors R_1 through R_4 are selected according to the binary weight being represented. The values of the resistors were calculated assuming that TTL logic ICs would be used. Such chips use 5V for 1 and 0V for 0.

Feedback resistor R_5 is made variable so that the output voltage can be trimmed to exactly the correct value. This is necessary because it is unlikely that we would find the output of a TTL logic IC to be precisely 5.000V when a logical 1 is presented. The range of R_5 is selected according to the order of magnitude being represented. In this example, scaling has been selected so that 100, 200, 400, and 800 μA will flow into the inverting input of the operational amplifier. These currents represent weights of 1, 2, 4, and 8. If resistor R_5 is set to a value of 10K, these currents will create output voltages of 1, 2, 4, and 8V. Other IC logic families may not use the standard 5V level for logical 1 as is the case in TTL and DTL families. HTL, for example, uses something higher to improve noise immunity, and CMOS can use any voltage between 5 and 18V. If those logic families are used, select resistor values such that output voltages occur which are 10 percent,

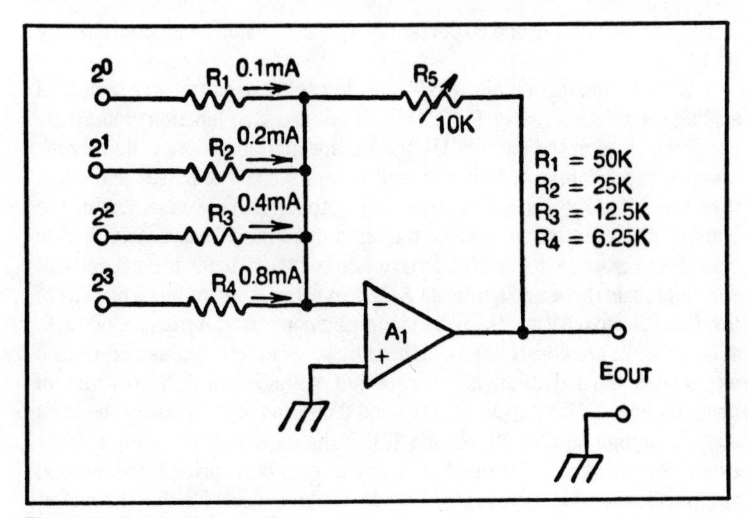

Fig. 9-18. Summation circuit.

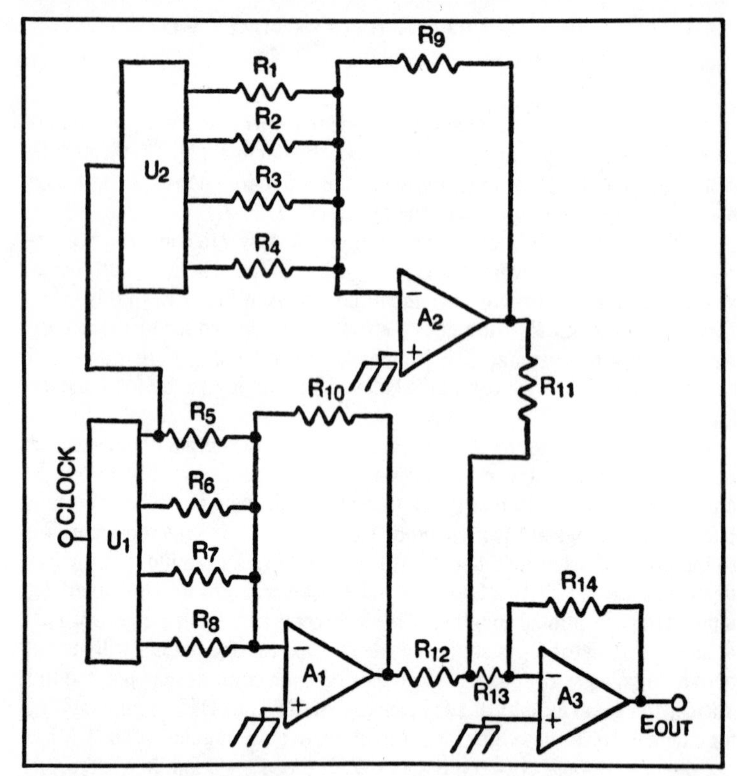

Fig. 9-19. Staircase generator.

20 percent, 40 percent and 80 percent of whatever value is selected as unity or 100 percent.

Both an application of digital-to-analog converters and an example of scaling can be seen in Fig. 9-19. This circuit is a step-function or *staircase* generator. Integrated circuits U1 and U2 are digital devices called *decade counters*. Such integrated circuits will accept a chain of pulses and count them continuously, and will deliver as an output a BCD word indicating the state of the count by tens. Since the circuit of Fig. 9-19 uses two decade counters in cascade, it has a total maximum count of 0 to 99. In such a circuit we could scale the least significant A/D converter, A_1, to produce outputs of 0.1, 0.2, 0.4 and 0.8V and the most significant converter, A_2, to produce 1, 2, 4, and 8V. We are constrained a bit here by some practical considerations if we want a third decade, because output voltages for a third order of magnitude would be 0.01, 0.02, 0.04 and 0.08V in the direction of the least significant digit and 10, 20, 40, and 80V in the most-significant-digit direction. The former is somewhat low for economy priced operational amplifiers, while the latter is too high for most devices. Neither, however, is beyond the reach of better components and clever design.

Amplifier A_3 serves a triple function: summation of the A_1 and A_2 outputs, buffer to the outside world, and inversion so that the output voltage is positive-going. The output will consist of a series of 99 individual voltage steps in increments of 100mV each.

Staircase generators are used in certain testing instruments, such as digital voltmeters (of a certain design) and semiconductor testers, where it is necessary to observe certain parameters under different conditions (which are successive voltage levels).

FM DEMODULATION

Figure 9-20 shows a novel technique for demodulating a frequency-modulated (FM) signal. This technique has been used in one form or another for many years, but only recently have operational amplifiers figured in its implementation. It is called the pulse-counting or *digital* detector, depending upon the source you read.

FM radio receivers, as well as TV audio sections which are also FM, normally amplify the i-f signal well beyond the point of clipping so that static and impulse noise, which tends to amplitude modulate the carrier, is cut off and eliminated. Signals strong enough to quiet the receiver noise will produce a chain of variable-period square waves at the input of the demodulator stage. By using these pulses to drive a monostable multivibrator, we can create a chain of pulses of equal duration and amplitude varying only in pulse repetition rate as the audio modulation of the radio carrier varies. We can recover the audio by taking the average of this output pulse train in an integrator circuit.

Figure 9-20 uses a TTL IC monostable multivibrator. Such ICs feature complementary outputs labeled Q and *not* Q. These outputs are of such a nature that while one is at the logical 1 state the other will be at logical 0. Both outputs Q and $\bar{Q}$ are integrated, and the respective audio outputs are fed to alternate inputs of a differential operational amplifier. This latter tactic allows us to increase the amplitude of the recovered audio.

The integrators can be either simple RC networks or active operational amplifier types.

This FM detector offers several features which tend to increase its appeal. One is independence of carrier frequency. This can be especially

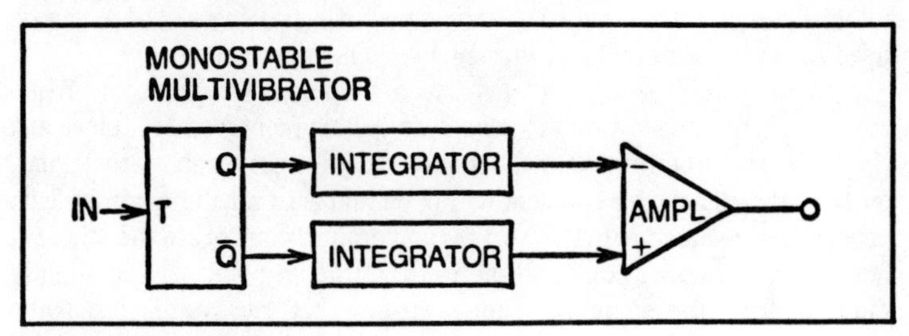

Fig. 9-20. Digital detector.

important in low-frequency tape recorders, or FM/FM telemetry systems, where it is typically necessary to modulate an audio-frequency carrier. Stability and accuracy of such systems tends to leave something to be desired as does the repeatability from one machine to another. This is caused by imperfections and variations (wow and flutter) in the tape transport speed which also tend to FM the carrier recorded on tape.

The pulse counting detector is superior in such systems because it simply adjusts to whatever carrier frequency is presented. This is not to imply, however, that the pulse-counting detector is limited to telemetry and FM analog data tape recording. The circuit also makes a fine detector for stable, fixed carrier frequency equipment such as found in FM stereo and FM mobile communications receivers. Heath Company, for example, uses the detector just described in its top-of-the-line Model AJ-1510 digital FM tuner. The circuit designed by Heath engineers achieves recovery of an audio signal with very low distortion, such as would be expected from a high-priced, superior tuner. The Heath design uses a TTL monostable multivibrator integrated circuit and a 709 operational amplifier for the differential stage. RC networks are used for the integrators.

TEMPERATURE CONTROLLER

It is sometimes desirable to control the temperature of some minienvironment in a precise and automatic manner. Such requirements exist in ovens used to stabilize the output frequency of an oscillator either by keeping the temperature of the whole circuit constant or by stabilizing the temperature of the piezoelectric crystal used to control frequency. In other applications, mostly medical and scientific, we might want to keep the temperature of some solution stable, a common requirement in chemistry laboratories.

Figure 9-21 is a simple circuit which can offer a measure of temperature control greater than that of the simple snap-action thermostat. In less crucial applications, of course, it is easier to use the snap-action type. Those devices control current through a heater element by thermal expansion of bimetallic elements. Different metals have different coefficients of expansion. A bimetallic strip made of dissimilar metals can be made to bend in a manner proportional to the temperature applied. When the critical temperature is reached, the strip will have deformed and bent enough to either open or close a set of electrical switching contacts. These can be used to control external circuitry such as a heating element.

Most home heating systems use a snap-action thermostat. When ambient room temperature drops below a certain point, contacts close and the furnace is turned on. When the room temperature rises above that point, on the other hand, the contacts will open and turn off the furnace. Two problems associated with this sort of temperature control are the inherent inaccuracy of the set point and the fact that the *on* point may be slightly different from the *off* point. This is to say that the system has some *hysteresis*.

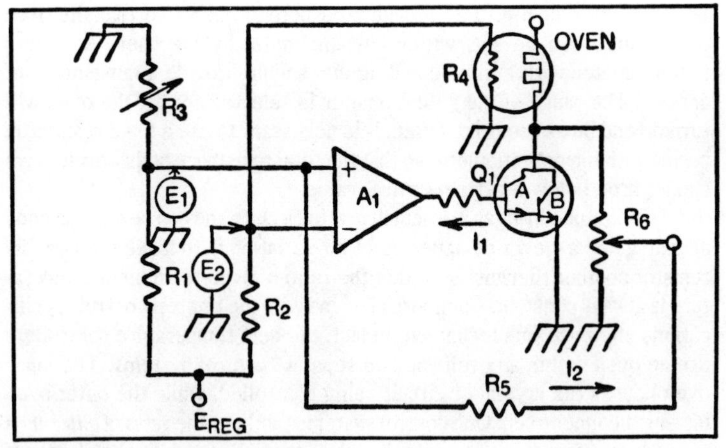

Fig. 9-21. Temperature controller.

The circuit of Fig. 9-21 narrows the hysteresis window of the system and makes the set point more accurate by using electronic control techniques. Resistor R_4 is a thermistor (temperature dependent resistor) coupled closely to the oven's internal environment. It has a resistance that is proportional to the temperature inside the oven. It is connected in a Wheatstone bridge arrangement along with resistors R_1, R_2, and R_3. If $R_1 = R_2$ and $R_3 = R_4$, voltages E_1 and E_2 will also be equal, and operational amplifier A_1 will be dormant.

If the temperature inside the oven changes, the resistance of R_4 will also change and the balance of the bridge will be upset. This will cause E_1 and E_2 to change relationship, creating a differential voltage at the inputs of A_1. Perturbing the input of the controlling amplifier causes current I_1 to flow, turning on the oven's heating element.

Oven control transistor Q_1 is shown here as a power Darlington device, but could just as easily be any number of power devices, including one of those hybrid power operational amplifiers used in some audio and servoamplifier applications. The Darlington device was selected here because it offers high gain (the total beta is equal to the product of the individual h_{FE} figures) and high power, in a package small enough for practical installation.

Keep in mind that whatever control element is selected, it must be capable of handling a fairly large amount of power *and* current. Heater control elements typically operate at high currents and have resistances low enough to accommodate those currents at reasonably low voltages. A sensitivity control is provided (R_6) which generates a feedback current proportional to the output voltage. This current is used to drive the noninverting input of the operational amplifier.

There are several possible variations on this type of circuit. One is to make the adjustable resistor opposite the thermistor in the Wheatstone bridge portion of Fig. 9-21 a calibrated potentiometer so that the oven temperature can be set, within certain limits, by the user. A 10-turn potentiometer with a turns-counting dial should provide a fair amount of control. The range of the potentiometer is selected so that the oven will turn off and on as required. Often, it is necessary to use a fixed resistor in series with the potentiometer so that the total resistance of that bridge arm cannot drop below a certain critical value.

Wheatstone bridges are actually ratio circuits and can be used to good advantage by a clever designer. Another variation is to make the variable resistor another thermistor so that the ratio of oven-to-ambient temperature is always constant. Commercial ovens with the tightest control specifications often use this technique. In fact, the best temperature controllers use an oven within an oven and two separate control systems. The inner oven houses the crystal or circuit being controlled, while the outer oven houses the inner oven. One control system stabilizes the ratio of *outer oven to inner oven* temperature while the other controller stabilizes the ratio of *ambient room to outer oven* temperatures. Such a circuit allows a very tight control over the temperature of the inner oven.

Thermistor manufacturers are as good as operational amplifier manufacturers when it comes to supplying literature covering design of circuits using their products. It would be worthwhile for a potential temperature controller designer to consult that source for ideas.

Control of a temperature is not the only application where the thermistor and the operational amplifier make good mates. There is also the possibility of making a flow meter for fluids or gases (see Fig. 9-22). The Wheatstone bridge is again pressed into service and is wedded to the

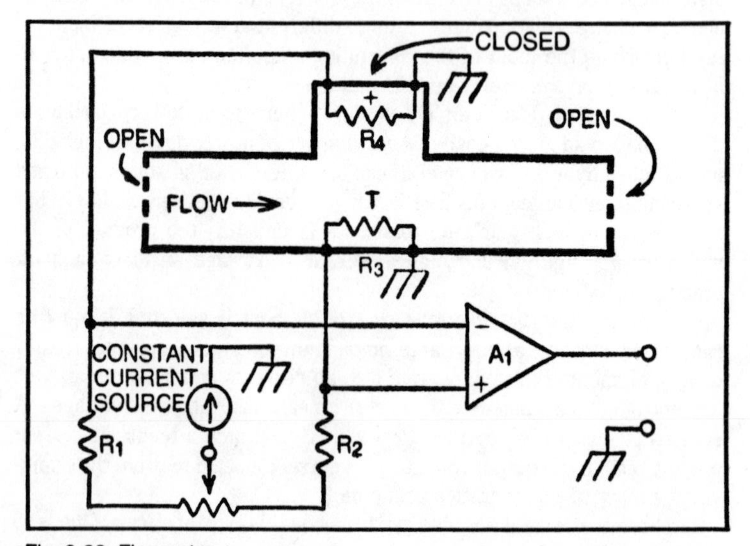

Fig. 9-22. Flowmeter.

operational amplifier. One of the thermistors required for this application is used to measure the temperature of the fluid or gas trapped in the side duct. Alternatively, it could be located in free air. This establishes a reference point. The temperature of the flowing fluid or gas is measured by the other thermistor.

The bridge excitation voltage is selected to be high enough to cause sufficient current to flow in the thermistors to allow a small amount of self-heating. The fluid or gas flowing in the pipe will cause some of the heat in the thermistor inside the stream to dissipate, causing a change in resistance. If there is no flow, then the two thermistors will have equal resistances, and the input voltage applied to the differentially connected operational amplifier will be zero. As flow causes the thermistor to rise in value, however, the balance of the bridge is upset and a voltage is created. The thermistors used in this flowmeter circuit must have response times fast enough to follow the changes in waveform (flow), if an accurate rendition of the waveform is desired. If a waveform is too fast for the response of the thermistors, the shape will deteriorate to a point and may be unrecognizable. The current source feeding this bridge circuit should be well regulated.

PRECISION VARIABLE REFERENCE POWER SUPPLY

Figure 9-23 shows a variable power supply which can be used as a precision reference source if adequate design and construction provisions are made. One of these provisions is the quality level of the active element, operational amplifier A_1. At the very least, assuming that some precision can be safely sacrificed, A_1 should be a low-bias-current, high-input-impedance type. If the power supply is to be precision, it will be necessary to use a very low-input-current, very low-drift device. This will probably mean use of a varactor bridge or chopper stabilized type, although some regular types are available which fill the bill. Capacitor C_1 must also be of high grade or performance will deteriorate. Use of a low-leakage type such as polystyrene, polycarbonate, or glass is almost mandatory. Resistor R_1 is a decade type in the precision supply, but it can be a simple multiturn potentiometer. A decade resistor will be variable from 0 to 99,999Ω in 1.0Ω steps.

Although the diagram shown in Fig. 9-23 shows a switch-selected decade resistor, some are equipped with shafts and closely resemble a multiturn potentiometer. In the former type, there will be a 10-position switch for each decade of value range. Use of a multiturn potentiometer for R_1 may cause a loss in repeatability and resolution. Although modern potentiometers can be purchased which offer good tracking and accuracy between true resistance and dial reading, they still suffer somewhat from poor resolution. Decade resistors, on the other hand, can be made to have a resolution of 1Ω or even 0.1Ω.

Voltage source E_1 is very crucial to the successful operation of this supply. It must be a very stable reference supply.

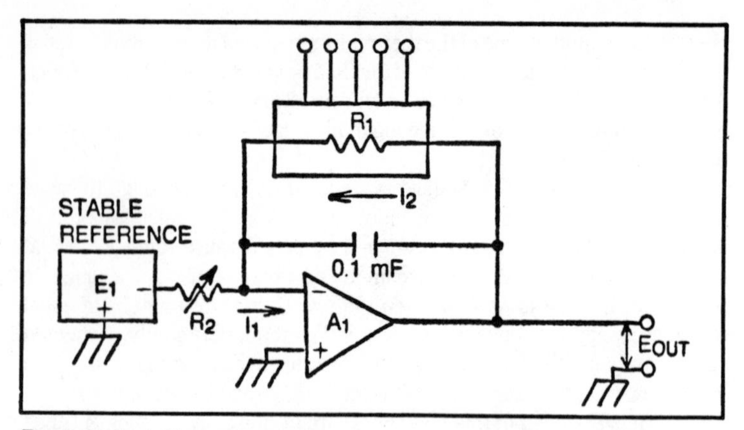

Fig. 9-23. Variable power supply.

Any drift in reference voltage will be reflected as drift in the output; that is hardly a desirable feature for a precision reference source. In the simplest case, E_1 might be a single zener diode connected through a series resistance to the minus power supply source. If this is the case, then, only "reference-grade" zener diodes may be used, because they have a better temperature coefficient than regular stock zeners.

In better power supplies, though, the reference source must be even better than a quality zener can provide. It should be an operational amplifier or other active-feedback type such as those described in the preceding chapter.

Another alternative is to start with a regulated voltage much higher than is needed for E_1 and then count down through a chain of dropping resistors and zeners. Successively lower zener voltages in each stage of the chain are obtained until a voltage for E_1 in the 1 to 10V range is reached. The value of resistor R_2 is selected so that an output of 9.9999V exists when the decade resistor is set to 99,999Ω. This requires the current $I_1 = I_2 =$ 9.9999/99,999 = 0.0001A. R_2 should, therefore, have a value of E_1/I_1.

A high degree of trimming resolution is offered by a combination of two methods (1) op-amp offset adjustment, and (2) the actual configuration of R_2. We will want to make R_2 a combination of two resistors; one is a fixed type and the other is a multiturn potentiometer. Whatever the configuration of R_2, all elements making up the total resistance must be temperature compensated or a drift component will be introduced.

Mechanical rigidity of both the circuit board (or other component support structure) and the cabinet is important. Vibration in the mechanics can throw off the setting of trimmer and panel controls sufficiently to disturb output accuracy.

When building any piece of precision test equipment, one must use only the best components and techniques available or be willing to suffer from a loss in precision.

Chapter 10

Unusual Op Amps and Related Devices

In this chapter, we examine certain unusual operational amplifiers and other related semiconductor devices. Some of these (such as the current difference and operational transconductance amplifiers) are generically close to actual operational amplifiers, while others merely incorporate an operational amplifier in a device intended for some other use. Examples of these are among some temperature and pressure measuring devices manufactured by National Semiconductor. One last category to be discussed are devices such as the special-purpose operational amplifiers, (including the dual FET input unity-gain follower and the programmable op amp) and digitally selected quad operational amplifiers.

CURRENT DIFFERENCE AMPLIFIERS

Until now the operational amplifier, which we have considered, have been classic voltage-difference devices. There is, however, a newer type not as well known but making significant inroads, especially in the automotive and mobile equipment markets. This is the CDA, or *current difference amplifier*. The appropriate schematic symbol for the CDA or *Norton* amplifier (shown in Fig. 10-1) is the normal op-amp triangle with the addition of a constant-current source symbol along the edge opposite the apex. Although it would not prove difficult to dissect the CDA relative only to itself, it might be easier to understand if we compared the CDA with the traditional operational amplifier.

Input Configuration

Figure 10-2 is a simplified version of the input stage of a classic voltage-difference op amp. Together with a constant-current source (CCS), transistors Q_1 and Q_2 form a differential amplifier. The CCS is the circuit

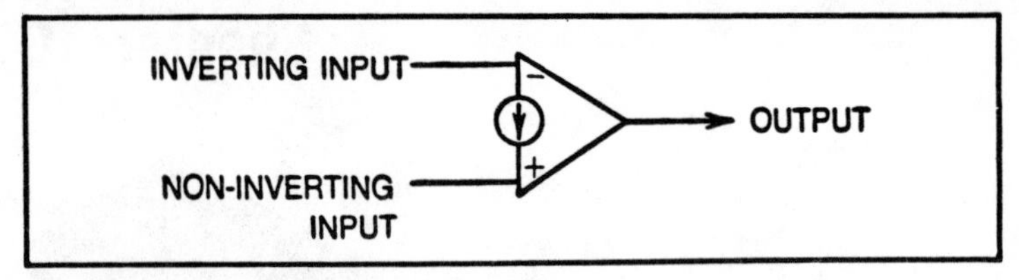

Fig. 10-1. Current difference amplifier (CDA).

shown as an inset to Fig. 10-2. It supplies the same value of I_1 regardless of the load conditions imposed by Q_1 and Q_2 of the op amp. Assuming the Q_1 and Q_2 are so well matched they are identical, currents I_2 and I_3 will be equal for equal values of E_1 and E_2. If E_2 is greater than E_1, current I_3 will increase. Since I_1 is a constant, and $I_1 = I_2 + I_3$, this can only result in less current being available for I_2. When E_2 is greater than E_1, voltage E_{OUT} will decrease. The base of Q_2, therefore, can be used as the minus or *inverting* input.

The other alternative is for E_1 to be greater than E_2. Under that

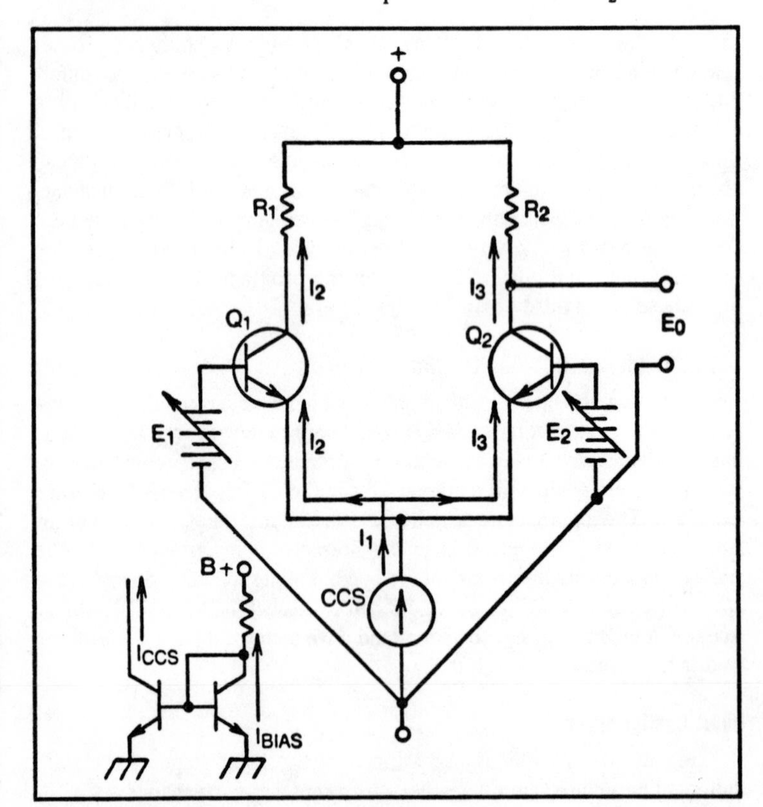

Fig. 10-2. Typical input circuitry for op amp.

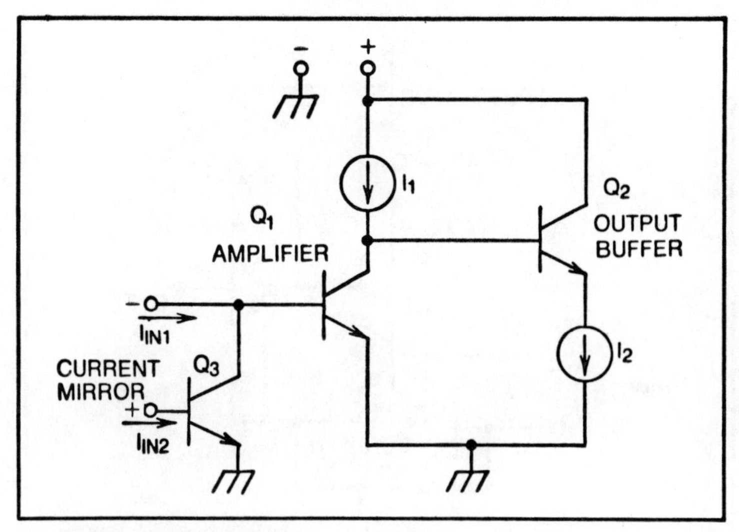

Fig. 10-3. Typical input circuitry for a CDA.

condition, I_2 will be larger than I_3. Since this will cause I_3 to decrease relative to its quiescent value, E_{OUT} will increase. This makes for a handy noninverting input at the base of Q_1. On that side of the differential amplifier, an increase of the input voltage will cause a corresponding increase in output voltage.

Figure 10-3 shows a simplified version of a typical CDA input amplifier stage. Transistor Q_1 is a standard common-emitter stage while Q_2 serves as an output buffer in an emitter-follower configuration. The base of Q_1 serves as the inverting input, which is the normal situation for a common-emitter stage.

The noninverting input is through transistor Q_5 (Fig. 10-4), a second common-emitter stage. This transistor, along with the diode shunting the base to emitter, form what is known as a *current mirror*. In most circuits employing the typical CDA device, there will be a permanent bias current of 5 to 100 μA flowing in the noninverting amplifier input.

Both the input amplifier and the output buffer derive their respective collector currents from constant-current sources. Figure 10-4 shows the same input stage expanded to include the constant-current-source transistors. Bias to the respective base terminals is from internally regulated reference power supplies. Current remains stable because the bias is stable.

Inverting ac Amplifiers

Figure 10-5 shows the normal circuit for using a CDA as an inverting ac signal amplifier. Note that the external circuit configuration resembles that of a traditional voltage-difference operational amplifier. Direct current to

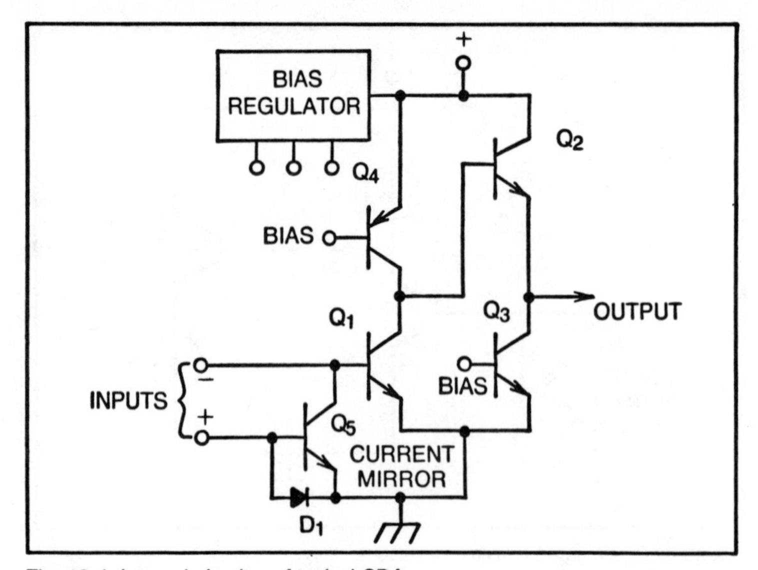

Fig. 10-4. Internal circuitry of typical CDA.

the input is blocked by a capacitor which has a reactance equal to about 10 percent the value of R_{IN} at the lowest frequency of interest.

In a traditional op amp, voltage gain can be predicted with a fair degree of accuracy from the ratio of the feedback to input resistances; a fact that makes designers happy. This procedure retains some of its utility when CDA devices are used, but will yield only an approximate value for A_V:

$$A_V \simeq R_F/R_{IN} \tag{10-1}$$

Several error terms are accounted for by the following equation for quiescent output voltage level:

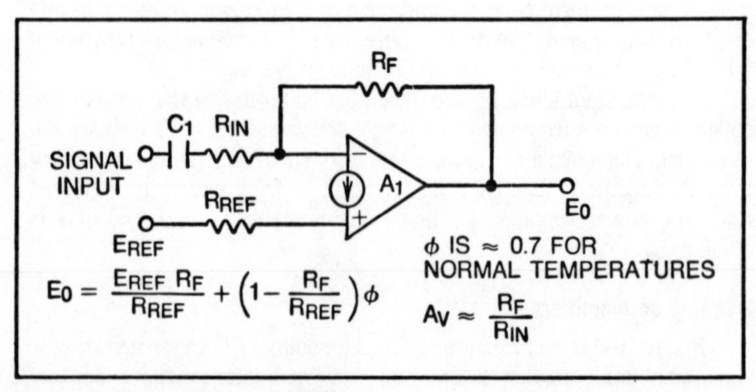

Fig. 10-5. CDA inverting ac amplifier.

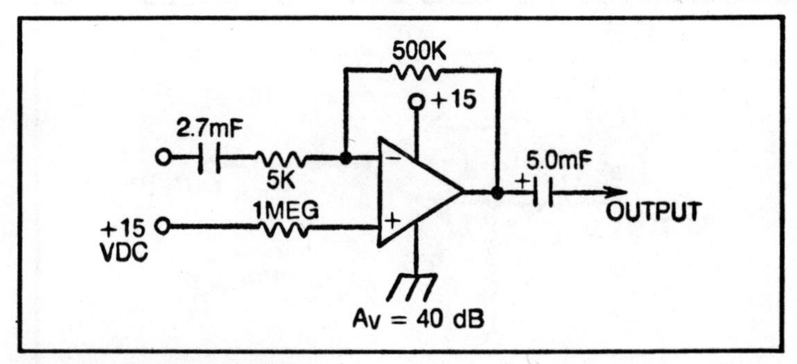

Fig. 10-6. 40 dB ac amplifier.

$$E_{OUT} = \frac{E_{REF} R_F}{R_{REF}} + \left(1 - \frac{R_F}{R_{REF}}\right) \phi \qquad (10\text{-}2)$$

The ϕ term represents the normal junction potential of the input transistors. Since these are silicon, most CDA manufacturers recommend using a value of 0.7 for this when the device is operated within normal temperature ranges. Figure 10-6 is a practical example of the former circuit offering a wide bandwidth ("full audio spectrum") with a voltage gain of approximately 40 dB. Note that in both examples the noninverting input is returned to B+ through resistor R_{REF}. The value of this resistor is set so that a current between 5 and 100 μA will flow.

Noninverting Amplifiers

The circuit of Fig. 10-7 shows the noninverting configuration for a CDA. In this case the signal is input through a current mirror. Note the major difference between this circuit and a similar function using opera-

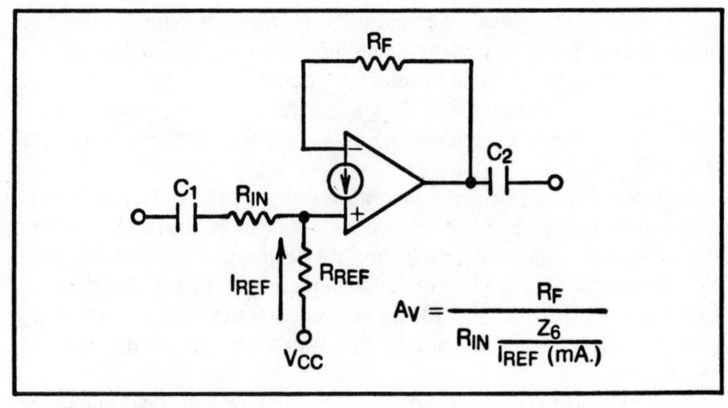

Fig. 10-7. Noninverting CDA.

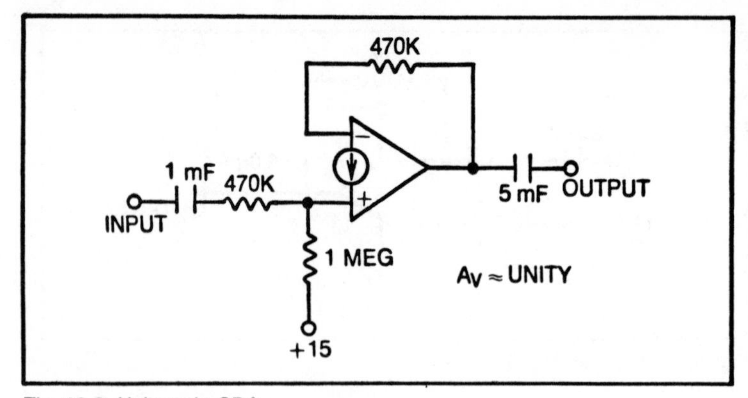

Fig. 10-8. Unity gain CDA.

tional amplifiers: R_{IN} is part of the plus input circuit instead of being connected from the minus input to common. The gain of a noninverting CDA is given by:

$$A_V = \frac{R_F}{R_{IN}\left(\frac{26}{I_{REF}}\right)} \tag{10-3}$$

where I_{REF} is in milliamperes.
An example of a unity-gain noninverting amplifier is given in Fig. 10-8.

General Design Procedure

The first step is to set the quiescent output conditions. During this part of the procedure, we will want to set the current flowing in the noninverting input to a value within the specified range of 5 to 100 μA.

For the majority of applications, it will be desirable to use one-half the supply voltage as the quiescent output voltage. Once a resistor is selected to supply the reference current in the plus input, choose one-half its value as the feedback resistance. Gain is selected through a consideration of the needs of the overall design. Once the gain figure is selected, however, we plug it and the value of R_F into either Eq. 10-1 or 10-3, as appropriate, and solve for R_{IN}.

Differential Amplifiers. In operational amplifier circuits, the device delivers an output which is proportional to the voltage gain factor times the *difference* between input voltages. In the CDA device, we will also make use of the two inputs to form a differential amplifier. In that case, though, the output voltage is proportional to the difference between input currents. Figure 10-9 shows one form of CDA implementation of the differential amplifier idea.

Mixer Circuits. A linear signal mixer is a circuit which will combine

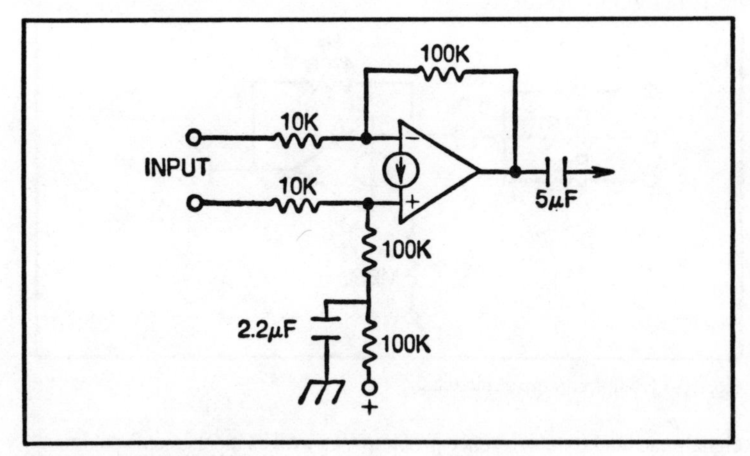

Fig. 10-9. Differential CDA.

into one channel analog signals from several sources without causing distortion to any of them. The circuits of Figs. 10-10 and 10-11 are examples of mixers using CDA devices.

The circuit in Fig. 10-10 uses one CDA as an output buffer amplifier fed by the outputs of several other CDA stages (only one channel is shown). This is a convenient arrangement, especially if only three channels are contemplated, since most CDA integrated circuits contain four amplifiers. One especially attractive feature of this circuit is the fact that any channel can be turned on or off simply by using a switch to ground the noninverting input bias current. It is generally agreed that signal switching is best handled by dc methods such as this, since switching audio and other ac

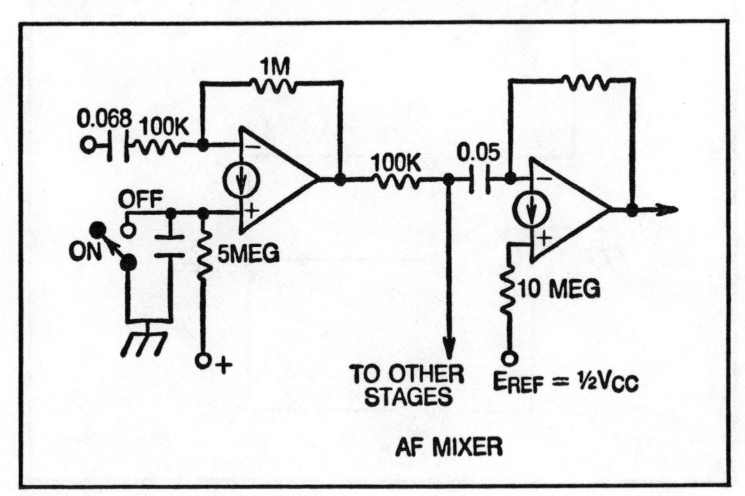

Fig. 10-10. CDA mixer circuit.

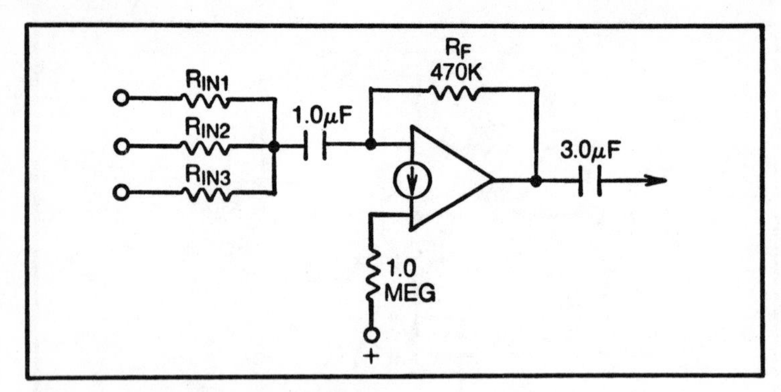

Fig. 10-11. Alternate mixer circuit.

signals can lead to interference problems, as well as mechanical problems, resulting from the attempt at fixing interference!

The mixer of Fig. 10-11 is an ac OR gate. This circuit has as its main virtue utter simplicity of design. The gain seen by any one input is approximated by Eq. 10-1; a fact which offers some intriguing possibilities for independent level controls.

Miscellaneous CDA Circuits

Illustrations of assorted and miscellaneous CDA circuitry that follows in this chapter often succeed better than anything in demonstrating utility of application. Figure 10-12 shows a method for using a CDA to regulate the

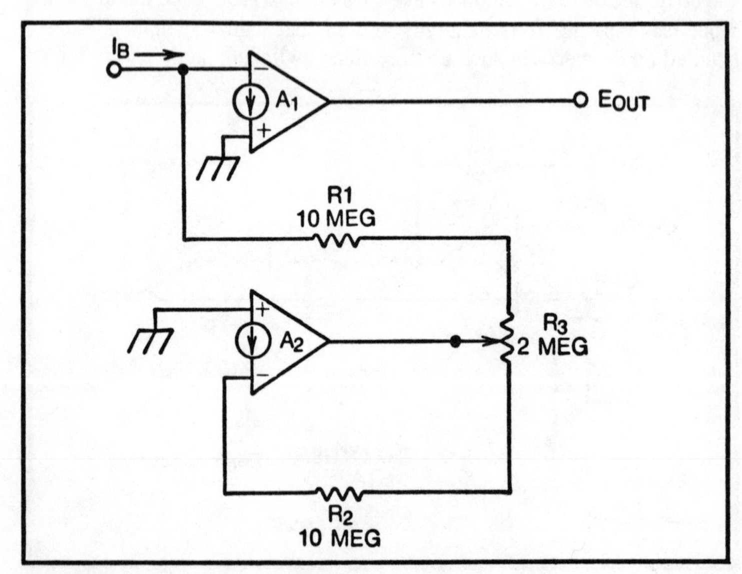

Fig. 10-12. Using CDA to regulate bias current of another.

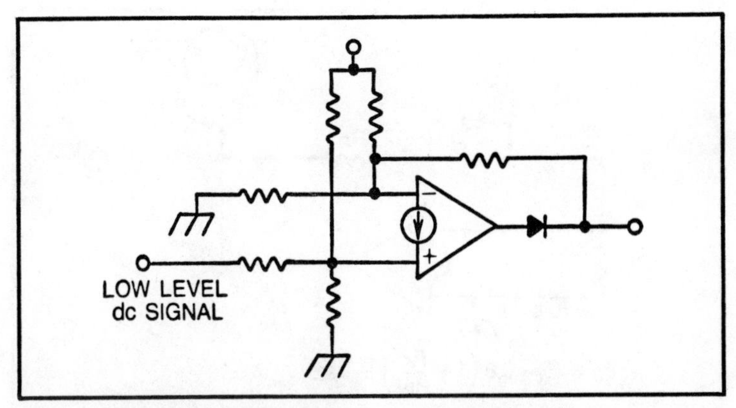

Fig. 10-13. Low level dc preamplifier.

reference bias of another CDA. In this circuit, potentiometer R_3 sets the current level (generated by amplifier A_2) flowing into the input of the first amplifier.

Low-level dc signals are not easy to handle as are larger high-level signals. This is probably because bias must be provided to the common-emitter input transistor. The circuit of Fig. 10-13 accomplishes this with an extra set of resistors.

A comparator circuit delivers an output that indicates either agreement or disagreement of two (or more) input voltages by delivering one of two mutually exclusive output voltages. One method for making a comparator is to connect the two voltages to an amplifier with grossly excessive gain; one that will saturate with any input signal at all. In the CDA comparator of Fig. 10-14, the excessive gain criterion is satisfied rather easily by the elimination of the feedback resistor. In that case, the CDA is running wide open with a gain equal to the open-loop gain of the device as specified by the manufacturer. Assuming resistor equality is maintained, we will generate a zero output when $V_X = V_{REF}$. This situation causes the two

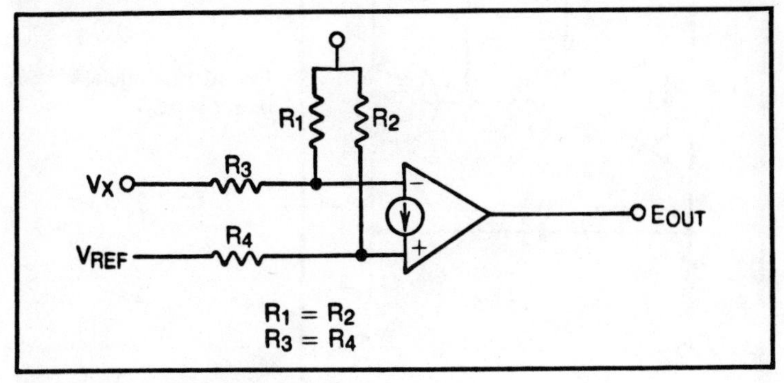

Fig. 10-14. Comparator.

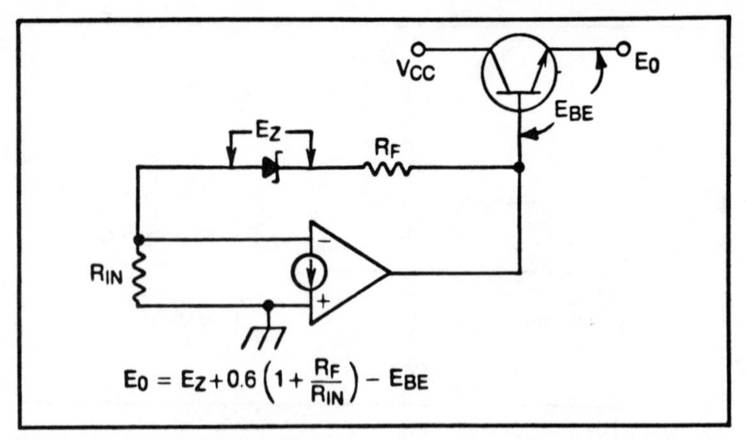

Fig. 10-15. CDA reference source.

inputs to see equal currents which will, therefore, have equal but opposite effects on the output voltage. A difference in the two input voltages, however, causes one input to have a greater effect on the output, resulting, due to the high gain, in amplifier saturation. The polarity will depend upon the polarity of the input difference voltage.

As stated in an earlier chapter, regulated power supplies offer characteristics and advantages which deserve our close attention. Figures 10-15 and 10-16 are examples of regulated power supplies using CDA devices to control a series-pass regulator transistor. The only essential difference between these circuits, as can be seen from a study of the respective schematics, is one of approach.

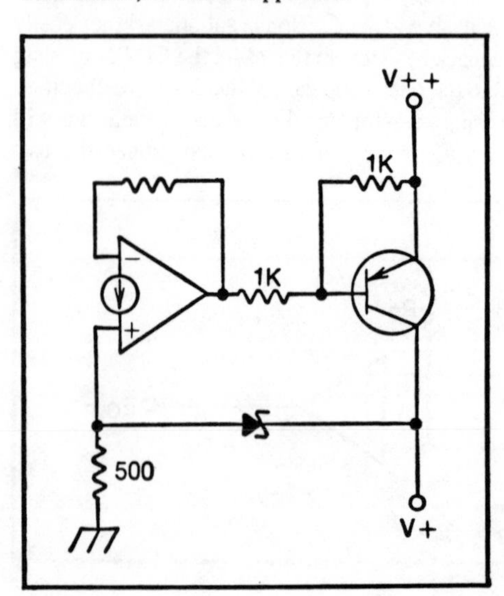

Fig. 10-16. Regulated power supply.

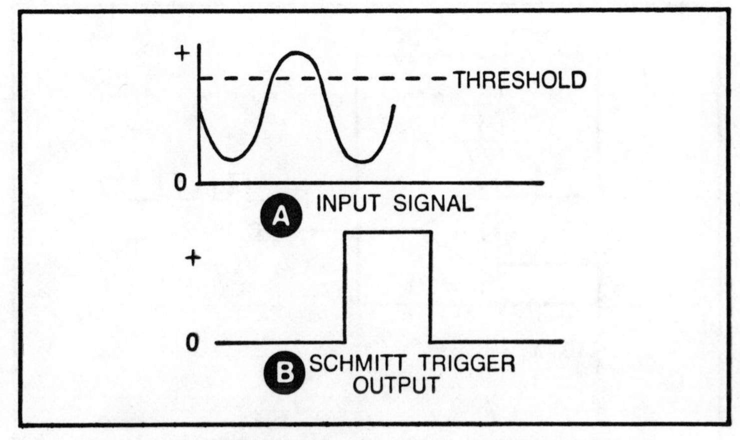

Fig. 10-17. Schmitt trigger characteristic.

A Schmitt trigger is a circuit used to square an input waveform. It maintains a zero output until such a time when the input voltage exceeds a predetermined threshold value. At that instant, the output snaps to some high (in our case positive) value. The output will remain at that level until the input falls back to the threshold level. This is shown in Fig. 10-17. Schmitt trigger circuits exist using almost every form of active electronic device (transistors, op amps, plus several digital logic IC families) so why not the CDA? Figure 10-18 is respectfully submitted.

One major application for the Schmitt trigger is the conversion of sine waves or irregular electrical signals into nice, clean, square pulses which digital circuitry can process. In fact, equipment such as digital counters require square waves for proper and accurate operation; a situation that calls for a lot of Schmitt triggers.

The multivibrator of Fig. 10-19 adds frequency-selective feedback to the trigger forming a self-triggering circuit which produces a square wave.

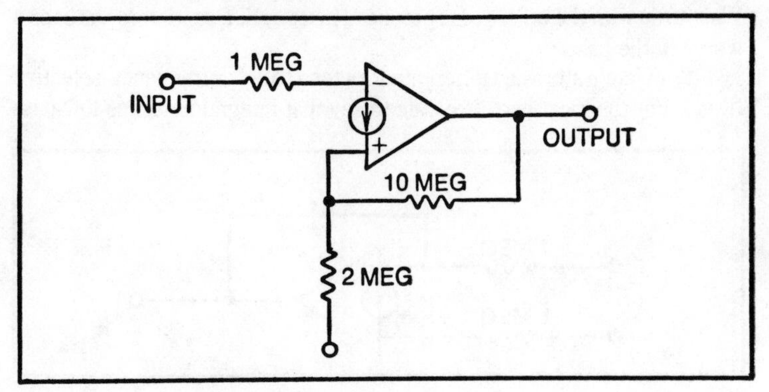

Fig. 10-18. CDA Schmitt trigger circuit.

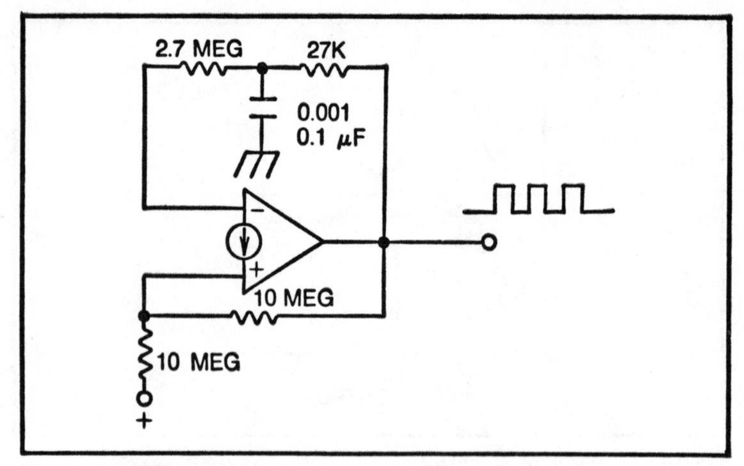

Fig. 10-19. Astable multivibrator.

The frequency of the output wave is a function of the RC time constant of the feedback network.

There are those of us who think of electronic integrators and differentiators only in the light of their outstanding performance of mathematical operations in analog computers. However, by doing this, we may well miss some of the neater applications in waveshaping and other areas. In Chapter 5, we illustrated some of the more popular waveshapes. Figures 10-20, 10-21, and 10-22 are CDA circuits which allow such applications.

Two differentiator circuits are the subjects of Figs. 10-21 and 10-22. In the first of this pair, we have a classic differentiator which produces results similar to the op-amp circuits of a previous chapter. Selectable triggering is an added wrinkle of the second circuit. The position of switch S_1 determines whether the differentiator responds to positive or negative going edges of the input waveform. This feature can be of great importance in circuits where single-polarity pulses from an input waveform are to be created. What to do with the other pulse produced in many differentiators has been a worry in the past.

Both integrators and differentiators tend to act as frequency-selective filters. For the most part, it is safe to say that integrators act as low-pass

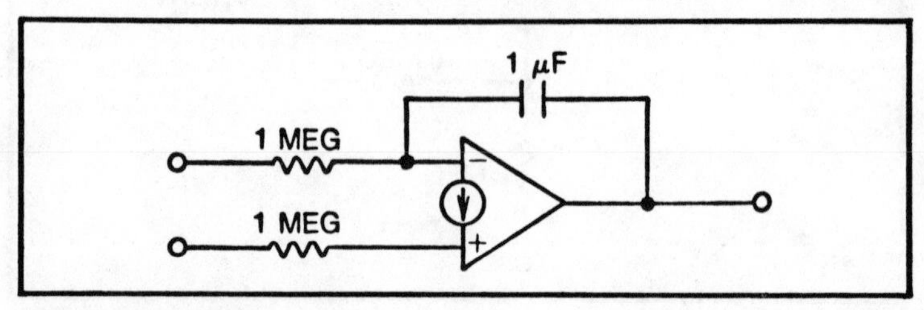

Fig. 10-20. Integrator.

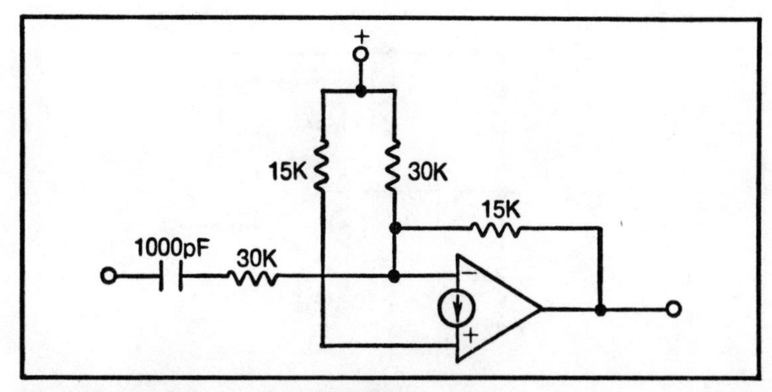

Fig. 10-21. One type of CDA differentiator.

filters and differentiators serve as high-pass filters. Such circuit action can be anything from highly desirable to accursed, depending upon the situation.

Besides the almost unintentional use of the above circuits as filters, we can and often do use other configurations. Figures 10-23 and 10-24 are examples of high- and low-pass filters. Note that both are reasonably standard adaptations of op-amp circuits discussed previously.

OPERATIONAL TRANSCONDUCTANCE AMPLIFIERS

There is a third type of operational amplifier making the rounds: the operational transconductance amplifier (OTA), offered by RCA and other sources. Classic op amps are defined by an output voltage generated by an input voltage and a gain factor. Norton (CDA) amplifiers are defined by an output *current*, transconductance factor, and input *current*. The OTA is defined by the classic transconductance formula:

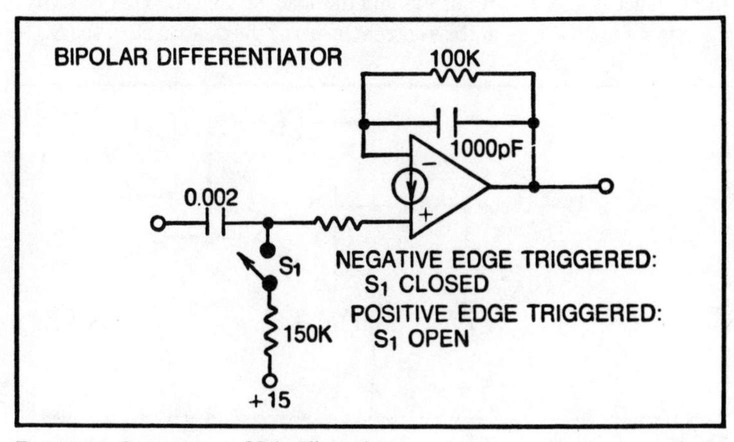

Fig. 10-22. Second type CDA differentiator.

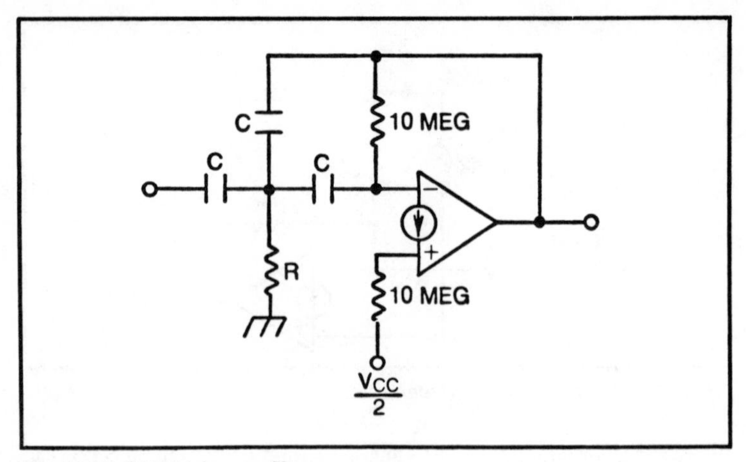

Fig. 10-23. CDA high-pass filter.

$$g_M = \frac{\Delta I_{OUT}}{\Delta E_{IN}} \tag{10-4}$$

where g_M is the transconductance in micromhos.

A symbolic representation is shown in Fig. 10-25 (the normal op-amp symbol of a triangle is used in circuit diagrams) while Fig. 10-26 shows the block diagram of internal OTA circuitry. Note that the OTA will perform all, or at least most, of the usual op-amp chores. There are, however, some functional differences.

For example, since the g_M is proportional to bias current, gain can be externally adjusted by varying the level of current applied to the bias terminal. The output voltage swing exhibited by the OTA is proportional to the product of the output current and the load resistance. That quantity, I_{OUT}, is set (for any specific bias current level) by the product of g_M and E_{IN}.

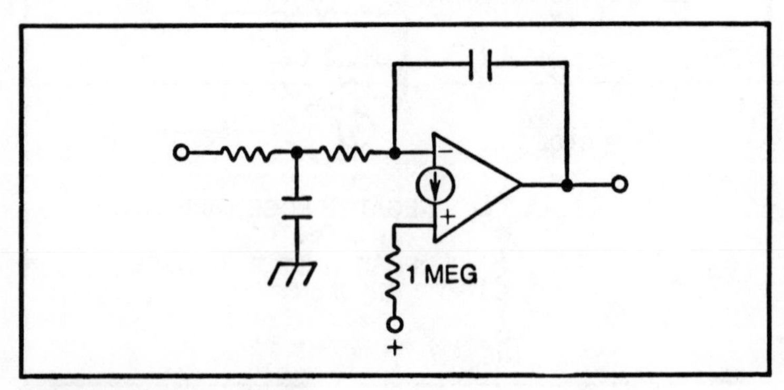

Fig. 10-24. CDA low-pass filter.

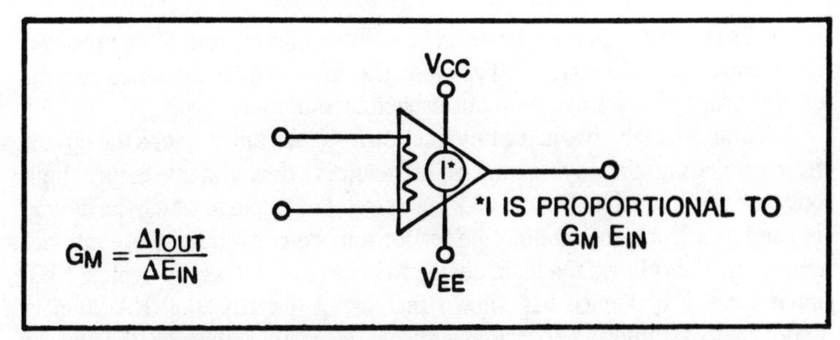

Fig. 10-25. Model of an operational transconductance amplifier (OTA).

HA-2000/HA-2005 FET INPUT FOLLOWERS

Harris Semiconductors offers this special dual operational amplifier in a standard 8-pin metal can. It is unique because both op amps in the device are unity-gain, noninverting followers designed for use as preamplifiers. Although their principal utility lies in service as front ends to regular operational amplifiers, the manufacturer's literature illustrates a number of other applications.

These devices feature JFET inputs and bipolar outputs, resulting in a combination with a very high input impedance—on the order of $10^{12}\Omega$, with a very low output impedance. Each preamplifier in the package will operate to 10 MHz and can deliver full output power to about 1 MHz. The JFET

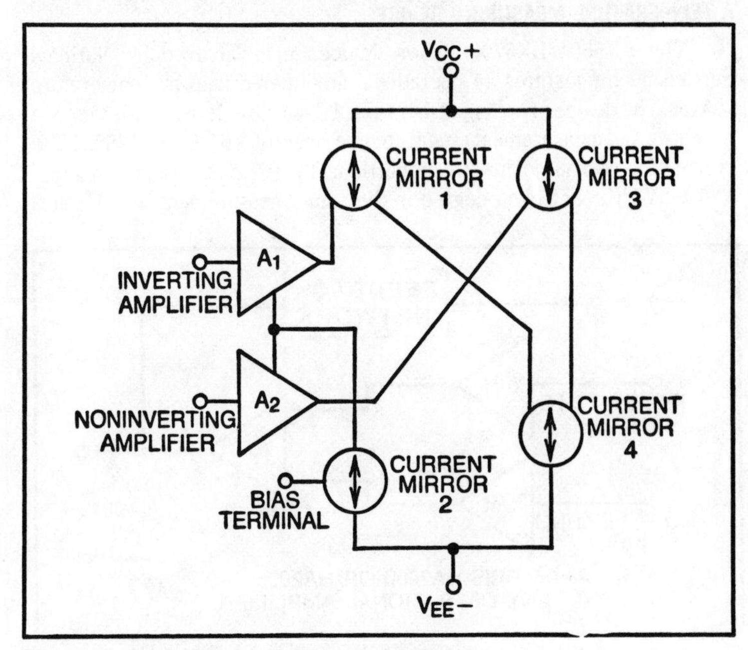

Fig. 10-26. Block diagram of OTA internal circuitry.

inputs create the high impedance and low input bias current often required in certain circuit applications. Typically, the device will exhibit bias current on the order of 1 pA and an input capacitance of about 5 pF.

Total gain, which is just a tiny fraction less than unity, keeps the circuit from oscillating at annoying times. The result is a device stable even at high operating frequencies. Figure 10-27 is a circuit example in which the device is used as a front end or input buffer for a more conventional operational amplifier. This allows the main device to behave as if it were a typical FET input type. Experience has shown that using the HA-2000/HA-2005 is superior to attempting to achieve the same virtues through the use of regular JFET transistors.

The Harris device allows better thermal tracking, a closer match between inputs (important to the maintenance of a good common mode rejection ratio), and the ability to use full input voltage swing rather than simply a fraction (as is the case when individual transistors are used). Feedback can be applied to the circuit of Fig. 10-27 around both the main op amp and the HA-2000/HA-2005 together, and not simply around the main amplifier.

The primary difference between the HA-2000 and the HA-2005 is in the temperature specification. The HA-2000 operates over the specified military temperature range of −55°C to +125°C while the HA-2005 only covers the commercial or industrial range of 0°C to +75°C.

A TEMPERATURE MEASURING DEVICE

The LX5600/LX5700 series devices manufactured by National Semiconductor features an operational amplifier driven by temperature sensor. The device is packaged in a 4-pin TO-44 case. It is intended for use in control and measurement circuits over a range of −55°C to +125°C. The output of the sensor is directly proportional to temperature and is at a rate of 10 mV/°K. (A Kelvin degree is the same measurement as a Celsius

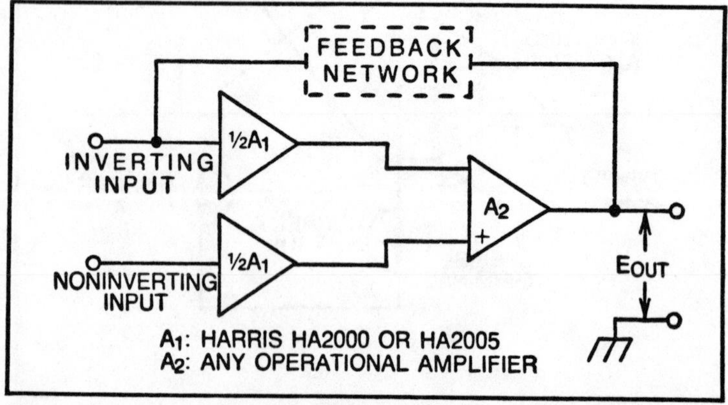

Fig. 10-27. Use of HA2000/2005 FET followers.

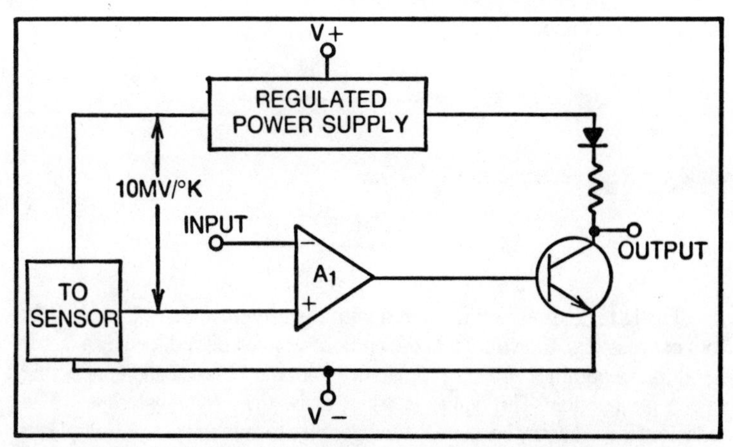

Fig. 10-28. Block diagram of the National temperature measuring device.

degree, but the Kelvin scale starts with a reading of 0°K at absolute zero, or −273°C. Celsius starts with 0°C at the freezing point of water. A conversion factor is that 0°C is approximately 273°K.)

An internal operational amplifier is connected with its noninverting input to the temperature sensor and the inverting input available to an outside terminal (see Fig. 10-28). This feature allows some control over the functions which can be accommodated in the design. The operational amplifier can be made to function either as a gain stage for measurement systems or as a comparator for control systems. In that latter mode, the operational amplifier can control outside circuitry because its output switches positive or negative as the temperature sensor goes through excursions back and forth across the comparator reference point. Since these devices will operate with output transistor collector voltages up to +35V, the device can be interfaced with most conventional operational amplifier, logic, and transistor circuitry.

This same manufacturer also offers a series of pressure sensor ICs built along the same lines as the temperature sensor just described.

PROGRAMMABLE OPERATIONAL AMPLIFIERS

This family of devices allows selection or programming of certain key op-amp parameters such as gain, bandwidth, slew rate, and power dissipation. The mechanism of control is selection of an externally controlled master bias current called I_{SET} (see Fig. 10-29A). For the Fairchild μA776, this current flows through pin 8 of the metal can and plastic *miniDIP* devices, and through pin 12 of the standard DIP devices. This master bias current can be varied from a low value close to 1.0 pA (at 25°C) to a maximum of 100 μA. The I_{SET} pin must be returned to either dc ground or V_{EE} of the power supply through a resistance R_{SET}. The value of this resistance is calculated using Ohm's law:

For R_{SET} to ground:

$$R_{SET} = \frac{|V_{CC}(+)| - 0.7}{I_{SET}}$$

while for R_{SET} returned to $V_{EE}(-)$:

$$R_{SET} = \frac{2V_{CC}(+) - 0.7}{I_{SET}}$$

The latter expression is offered with the provision that $V_{CC} = V_{EE}$. In both expressions, the voltage in the numerator must be reduced by a factor equal to the nominal voltage drop across a forward biased and conducting silicon pn junction. This value is taken to be 0.7V for most cases. The reduction is necessary because the master bias terminal is at a potential just one diode drop (0.7V) from $+V_{CC}$.

When I_{SET} approaches 100 μA, the device will function very much like a device from the low-cost 741 family. As the bias current level drops, however, a number of the device parameters change and a new world of possibilities opens up to the designer. One new characteristic, for example, is the ability to operate as a nanowatt amplifier with a low quiescent power consumption to allow its use in battery powered equipment. A further attribute of the μA776 which also enhances its value in battery equipment is the fact that it has a useful range of V_{CC} and V_{EE} values of 1.2 to 18V, implying that it could easily be operated from a pair of dry cells—one each for V_{EE} and V_{CC}.

Examination of the μA776 data sheet reveals several parameters which are dependent upon the master bias current. One of these which turns out to be very useful is the gain—bandwidth product. This is a specification often used in conjunction with transistors and operational amplifiers to

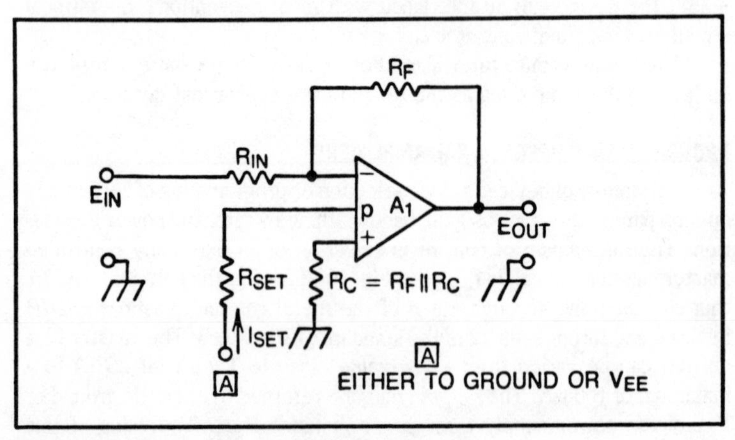

Fig. 10-29A. Circuit of programmable op amp.

indicate in a rough-but-useful manner the capabilities of the device over a wide frequency range. Gain—bandwidth product or f_T has units of frequency (hertz) and is the frequency at which the gain of the device drops to unity ($A_V = 1$). An expression for f_T is:

$$f_T = A_V f_1$$

where f_1 is the operating frequency, A_V is the gain, and f_T is the gain—bandwidth product (a constant). The value for f_T usually given in specification sheets is the value of f_1 existing when A_V is equal to 1.

Once we know the value of f_T as given is the data sheet, we calculate the gain which can be expected from the device at any frequency less than f_T. If the value of f_T is 1 MHz, for example, we could easily calculate the gain available at any lower frequency. At 100 kHz, for example:

$$A_V = \frac{f_T}{f_1}$$

$$= 10^6/10^5$$

$$= 10^1$$

$$= 10$$

On the other hand, suppose we have a design requirement for a gain of 70, and we want to ascertain whether the programmable operational amplifier can handle that at the frequency of interest:

$$f_1 = \frac{f_t}{A_V}$$

$$= (10^6)/(7 \times 10^2)$$

$$= 1429 \text{ Hz}$$

If the maximum frequency is less than this frequency, then the device can be used. Keep in mind that nonsinusoidal waveforms contain harmonics considerably higher than the fundamental frequency, and all of these which make up a significant portion of the total voltage at any point on the waveform must be less than the value of f_1.

The gain-bandwidth product is one of the parameters which can be set by manipulating the master bias current. From the graph shown in Fig. 10-29B, we ascertain that with a $+V_{CC}$ of 15V a master bias current of approximately 13 μA is required to yield an f_t of 10^6.

Slew rate is another important specification and especially where large signals are to be processed. Slew rate is also a function of the master bias current. In our previous example, we required a current of 13 μA. From the data sheet, we find that a 13 μA master bias current results in a slew rate of 800 mV/μSEC. Figure 10-29C shows the frequencies which can be handled

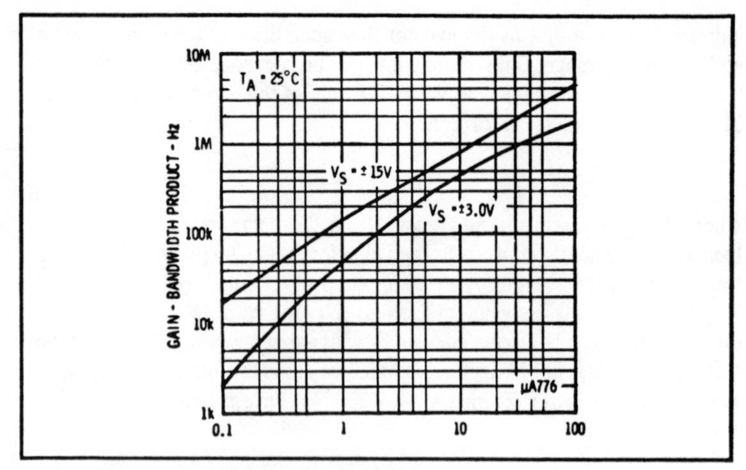

Fig. 10-29B. Slew-rate vs frequency graph.

at various slew rates with no distortion due to excessive rate of change. For the 800 mV/μsec figure, the device can handle signals with peaks of 1.0V out to frequencies in excess of 50 kHz. For signals with an 8V peak, it can only handle frequencies out to approximately 10 kHz. Obviously, for small signals, those with peaks less than 1.0V, the device is *frequency-response limited*. For large signals it is *slew-rate limited*.

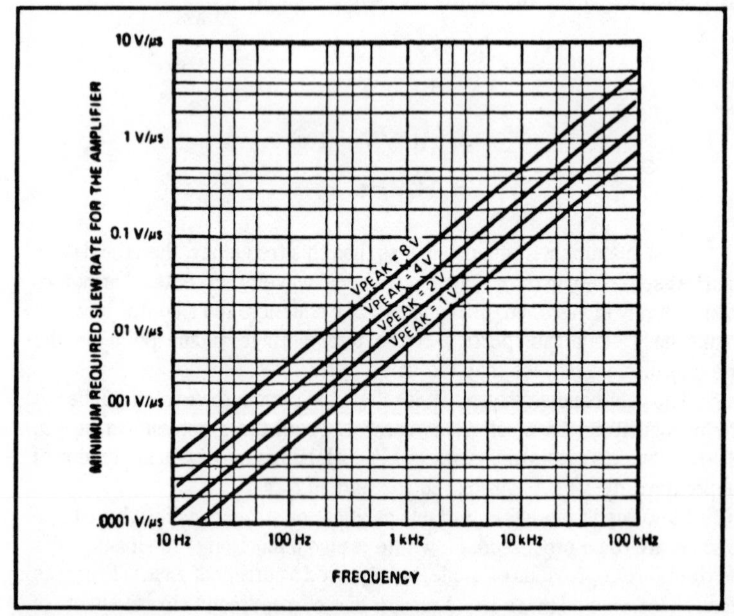

Fig. 10-29C. Gain-bandwidth product for Fairchild μA776.

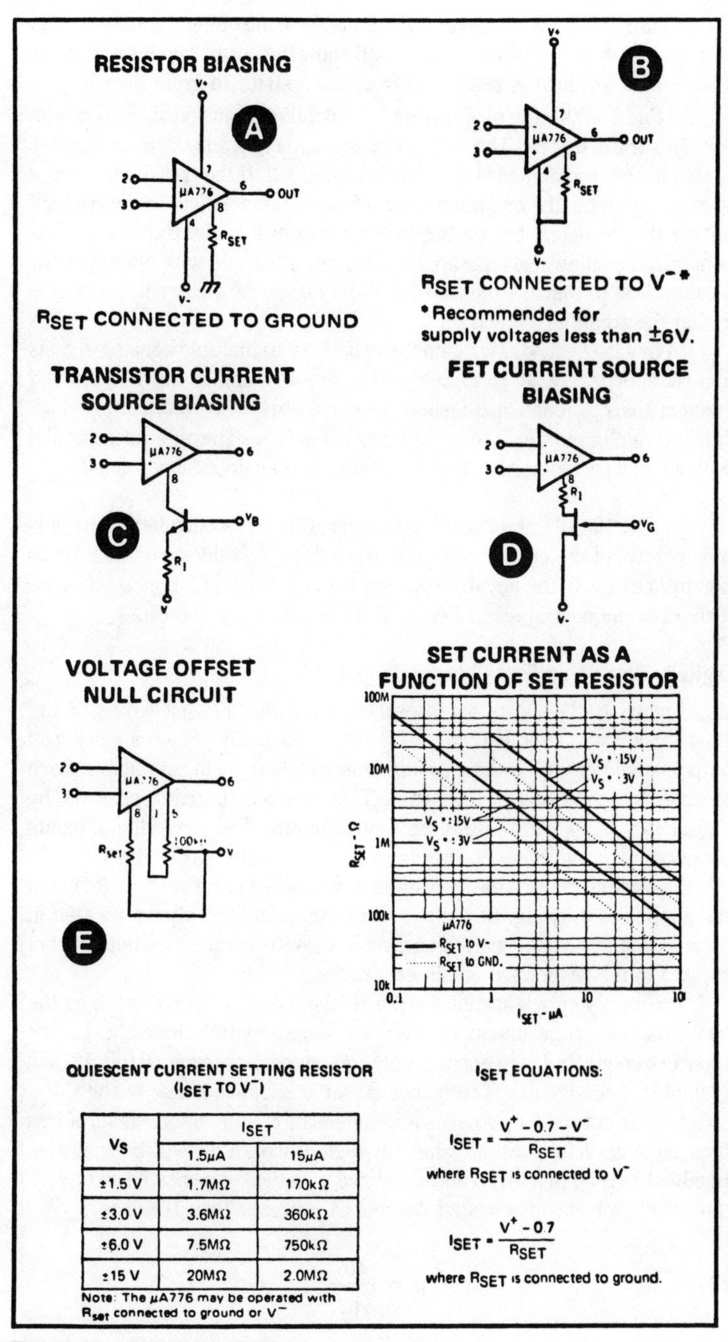

QUIESCENT CURRENT SETTING RESISTOR (I_{SET} TO V^-)

V_S	I_{SET}	
	1.5μA	15μA
±1.5 V	1.7MΩ	170kΩ
±3.0 V	3.6MΩ	360kΩ
±6.0 V	7.5MΩ	750kΩ
±15 V	20MΩ	2.0MΩ

Note: The μA776 may be operated with R_{set} connected to ground or V^-

I_{SET} EQUATIONS:

$$I_{SET} = \frac{V^+ - 0.7 - V^-}{R_{SET}}$$

where R_{SET} is connected to V^-

$$I_{SET} = \frac{V^+ - 0.7}{R_{SET}}$$

where R_{SET} is connected to ground.

Fig. 10-30. μA776 bias circuits.

Figure 10-30 shows several methods for controlling the master bias current I_{SET}. Figures 10-30A and 10-30B show the normal modes where the master bias terminal is returned through a resistor to ground, or V_{EE}.

In Fig. 10-30C, the bias current is controlled by an npn silicon transistor. This transistor must be a very low-leakage type, and the manufacturer of the op amp recommends the Fairchild 2N5962. If the transistor is not a low-leakage type, the minimum control function current will be determined not by the designer, but by the leakage currents of the transistor. This configuration allows several applications not allowable with plain resistor biasing. One of these is modulation of the master bias current; another is gating the amplifier on and off.

In this latter mode, we gain the capability to multiplex analog signals almost effortlessly. It is merely necessary to parallel the outputs and connect the I_{SET} control transistor to some sort of logic circuitry which selects which amplifier is to be on at any given time. The outputs in parallel will not load each other because they become high impedance when I_{SET} is blocked.

In Fig. 10-30D, the master bias current is FET-controlled. This permits control of the entire range of permissible I_{SET} values with as little as 500 mV change in the negative voltage applied to the JFET gate terminal. This is at the cost of less freedom from temperature variations.

Digitally Selectable Four Channel Op Amp

Figure 10-31 shows a representation of the internal works of the Harris Semiconductor HA2400/HA2405 devices. They have a unity gain output amplifier driven by any (or none) of four input amplifiers, each selected by an internal analog switch. This switch is set to its "position" by digital signals applied to its three control inputs. The three digital inputs connect input amplifiers according to the truth table in Fig. 10-31.

The actual control mechanism is a little different from that shown in the simplified drawing. In reality, all of the amplifier outputs are tied in parallel and the analog switching circuitry controls the operating current applied to the respective amplifier circuits.

Frequency compensation for the HA2400 device is dominated by the compensation requirements of whatever stage requires the highest value capacitor connected between the single compensation terminal (pin 12) and ground (for ac signals). The manufacturer recommends use of the $+V_{CC}$ supply as ac ground for purposes of compensation. For voltage gains of less than 10, a capacitor with a value between 1 and 15 pF will be required. Bandwidths β up to 8 MHz can be realized with the compensated configuration, while for uncompensated designs (A_V greater than 10) it is:

$$\beta = \frac{40}{A_V}$$

Slew rate will vary from 15V/μsec to over 50V/μsec, as the value of the compensation capacitor is changed from its maximum value down to zero.

The number of applications possible for a device such as the HA2400/HA2405 is extremely large and highly varied. For the most part, we are free to connect any feedback network between the common output and any of the four pairs of channel inputs, and are limited only by the normal rules applying to operational amplifier feedback networks. The only appreciable limitations result from any possible loading effects which might be present in some types of circuits if the networks tend to interact. Offset adjustment for the HA2400 is best accomplished using the current summing method, where a tiny bucking current is fed either from V_{CC} or V_{EE} (as needed) to null the output to zero when the input is also at zero.

The *enable* terminal can be used to disconnect all of the amplifiers from the common output amplifier. Under some circumstances, this "position" of the analog switch results in a minute but potentially bothersome dc drift of the output toward the $-V_{EE}$ supply voltage. This can be overcome by connecting one of the amplifier sections as an inverting follower and grounding its noninverting input. Such a configuration will tend to clamp the output to zero and prevent drift.

Output limiting can be accomplished by shunting diodes from the compensation terminal (pin 12) to either V_{CC} or a positive point on a voltage

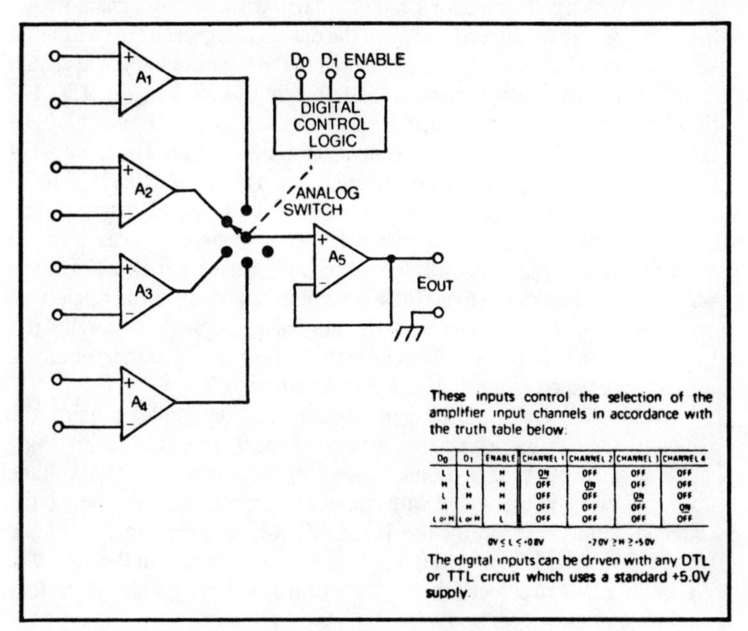

D0	D1	ENABLE	CHANNEL 1	CHANNEL 2	CHANNEL 3	CHANNEL 4
L	L	H	ON	OFF	OFF	OFF
H	L	H	OFF	ON	OFF	OFF
L	H	H	OFF	OFF	ON	OFF
H	H	H	OFF	OFF	OFF	ON
L or H	L or H	L	OFF	OFF	OFF	OFF

Fig. 10-31. Harris digitally selectable four channel op amp.

divider network. The maximum current which can be drawn through the compensation terminal is 300 μA.

Under normal operation, with *enable* high, inputs D_0 and D_1 will select the input amplifier according to the rules of the truth table. If the enable input is low, none of the input amplifiers will be connected to the output amplifier. Unused analog inputs can be left floating, or be strapped to ground as required. The best noise immunity is obtained when the inputs are grounded. The digital inputs may be either grounded or strapped to a +5V source. It depends upon whether a permanent *high* or *low* condition is preferred.

HA2400/HA2405 APPLICATIONS

One application which springs to mind almost immediately is analog multiplexing. In such a system, four or more signals could be passed into a single channel for either processing or communication, as needed. A multiplexer will transmit a tiny portion of each signal, selecting from each channel sequentially. If the sampling rate is high enough, the signals being multiplexed can be reconstructed at the other end of the line with little or no loss in shape or other information content.

In the simplest configuration using the HA2400/HA2405, all four inverting inputs are strapped together and are returned to the common output terminal. This results in a bank of four noninverting unity-gain followers with a common output and separate inputs. Analog signals are fed to the respective noninverting inputs, the enable is high, and the two digital selection inputs, D_0 and D_1, are connected to the logic circuitry. This could consist of a clock (pulse generator) and a single CMOS, TTL, or DTL, J-K flip-flop. The clock pulses could be connected to the D_0 input of the HA2400/HA2405 and to the toggle input of the J-K flip-flop. The Q output of the flip-flop will then be connected to the D_1 input of the HA2400/HA2405.

Such a simple circuit will generate the 00, 01, 10, 11 binary coding needed to select input amplifiers in a 1, 2, 3, 4 sequence. In cases where more than four channels are needed, up to four channels per HA2400 can be accommodated and up to four HA2400 outputs can be fed to the respective inputs of a fifth HA2400. The digital inputs can be connected in parallel (D_0 to D_0 and D_1 to D_1). The enable inputs are then connected to another digital logic circuit which is used as a *chip select* circuit.

It is also easy to make a programmable gain amplifier using the HA2400/HA2405. In such a circuit we could strap together the noninverting inputs and use them as a common signal input for the circuit. A voltage divider network is connected with one end to ground, and the other to the common output terminal of the HA2400/HA2405. Each junction of the voltage divider is connected to a different input amplifier in the HA2400. We are then able to select gain (R_F/R_{IN} ratio) by selecting which of the four amplifiers is turned on by the digital logic circuit.

The same idea can also be used to make a programmable attenuator. In that case the inverting inputs are strapped together and returned to the common output, once again resulting in four unity gain, noninverting followers. In this case, though, we place the voltage divider across the signal input line and connect the respective channel amplifier noninverting inputs to the voltage divider junctions. If a *nonattenuated* position is desired, the input of one of the amplifier sections can be connected directly to the signal at the top of the voltage divider network.

The manufacturer's literature points out that two of these amplifiers can be connected in this manner and then be used as a programmable attenuator for balanced audio lines. One potential application for such a circuit is in broadcast stations where the engineer might want to control gain and signal level applied to a line from a remote location using AFSK (audio-frequency-shift-keyed) signals to create the digital selection signals.

The HA2400/2405 can also be used in a unique low-pass filter circuit that permits remote or local selection of four different values of cutoff frequency by changing the digital input coding. In that application, there will be four 3-terminal RC networks, one for each value of cutoff frequency f_C. The inputs of the networks are strapped together and this point is used as the circuit input. The common terminals of the RC networks are also strapped together and are connected to the HA2400/HA2405 output. The respective RC network outputs are connected to the respective individual amplifier inputs. By digital selection of which amplifier section is active, we can select the cutoff frequency of the whole filter.

Chapter 11

Operational Amplifier Measurements

This chapter is devoted to explaining how several of the operational amplifier parameters are measured. Understanding how these are obtained can help to better understand the abilities and limitations of any particular device.

VOLTAGE GAIN

Voltage gain is the ratio of signal output voltage to signal input voltage, or

$$A_V = \frac{E_{OUT}}{E_{IN}} \tag{11-1}$$

Obtaining closed-loop gain is a relatively simple matter of applying an input signal of known amplitude and then measuring the output level thus generated. These figures can then be plugged into Eq. 11-1 and the figure for A_V comes cranking out. The only thing to watch for is saturation of the output. The input signal must have a level high enough to produce a meaningful output (i.e., easy to measure accurately), but low enough to prevent overloading the amplifier. It is preferable to keep the test frequency either close to the center of the passband or, more often, a specified test frequency such as 1 kHz. When the input signal necessarily is of very low level, such as might occur if the stage had extremely high gain, a means should be provided to null dc offsets because these might well approach or exceed the amplitude of the test signal. Measurement of open-loop gain is the same, except that input signals in the microvolt range are needed.

INPUT OFFSET CURRENT

Input offset current is measured in a test circuit such as that shown in Fig. 11-1. Input offset current can be specified by the relationship between two output voltages taken under different input conditions:

$$I_{IO} = \frac{R_{IN}(E_{OUT1} - E_{OUT2})}{R_2(R_{IN} + R_F)} \qquad (11\text{-}2)$$

The first output voltage, E_{OUT1}, is taken with resistors R_1 and R_2 still connected in the circuit. E_{OUT} is that output voltage taken with these resistors shorted out, but with all other conditions the same. The resultant output voltage can, along with E_{OUT1}, be plugged into Eq. 11-2.

INPUT OFFSET VOLTAGE

Input offset voltage is the voltage required to force the output (E_{OUT}) to zero when zero input voltage is present. The op amp is connected in an inverting amplifier configuration such as Fig. 1-7 (Chapter 1). To make the measurement, the E_{IN} terminal is connected to ground. The input offset voltage is found by measuring the output voltage and plugging it into the standard voltage divider formula:

$$E_{IO} = \frac{E_{OUT} R_{IN}}{RF + R_{IN}} \qquad (11\text{-}3)$$

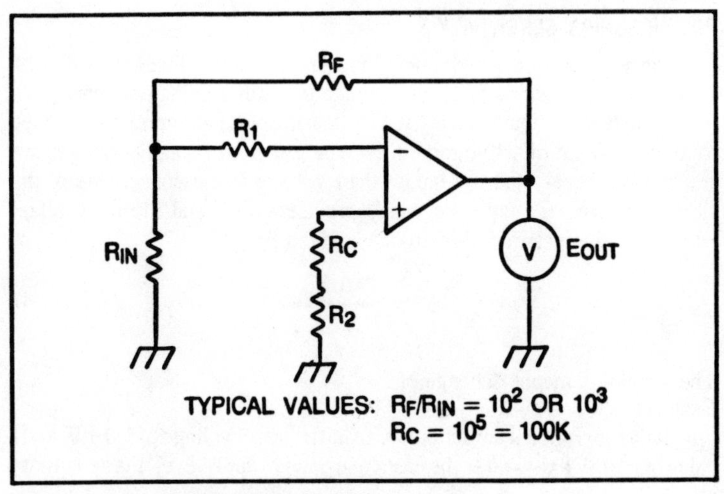

Fig. 11-1. Input offset current test circuit.

Greater accuracy is obtained if R_F/R_{IN} has a value of 100 or 1000 (or even higher).

INPUT BIAS CURRENT

This test requires a pair of closely matched resistors connected between the op-amp inputs (inverting and noninverting) and ground. Power is applied to the operational amplifier without an input signal. The actual value of the two resistors must be high enough to produce a measurable voltage drop at the level of current anticipated. Although the values of the resistors are not crucial, the match between the resistors is very important. (Unmatched resistors will cause an error factor in our calculation.) As to what constitutes a *readable* voltage drop, that may well depend on the instrumentation available to do the job. For example, if the resistors are 2200Ω and the actual bias current is 5 μA:

By Ohm's law:

$$E = IR - (2200)\,(0.000005) = 11 \times 10^{-3}$$
$$= 0.011\text{V}$$
$$= 11 \text{ mV}$$

If your voltage measuring equipment is not capable of measuring these levels, higher resistor values would be required.

If the two inputs had ideally equal input bias currents, only one measurement would be needed. Since a real device has unequal bias currents, however, it is necessary to measure both and use the higher bias current value.

POWER SUPPLY SENSITIVITY

Power supply sensitivity ψ is the change of input offset voltage for a 1.0V change of *one* power supply voltage (the other being held constant). The same test configuration is used to measure this parameter as was used to measure input offset voltage. First, the two power supply voltages are set to equal levels and the input offset voltage is measured. One of the supply voltages is then changed by precisely 1.0V and the input offset voltage again measured. Sensitivity is given by:

$$\psi = \frac{\Delta E_{IO}}{\Delta E_{OUT}} \tag{11-4}$$

The symbol Δ means "change of . . ."
Example:

If the operational amplifier has an initial offset voltage of 5.0 mV, and a value of 6.2 mV exists after the change in power supply level, the sensitivity is:

$$\psi = \frac{6.2 - 5.0}{1.0} = 1.2 \text{ mV/V}$$

Actual true sensitivity might be different under different conditions, so measurements are made using both ±1.0V excursions of first V_{CC} then V_{EE}, and the worst case taken as the sensitivity.

SLEW RATE

Slew rate is the ability of the operational amplifier to shift or race between opposite output voltage extremes while supplying full output power. It is usual to measure slew rate in the noninverting unity-gain voltage follower configuration, because this circuit generally has the poorest slew rate in most op-amp devices. Here, as in previous tests, the worst case should be the published case (which is a practice op amp manufacturers hopefully follow).

The unity-gain follower is driven by a square wave of sufficient amplitude to drive the device well beyond full saturation. This criterion is necessary to eliminate the rounded curves which will exist at points just below full saturation. The output waveform can then be examined with a wideband oscilloscope which has a time base fast enough to allow for a meaningful examination. The trace will be a straight line with a certain slope. Adjust the time base of the oscilloscope so that the slope is low enough to cover at least several horizontal scale divisions. Slew rate S_R is given by:

$$S_R = \frac{E_{OUT}}{t} \tag{11-5}$$

which is the slope of the trace shown on the oscilloscope.

PHASE SHIFT

The phase shift ϕ of an operational amplifier, or almost any other linear electronic circuit for that matter, can be measured using a sine wave and an oscilloscope. In one version of this technique, a single-trace scope is used. The input signal is applied to the vertical channel of the scope while the op-amp output is applied to the horizontal channel. Gains for the two respective channels are set so that equal beam deflections are produced. The phase shift can be computed from:

$$\phi = \text{Arc sin}\left(\frac{Y_1 - Y_2}{Y_4 - Y_3}\right) \tag{11-6}$$

See Fig. 11-2 for a graphic illustration.

An alternative approach is to use a dual-trace oscilloscope which has the op-amp input signal on one channel and the output on the other channel (see Fig. 11-3). Adjust the *gain* and *position* controls so that the traces are nearly the same height and overlay each other. The time base is then adjusted so that one cycle nearly fills the screen (it rarely works out that a

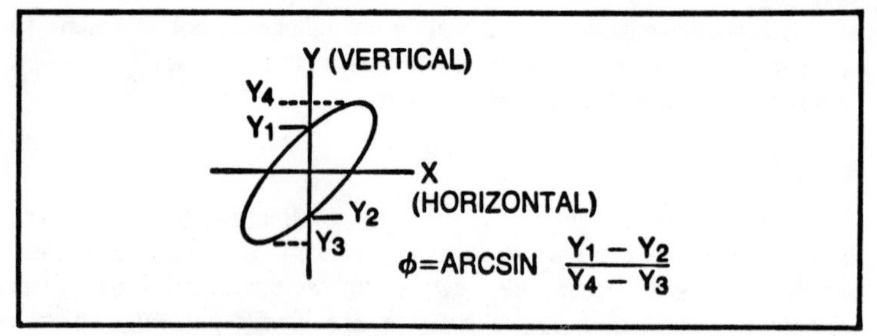

Fig. 11-2. Phase determination by Lissajous figures.

calibrated value of time base exactly fits). The trace of the output signal will be delayed in time slightly with respect to the input signal. Phase shift is proportional to the time shift.
Example:

$$\phi = \frac{360B}{A} \text{(See Fig. 11-3)} \qquad (11\text{-}7)$$

If the trace occupies 9.5 divisions on the horizontal scale and the time shift is 0.8 divisions, shift of phase is:

$$\phi = \frac{360\ (0.8)}{9.5} = 30.3^\circ$$

Of course, this is a highly magnified value relative to what can actually be expected with most op amps, but it does serve as an illustration. An oscilloscope with ×5 or ×10 time base expansion will give readable results with phase shifts likely to be found in typical op amps.

COMMON-MODE REJECTION RATIO

Common-mode rejection is defined as the ratio:

$$\text{CMR} = \frac{A_{V(DIFF)}}{A_{V(CM)}} \qquad (11\text{-}8)$$

where the numerator is the differential voltage gain and the denominator is the common-mode gain. This latter gain is not always a linear function of

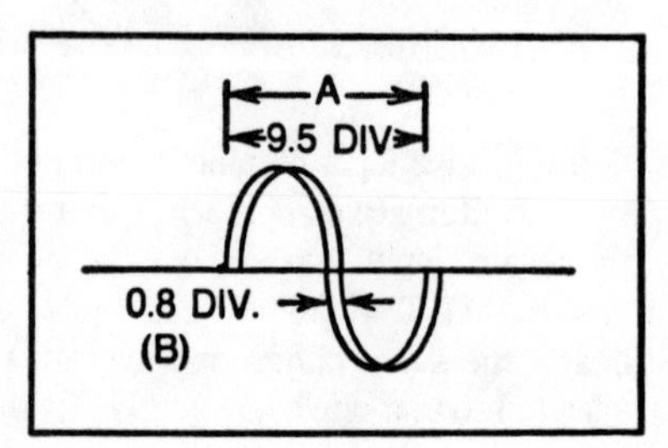

Fig. 11-3. Alternate phase determination method.

common-mode input voltage (E_{CM}), so it is usually specified at the maximum allowable value for E_{CM}. The amplifier is connected in a differential amplifier circuit such as Fig. 3-12 (Chapter 3).

CMRR is:

$$\text{CMRR} = \frac{(R_F + R_{IN})\, E_{IN}}{R_{IN} E_{OUT}} \tag{11-9}$$

provided that R_F is much larger than R_{IN} (i.e., R_F = 100K and R_{IN} = 100Ω).

Chapter 12

Useful Circuits and Interesting Applications

This chapter is included to comply with suggestions of several friends who felt, after reading the manuscript, that their own areas of interest were slighted. These included physics, biology, chemistry, and several engineering disciplines. Although we have not been able to address each and every one of them, much of the material is useful to all.

USING LIGHT IN OP-AMP CIRCUITS

Photoelectricity is a phenomenon in which certain substances generate a voltage, change electrical resistance, or emit electrons. The emission of electrons is proportional to the properties of an impinging light beam. The energy imparted to any given electron is not dependent on the intensity of the light, however. Only the number of electrons emitted changes with changing intensity. This phenomenon, called *photoemission*, is the basis of operation for such devices as the photomultiplier tube.

Photoconductivity is a phenomenon which refers to the ability of certain materials to change their electrical resistance when illuminated by light. The amount of change can be quite high. Dark/light resistance ratios are of an order that is surprising. Investigation of typical photoresistor spec sheets indicates the fact that dark resistances range from several hundred thousand to several million ohms. Lighted resistances, on the other hand, will vary from a few hundred to a few thousand ohms. What really makes these devices so appealing is that most of them are economical.

One last type of photocell which we will mention here is the photovoltaic or *solar* cell. These devices will produce an output voltage when illuminated. A number of different cells exist in this category, including silicon, selenium, cadium sulfide (CdS), and so forth. Low cost, but reasonably accurate, photographic exposure meters are made using devices such

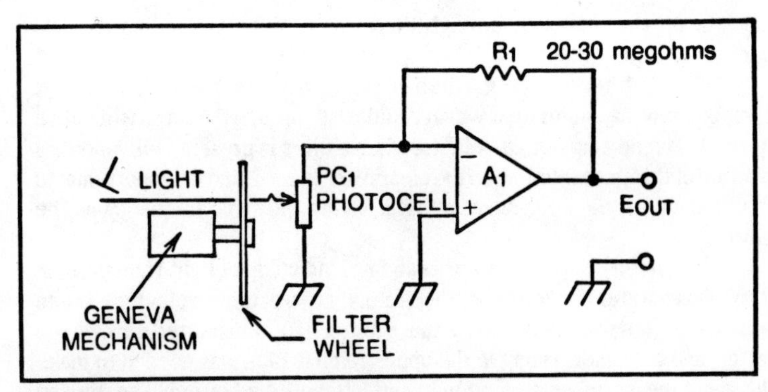

Fig. 12-1. Cohen's spectral photometer.

as this. Outputs from the various types of photovoltaic cell range from less than a hundred millivolts to about half a volt.

Spectral response can be of concern when using any type of photocell. Most of these devices do not offer a flat response to all wavelengths of light. In fact, most will offer what seems to be a poor response in the visual range and will peak most often in the infrared, or sometimes in the ultraviolet. This might not be too bad, of course, if your interest lies in the same region as the best response of the cell being used, but it can be trouble if the peaks are at inopportune points. In some cases, it may be possible to smooth out the peaks by using an optical filter between the cell and the light source. Peaks in the response range can be evened out by using a filter element. The filter should have its maximum attenuation in the wavelength band where the photocell has its main response peak. A photographer's daylight filter, for instance, can get a cheap method for preventing ultraviolet from saturating the cell, if that happens to be a problem.

Figure 12-1 is a circuit contributed by physicist Norman Cohen president of EHI Electronics. Operational amplifier A_1 is used to amplify the output of photovoltaic cell PC_1. The op amp must be a low-drift type with high input impedance. Resistor R_1 will have a value in the megohm range because this circuit was designed for low-light-level application. This makes stringent requirements for the specifications for both the amplifier and the resistor. The amplifier and the resistor must for example, be low-noise types or some of the weaker signal components will be buried in the *grass*.

In the specific application for which this circuit was designed, zero temperature coefficient for the system must be maintained. This means that the resistor should have a temperature coefficient of a polarity and amount which will tend to cancel that of the operational amplifier.

A filter wheel connected to a Geneva mechanism can be pulsed in such a way that filters for different wave-lengths can be placed successively in front of the photocell. One of the filter positions is clear so that white light can be used to calibrate the system. The output voltage generated when daylight hit the photocell through the clear position is used as the 100 percent or unity value.

As each filter is brought into place in front of the cell, only that component of the white light which could pass through the filter will fall on the cell. The op amp output voltage, when a filter is present, will be only a fraction of that generated when the clear filter is used, and is proportional to the intensity of the component of light having the same frequency as the filter.

This circuit was used in an oceanographic study of light transmission through sea water at various depths. Actually two of these detector circuits were used. One was needed to measure direct light transmitted through the water, and the other, facing in the opposite direction, was needed to make the same measurements using light reflected off the bottom. The op amp output voltages were used to modulate voltage-controlled oscillators (VCO). The VCO delivered an audio tone whose frequency varied as the light intensity varied. Such signals were then passed to the surface via telephone wires and tape recorded for eventual demodulation and study ashore. This project was a good demonstration of how a clever scientific worker could profit from a little op amp know-how and thereby function without the need for a sophisticated electronics model shop.

X-Ray Detector

A reasonably decent X-ray detector can be fashioned, for very low cost, which will allow viewing of the time/intensity output of an X-ray machine on an oscilloscope. Several manufacturers of photocells were consulted on the X-ray response of their products, but the survey was negative. It seems that those which would operate much above visible light regions were too expensive to meet the specification.

A field engineer with the service department of a major X-ray manufacturer, however, demonstrated a homebrew device used by many in his profession. It is a reasonably good solution, yet was so inexpensive as to leave one incredulous. The sensor head consists of a sandwich of a piece of fluorescent material, often found in X-ray rooms, and three low-cost selenium solar cells. This assembly is mounted inside a light-tight plastic housing which has a communications-type BNC output connector on one end. The output of the sensor head is connected to the input of the oscilloscope. If the sensor is placed in the path of the X-ray beam, the material inside will emit light when struck by the beam. This will, in turn, causes a tiny output voltage to appear across the terminals of the solar cell. The output of the cell is proportional to the intensity of the beam.

Of course, the X-ray beam may be on for too short a time for critical oscilloscope examination. In that case, a storage oscilloscope or a scope equipped with a Polaroid camera is used.

The design I examined used three series-connected selenium cells of a brand and type number often seen dangling from a pegboard in electronics chain stores.

Rise time for the three-cell combination was not too exciting—on the order of 3 msec. This can be improved by reducing the number of cells if a lower output voltage can be tolerated. If a high-level output and faster rise time is needed, we could try using an operational amplifier in the noninverting follower mode between the sensor and the oscilloscope input. This area seems ripe for some clever soul to give free play to imagination.

Perhaps it would prove fruitful to try several different low-cost photosensitive electronic devices which may well give the required rise time and output voltage, yet can withstand being placed directly in the path of the X-ray beam. Also, consider the fact that such sensor devices need not be restricted to oscilloscope applications. It could, for example, be used to pulse a Schmitt trigger circuit, which could then be used to gate a period counter. This gives us the ability to measure the time duration of the X-ray beam.

Optical Measurements

Some phenomena are studied by passing light through a device to a photodetector. A simple apparatus for such experiments should operate nicely unless the intensity of the transmitted light is important. If that is a parameter of the test, we find that unintentional intensity variations in the light source become acutely important. Of course, one could use a super-stable light source, but this may not be necessary. Figure 12-2 shows a way out. In this circuit, we direct light from the source through a *beam splitter*, a partially silvered mirror which transmits a portion of the light and reflects the rest.

The transmitted portion is directed through the material being investigated (which we will call the *medium* for lack of a better word) and falls on photodetector A. This produces a voltage at the output of the detector's operational amplifier (Fig. 12-2) proportional to the intensity of the transmitted light beam.

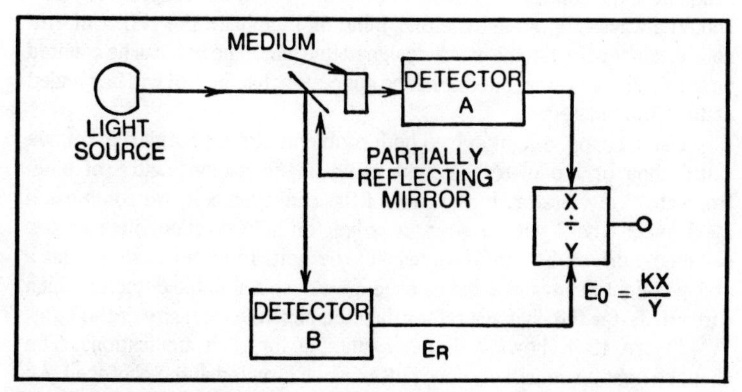

Fig. 12-2. Scheme to eliminate artifacts from light source variations in photoelectric systems.

Nice. But what happens if the intensity of the light beam varies due to problems in the light source rather than changes in the medium? When the output of the light source wiggles a bit, we generate a change at the output of the op-amp circuit. We can eliminate this problem by causing the reflected light beam to fall on a second, identical, detector to create a reference voltage proportional to the intensity of the incident beam, but unaffected at all by what happens to the transmitted beam. These two voltages can be combined in a ratio-connected analog multiplier (divider) to create a voltage E_{OUT} proportional to the ratio E_t/E_{REF}.

Crude, perhaps, but clever crudeness counts when you work on a budget. This system works on the principle that light source intensity variations will affect both detectors in a like manner, but variations in the medium will affect only detector A (E_t).

Chopped Light Detector

There are times when constant-intensity light systems that are used as alarms, etc., will fail miserably. Consider two such situations: burglar alarms and conveyor-belt motion sensors. A popular and reasonably priced burglar alarm uses a light beam across an entrance as an intruder alarm. As long as light falls on the detector, everything is fine. When an intruder breaks the beam, even for a brief instant, the photocell will react to the sudden loss of intensity and will activate the alarm. But what happens when the burglar is clever enough to come equipped with a flashlight to shine into the detector as he crosses the entrance? As far as the photocell is concerned, the beam still exists, but the burglar is inside the premises. This doesn't appear to be such a good alarm system!

Consider the other situation where a photocell is used in a plant to count moving objects on a conveyor belt. The counter should also work as an alarm so that everyone will be aware of the problem if the belt stops. Depending on the circuit design, a photocell-lamp combination would be adequate if the conveyor system, were consistent in this respect: The belt should always stop so as to either blind or illuminate the cell. Unfortunately, conveyor systems aren't designed this way. The belt can be counted on to occasionally stop, but there is no guarantee that the cell will be blinded or fully illuminated.

Using chopped light solves both problems. In the burglar alarm, we could chop or modulate the light using an electronic switch of electromechanical vibrator. In the case of the conveyor belt, we could use a mechanical wheel with a serrated edge (or holes drilled) in a proper sequence, driven by the movement of the belt. In either case we get a chopped light beam and it can be used if we have a suitable detector which cares more for the changes rather than the absolute intensity of the light.

Figure 12-3 shows a detector suitable for such applications. The chopped light beam will produce pulses when directed at the photocell. An RC differentiator consisting of resistor R_4 and capacitor C_1 passes only

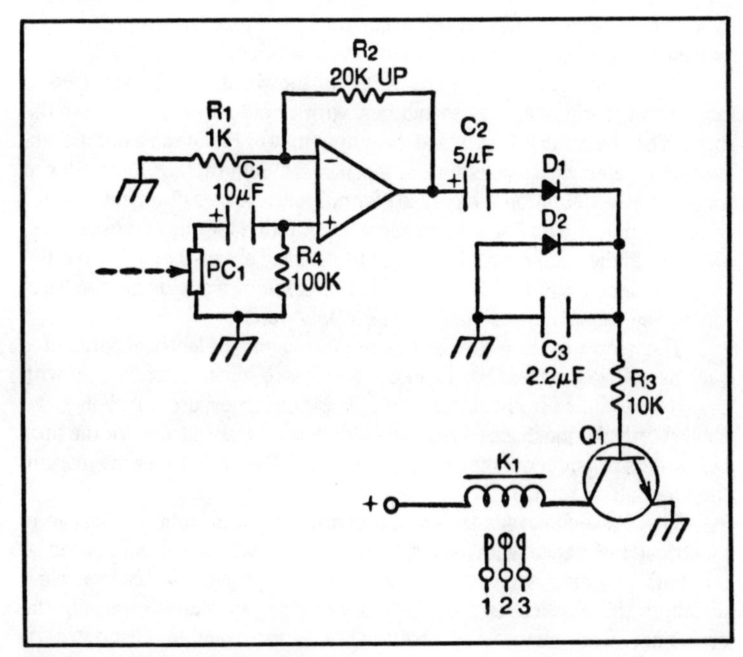

Fig. 12-3. Chopped light detector.

pulses to the input. Should the light beam either fail or remain steady (as if a burglar was shining a flashlight on the cell), the output of the photocell will go either to zero or some steady value. In either event, the differentiator only passes *changing* signals, so this will eliminate the input to the amplifier. This network also prevents high ambient light levels from affecting the amplifier.

Resistors R_1 and R_2 set the circuit gain. These will probably have to have a high ratio to provide sufficient amplification to handle the small output pulses expected from the photocell. The amplified pulses at the output of the op amp A_1 are fed through a half-wave voltage doubler (C_2, D_1, D_2) where they are rectified and used to charge capacitor C_3. The voltage across this capacitor is used in this example (but by no means universally) to turn on relay control transistor Q_1. It is an easy matter, though, to adapt the control portion of such a circuit to many applications.

TRANSDUCERS AND TRANSDUCER SYSTEMS

In the treatment of differential amplifiers in Chapter 3, we briefly discussed the famous Wheatstone bridge. We emphasized the fact that we could use an operational amplifier to either buffer and isolate the bridge from the outside world, or to amplify the normally small bridge output voltage. In this section, though, the emphasis is on transducers which are used in the measurement of certain physical parameters. This will include

Wheatstone bridge types as the major topic, because they represent the largest percentage of transducers in actual service.

A transducer, in the general sense of the word, is a device used to convert one form of energy to another, with an output proportional to the input. The signals in the input and the output may be of the same or different types, i.e., electrical, acoustical, or mechanical. Some authorities prefer to include in the definition the phrase "for purposes of measurement, control or acquisition of data." In a more specific definition for our purposes here, we will add the further stipulation that the form of energy being "converted to..." is electrical; after all, operational amplifiers work using electrical inputs and cannot, for example, amplify salt water!

The secret to transduction lies in making some electrical parameter such as voltage, current, resistance, capacitance, or inductance vary with changes in whatever physical parameter is being measured. Although we shall shortly demonstrate capacitive and inductive transducers, for the time being, let's consider only the resistance types. They are, by a wide margin, the most often seen.

There are numerous resistor configurations which allow a change in electrical resistance with changes in some nonelectrical parameter or stimulus. In some devices, the composition of the resistor will change while in others the physical size of the resistor changes, thereby varying the resistance. Thermistors and photoresistors, for example, change resistance when heat or light, respectively, changes their composition. In other devices, a force or pressure is applied to the resistor and alters its size.

Figure 12-2 shows two crude, but somewhat effective, methods used to generate an output voltage which will vary with variations in the resistance of the sensing device. Figure 12-4A is a simple voltage divider excited by a constant voltage supply. Resistor R_2 is the sensor and it changes value in proportion to changes in an applied stimulus or parameter.

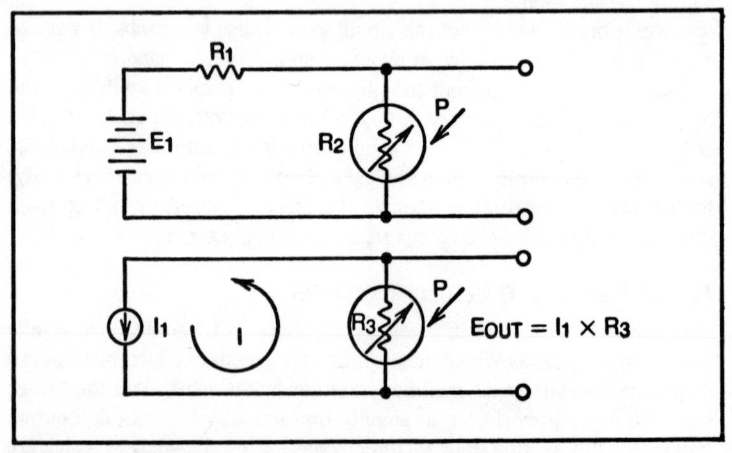

Fig. 12-4. Elementary, albeit almost useless, transducers.

An alternative method is shown in Fig. 12-4B where we use a single resistor excited by a constant current source, I_1. Since the value of I_1 will remain stable regardless of changes in the value of $R3$, we know (by Ohm's law) that E_{OUT} will have to vary.

Although both of these circuits are found in use, neither is really satisfactory for most applications. The first of the two examples suffers from gross errors in the voltage representation of the applied parameter, unless the value of R_1 is much greater than the nominal value of R_2. This means that obtaining an easily managed output voltage may require a very high excitation (E_1) voltage. The second circuit is insensitive to small changes in resistance, unless a high value of I_1 is chosen. That solution would be fine except that such current levels would possibly heat the resistor enough to either damage it or temporarily change its value. This restricts the use of circuits such as Fig. 12-4B to applications where resistance changes are expected to be large. Such cases might be where the sensor is a thermistor or photocell. Some of those devices exhibit very large resistance changes under influence of relatively small changes in light intensity or temperature.

Where the application is the measurement of pressure, force, strain, and so forth, the sensor is generally of the type which deforms a resistive element. This means that the expected change in resistance will be small and the output voltage will be small. Even if the output voltage was large enough to ensure that no problems in data collection would appear, there is still one problem with both of these circuits: an unwanted output offset voltage even when the stimulus is at zero or at its reference value. We can avoid this by two methods: an offset control in the operational amplifier (such as Fig. 4-6) or by not using the circuits of Fig. 12-4, and instead use a Wheatstone bridge circuit.

Figure 12-5 shows a basic bridge circuit in which three elements are fixed and one varies in resistance with changes in the applied stimulus. Since we covered the simple arithmetic of the bridge in Chapter 3, we shall not reiterate here. Recall, though, that Δ in the equations presented means "small change in..." and will have a value of zero when the system is unperturbed (at rest).

Perturbing the system (i.e., changing the temperature, applying a pressure, etc.) will cause the value of R_4 to change for R to ΔR. This upsets the bridge balance and generates an output voltage. Once again, we shall opt for the convention stipulating that, in our bridges, $R_1 = R_2 = R_3 = R_4 = R$. This is done for simplicity. However, most commercially available transducers use this same arrangement.

There are a few terms associated with bridges and transducers which might require a slight explanation. Gauge factor (GF), for example, is the change in resistance R caused by some unit change Δ in the physical parameter x being measured. For example, in a pressure transducer:

$$GF = \Delta R/(\Delta x/x)$$

$$= k/\Delta x \qquad (12\text{-}1)$$
$$\text{where } k = x/R$$

As an example, consider a medical blood pressure transducer where a fluid pressure of 100 torr (mm Hg) changes a slight amount to 101 torr. This causes resistance R to change from 200 to 202Ω. By the formula of Eq. 12-1:

$$GF = \frac{(100)\ (2)}{(200)\ (1)}$$
$$= \frac{200}{200}$$
$$= 1.$$

When we know the gauge factor of a transducer system, we are in a position to evaluate it relative to other transducer types.

Linearity is a measure of the accuracy of the bridge in representing the physical parameter applied to it. Linearity is measured by the amount of deviation from a straight line in the response curve (see Fig. 12-6). Part of the overall nonlinearity can be due to the particular type of transducer selected. If all else is equal, a transducer in which only a single bridge arm is allowed to vary in proportion to the variations in the external parameter being measured will have the worst error.

Most Wheatstone bridge transducers with a single variable element exhibit a 5 percent error for a 10 percent change of the input parameter.

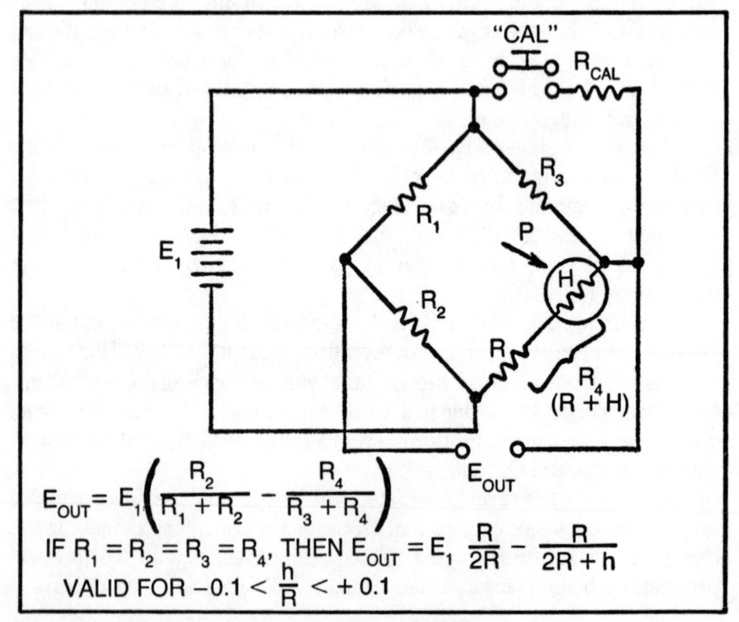

Fig. 12-5. Basic Wheatstone bridge with calibration resistor.

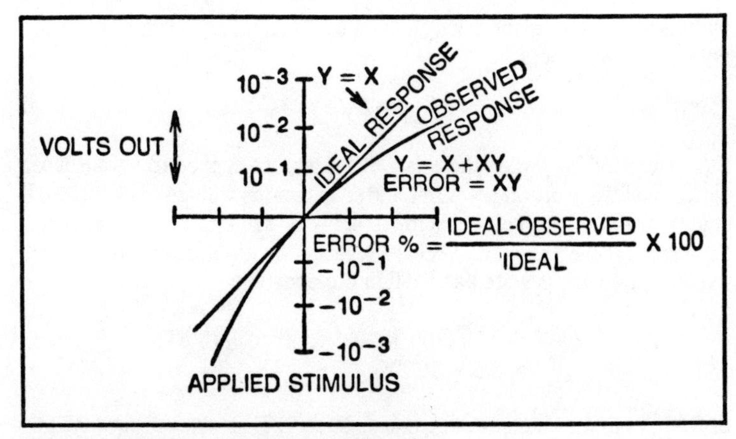

Fig. 12-6. Example of transducer nonlinearity.

This means a 5 percent change of values exists over a range of −0.1 to + 0.1.

Such nonlinearity can be all but eliminated by making either two or, preferably, all four elements of the Wheatstone bridge variable. Many fluid pressure transducers incorporate this approach in their design to improve the overall linearity to ±2 percent over a wide range and ±1 percent for a limited calibrated range. The expressions for the bridges with two and four active elements are:

For two elements;

$$E_{out} = \frac{E_{in}\Delta R}{2R} \tag{12-2}$$

For four elements;

$$E_{out} = \frac{E_{in}\Delta R}{R} \tag{12-3}$$

Note that improved linearity is not our only gain from going to multielement transducers—the output voltages are also higher. Most common transducers are of the two element variety.

Sensitivity factor ψ is one specification of primary importance when trying to incorporate a transducer into an electronic measurement system. Sensitivity is usually quoted as "output volts per volt of excitation per unit of stimulating parameter", or E_{out}/E_1/p. Take as an example the type of fluid pressure transducer used in medicine to monitor human blood pressure. A typical transducer may have a sensitivity specification of "100 μV/v/T. This means that it will produce an output signal E_{out} of 100 μV per volt of E_1, the excitation voltage, for every torr (T) pressure. Since most transducers are designed for operation with a 4—10V excitation voltage, we are going to use 5V as the excitation for a hypothetical transducer for purposes of making some calculations. For determining the range of output voltage we will use:

$$E_{out} = E_1 \psi p \tag{12-5}$$

Example: Find E_{out} when there is a 50T pressure applied to a transducer with a sensitivity of 100 μV/V/dT and an excitation voltage of 5V. (The dT stands for *dekatorr*, a unit equal to 10 torr—the same as 1 cm of mercury.) First convert the pressure to dekatorr. Since the dekatorr equals ten torr, the 50T pressure is stated as 5 dT in the equation:

$$\begin{aligned} E_{out} &= (5V)\ (100 \times 10^{-6}\ \mu V/V/dT)\ (5\ dT) \\ &= 2.5 \times 10^{-3} V \end{aligned}$$

or 2.5 mV output when pressure equals 50 torr. Thus, we will have 2.5 mV signal to work with when the applied pressure is 50T.

The next step in designing a usable measuring system is to calculate the gain required from the operational amplifiers. Of course, we could use arbitrary figures with an A_V, which is large enough to give an output to drive a meter or other indicating device. We could then recalibrate the face of the meter to pressure units, but this is too crude an approach for elegant tastes! Besides, unless an extensive graphic department is handy, it will prove to be a pain in the neck to draw, by hand, a meter face that looks decent.

A nicer and far more elegant solution would be to scale the amplification so that the output voltage will have the same digits as the applied pressure. For example, we could stipulate that the full range of the instrument to measure pressures averaging 50T will be 0—100 torr. Since most low-cost operational amplifiers can easily deliver output voltages between −10V and +10V, we could further stipulate that +10V will be used to represent 100T pressure. We could also design the system so that −10V represents a complementary vacuum, but this is not usually possible unless the transducer actually provides an output from negative pressures.

Alternatively, we could also allow 1.00V to equal 100 torr, if desired. With modern digital panel meter readouts, this would not impose any great hardship on accuracy, since most digital meters usually will measure to 1.999V. In our example, though, we will stick with the 10V standard.

In the example worked above we found that the tranducers will produce 2.5 mV when a pressure of 50T was applied. If 10V represents full scale (100T) in the unit being designed, half-scale will be 5V for 50T. The amplification should be:

$$A_V = (5.00)/(0.0025) = 2000$$

If the operational amplifier following the Wheatstone bridge transducer can give a gain of 2000, certainly not a big strain for even low-cost devices, the output voltage will be nicely scaled for readout by a simple digital panel meter.

Bridge calibration is often required so that meters, external oscilloscopes, and other indicating instruments can be calibrated without actually perturbing the system with the stimulus. Many transducers either come supplied with a suitable calibration resistor or the manufacturer will specify a value which the user can obtain from any electronic supplier. Figure 12-5 shows how such a resistor is connected into the classic Wheatstone bridge circuit. The value of R_{cal} can be computed from:

$$R_{cal} = R\left[\frac{1 - 2\psi}{4\,p\psi}\right] \tag{12-6}$$

where:

R is the resistance of a single bridge arm

p is the pressure (for other stimulus) which is to be the calibration point

ψ is the sensitivity factor expressed in μV/T.

Again using the 50T pressure and a 100 μV/V/dT sensitivity, let us calculate a value for a calibration resistor. First, we must ascertain the resistance of each arm of the Wheatstone bridge. There are several methods for doing this, but the easiest is to simply look it up in the manufacturer's literature. Either the catalogs or the specification sheet accompanying the transducer should give this data. If it is not known, try measuring the value with an ohmmeter. It may be necessary to disconnect some of the internal wiring in order to make a meaningful resistance reading. Let us assume that the manufacturer of our hypothetical transducer lists a value for R of 200Ω, then,

$$R_{cal} = R\left[\frac{1 - 2\,p\psi}{4\,p\psi}\right]$$

$$= \frac{(200)\ (1 - (2)\ (5\ \text{dt})\ (100 \times 10^{-6})}{(4)\ (5\ \text{dt})\ (100 \times 10^{-6})}$$

$$= 999 \times 10^{4}\Omega$$

$$= 99{,}900\Omega$$

Note that the value of R_{cal} isn't one of the standard values available on an off-the-shelf basis. This is why some manufacturers have odd calibration points. They use the lower cost standard value resistor closest to the calculated value which might result in a calibration point of perhaps 53.5 torr rather than a nice even 50T.

Fixing Wheatstone Bridge Transducer Problems

There are several problems encountered in the use of the Wheatstone bridge and in other forms of transducers. Most of these can either be treated and fixed or rendered inconsequential in their effect. One very annoying problem is the matter of drift in the output, (not due to variation in the stimulus). There are several different causes of such drift, including instability of the operational or instrumentation amplifier used to boost the output, temperature dependent drift in the values of the resistors forming the bridge elements, and variation in the value of E_1—the excitation voltage.

In the first instance, op-amp drift, we can cure the problem by selecting only top-grade, low-drift devices and by employing the tactics of Chapter 4 to more stubborn cases. For most users, we can cure the second problem by shunting any bridge which has resistor "drift." The temperature characteristics of the bridge is a specification available from the manufacturer. This will indicate the percentage drift within a specified temperature range.

In most all cases where experiments or measurements are carried out at "room temperature" (about 21°C), the temperature compensation of most tranducers is adequate. In nonstandard environments, or where measurements are to be extremely accurate, the temperature compensation of some transducers might prove to be insufficient. For the last problem mentioned above, we can use a highly regulated power supply for E_1 and the analog divider scheme of Fig. 12-7 to overcome the drift problem.

Recall that the Wheatstone bridge (and most other forms of transducers) have the E_1 term in the expression for output voltage. If this varies, so will the output voltage and that means the apparent reading of the parameter value will also vary. In the circuit of Fig. 12-7, we see an analog

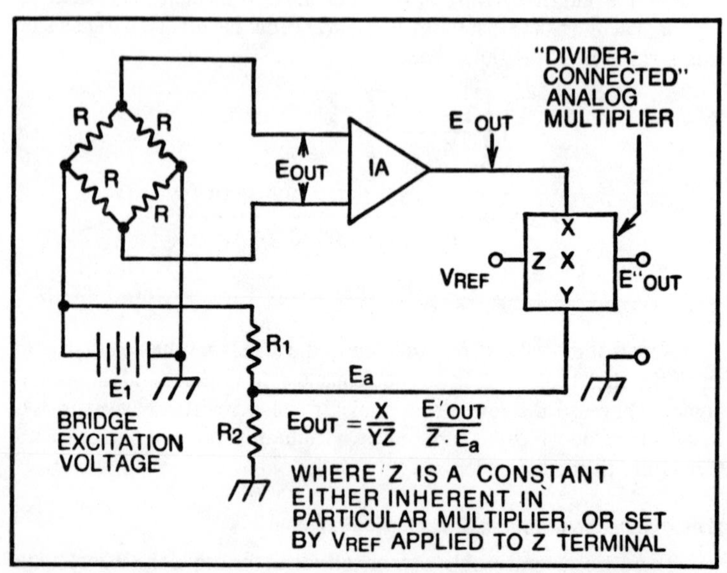

Fig. 12-7. Elimination of drift effects due to unstable bridge excitation voltage.

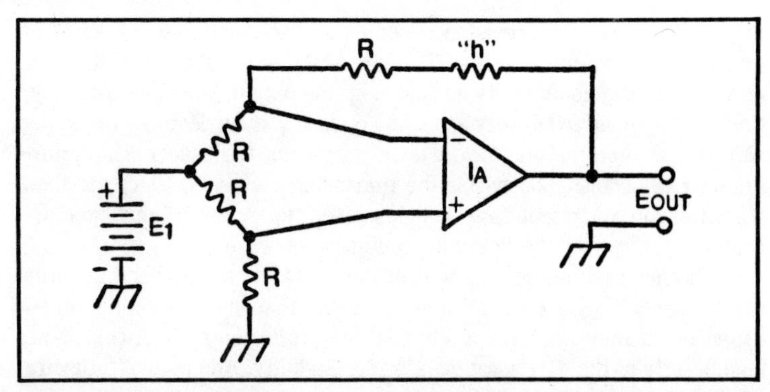

Fig. 12-8. Five-wire bridge circuit places active element of transducer in op amp feedback loop.

multiplier ratio-connected so that it divides the output voltage of the instrumentation amplifier by either the reference voltage (E_1), or a fractional sample of that voltage. The value of E_A will be equal to $E_1(R_2(R_1 + R_2))$. Whether or not the voltage divider is actually used may depend upon the particular design and what ranges of input voltage will make the multiplier/divider operate in the most accurate manner.

Unfortunately, reference voltage artifacts are not the only source of error in transducer applications. One of the problems is the fact that sometimes ΔR may vary in a nonlinear manner with respect to the change in the stimulus. Returning to our fluid pressure transducer of previous examples, we find that all is not so perfect in certain portions of the "safe" range. Typically, such transducers have a thin diaphragm connected to the variable resistance elements of the Wheatstone bridge. In most cases, the resistors are actually formed as part of the diaphragm so that they change their dimensions when a pressure perturbs the diaphragm surface.

Consider a case where 100T is applied to the diaphragm. A specified change in that pressure should produce a specified change in output voltage. Let us say that a 2T change in pressure should result in a 10 mV change in the output voltage. In certain portions of the range over which the transducer can safely operate without being destroyed, specifically the high and low extremes, such a 2T change might result in only a 7 or 8 mV change of output voltage. This results in a serious output error due to nonlinearity of the transducer. While there is little the user can do to overcome the causes of most nonlinearity in transducers, fortunately, at least a few of the effects can be corrected through application of a few little circuit tricks.

Others, though, may prove difficult or impossible to identify and eliminate. In fact, the total elimination of all problems from all portions of a transducers range may prove impossible. Trying to eliminate all errors in any particular transducer, all of those of a particular brand, will prove to have about the same frustration quotient as trying to skin an amoeba.

Figure 12-8 shows one method for linearizing the bridge circuit modified so that the variable resistance element is placed in the feedback loop of a high gain operational amplifier. This allows the action of the feedback loop to servo out the nonlinearity and clean up the output data. Unfortunately, this technique, although very appealing on first glance, develops problems almost immediately. One of these is the habit some transducer manufacturers have of permanently wiring the transducer elements, which are then placed inside an impregnable stainless steel fortress-like container! Of course, they opt for the four wire-configuration.

Another problem is a slow drift due to the extra connecting wires needed for a 5-wire configuration. It seems that the connecting wires, especially if they are over a few centimeters in length, can contribute significantly to the deterioration of bridge stability. Adding that fifth wire can only aggravate the problem.

This makes it just about imperative to install the operational amplifier circuit either inside or at least very close to the transducer assembly. The single saving grace of the five-wire circuit is that it allows the transducer to be used over a much wider than normal range of pressures. For most common bridge-type transducers, the total usable range covers those values for which $\Delta R/R$ is less than about 0.05, which isn't very much! Use of the five-wire technique and the operational amplifier allows widening the range to almost 2.

There are at least two more methods for ridding our signals of bridge errors. These are called the *implicit solution* method and the *inverse function* method. In some really accurate systems, both of these may be used. The implicit technique is illustrated in Fig. 12-9. Consider what terms make up E_{OUT} in the usual bridge circuit. In Fig. 12-6, we can see that in an ideal bridge the output will satisfy an expression of the form $X=Y$—clearly a linear expression. A real transducer, however, will actually have an output function similar to:

$$Y = \frac{XE_2}{1+X} \qquad (12\text{-}7)$$

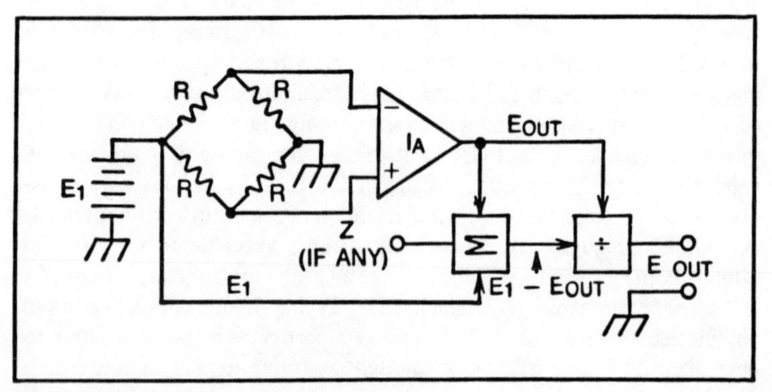

Fig. 12-9. Bridge linearization technique.

which can be shown to have, as an implicit solution:

$$XE_1 = Y + XY \tag{12-8}$$

or, as in a case such as Fig. 12-9;

$$E_{OUT} + XE_{OUT} = XE_1 \tag{12-9}$$

By algebraic manipulation:

$$\frac{E_{OUT}}{X} + E_{OUT} = E_1 \tag{12-10}$$

$$\frac{E_{OUT}}{X} = E_1 - E_{OUT} \tag{12-11}$$

$$\frac{X}{E_{OUT}} = \frac{1}{E_1 - E_{OUT}} \tag{12-12}$$

$$X = \frac{E_{OUT}}{E_1 - E_{OUT}} \tag{12-13}$$

The term in the denominator of Eqs. 12-12 and 12-13 is generated in the circuit of Fig. 12-9 by an operational amplifier connected as a subtractor. This is the special case of the summation amplifier introduced in an earlier chapter. With E_{OUT} applied to the minus input and voltage reference E_1 applied to the plus input, the subtractor will produce an output voltage equal to the $(E_1 - E_{OUT})$ term needed in the denominator of Eq. 12-13. The output voltage generated by the ratio connected analog multiplier is of the form ZA/B where Z is the division constant of the particular analog multiplier/divider selected. This may be either fixed or programmable. The actual output of a circuit such as Fig. 12-9 is:

$$ZX = \frac{E_{OUT}}{E_1 - E_{OUT}} \tag{12-14}$$

This solution works nicely for normal bridge circuits where errors are dominated by the $\Delta R/R$ term. In cases where the major error is due to actual nonlinearity of the ΔR term with respect to changes in the stimulus, it may be necessary to follow a circuit such as Fig. 12-9 with another circuit which takes the inverse of the erroneous function and sums it with the output voltage.

A perfectly linear transducer will produce an output of the form $Y = MX$, which graphs as a straight line through the origin. Real transducers, however, graph in a nonlinear fashion, producing an output voltage curve which resembles $F(X)$ in Fig. 12-10. In fact, this curve looks almost exactly like the curve of many pressure transducers in the lower 5-10 percent of their operational range. Function $F(X)$ can be linearized by summing it with its inverse, $F^{-1}(X)$, labeled $g(X)$ in Fig. 12-10. The summation of these two curves creates a third curve, $P(X)$. This new function is equal to $P(X) = F(X) + g(X)$.

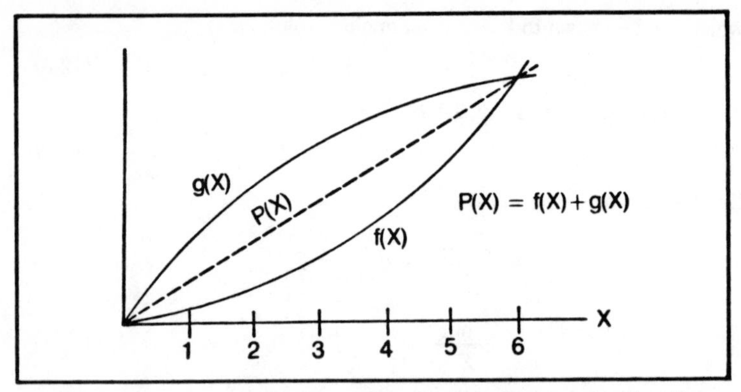

Fig. 12-10. Use of inverse function to linearize transducer's output function.

A system for implementing the linearization of *F(X)* is shown in Fig. 12-11. The nonlinear transducer signal is amplified by an instrumentation amplifier, and may also be processed in a stabilizing circuit (Fig. 12-9) to eliminate power supply drift components. The nonlinear output of the instrumentation amplifier is fed to both the summation circuit and to the inverse function generating circuit. The *g(X)* output of this circuit is then fed to the remaining summing input. The output of the summation amplifier will graph very close to the straight line defined by *P(X)*.

One method for generating the function *g(X)* is shown in Fig. 12-12. This linearization technique can be made accurate to within 0.1 percent, and has the advantage that linearization is almost totally continuous. The circuit works by parallel operation of a number of circuits called diode break-point generators. These circuits each generate small portions of the *g(X)* function from an *F(X)* input signal. A rough definition of a "breakpoint" is that it is a point on *X* where *F(X)* changes slope appreciably. Just what is meant by "appreciably" varies from one designer and application to another. The particular meaning for the circuit under consideration must be made by

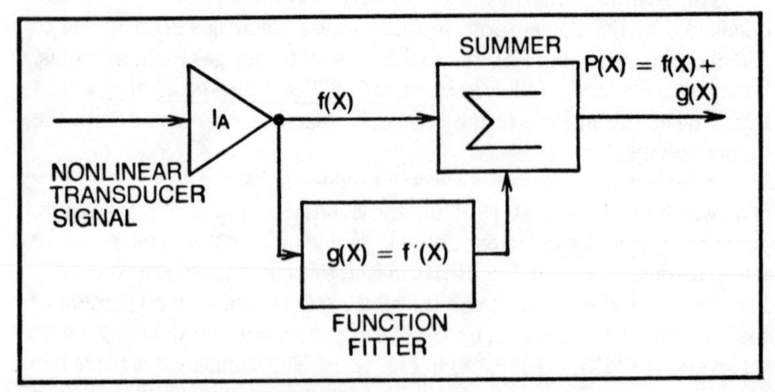

Fig. 12-11. Practical implementation of Fig. 12-10.

analyzing the situation. Lower error means less change of slope per break-point and this implies that more break points are needed if the function departs very much from a linear function. The amount of error which can be tolerated is a crucial decision in determining the number and placement of break points.

The circuit in Fig. 12-12 shows only four break points so that clarity is not sacrificed. Three factors determine where on $F(X)$ each break-point amplifier begins to operate: reference potential (V_{REF}) the values of resistors R_{AN} ($n = 1, 2, 3,...n$), and the nature of the current-voltage characteristic of the particular diodes selected. One amplifier, A_1, merely amplifies

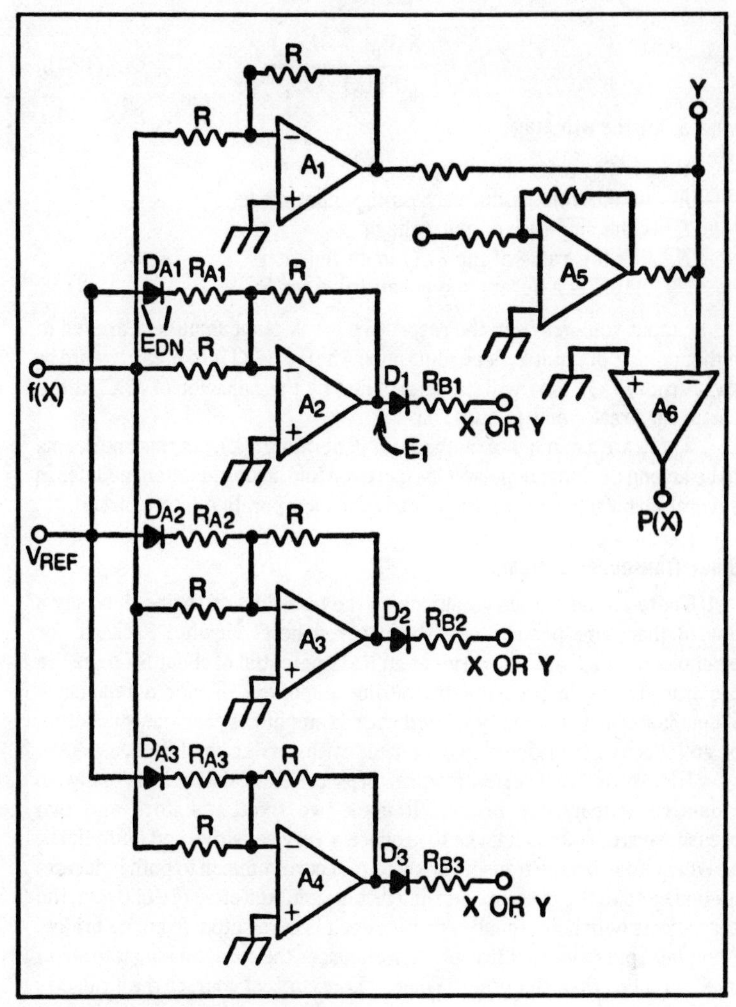

Fig. 12-12. Diode function generator.

$F(X)$ and needs no extra circuitry over and above that required for an ordinary inverting follower. In the other amplifiers, breakpoints are determined by exponential diode characteristics ($I = ME^{nV}$ where M and n are constants peculiar to the type of diode used).

From this relationship, we can determine experimentally the value of the highest voltage which will not cause appreciable current flow in the diodes. For most silicon devices, which are fully conductive at 600—700 mV, this value will lie somewhere between 200 and 350 mV. The output voltage of each amplifier, E_1, is selected so that it corresponds in value and slope to a particular breakpoint on $F(X)$. The value of the resistances required for each amplifier can be computed from:

$$R_A = \frac{R(V_{REF} - E_{DN})}{F_N(X) - E_1} \tag{12-15}$$

where, for the nth stage:

V_{REF} is the reference voltage
E_{DN} is the voltage drop across the input diode
E_1 is the amplifier output voltage
$F_N(X$ is the value of the $F(X)$ input function
10K is a decent and useful value for R.

Output voltages from the respective break-point amplifiers are fed to either point X or point Y, depending upon whether $g(X)$ is to break toward or away from $P(X)$. This will be determined by the behavior of $F(X)$ at the particular break-point in question.

There are a number of methods for generating $g(X)$, but this one seems to be among the most popular. One can even find analog function modules in several manufacturers' catalogs ready for incorporation into a circuit.

Other Transducer Systems

There are numerous variations on the transduction theme, but only a few of the more popular need be covered here. Hewlett-Packard, for example, uses a 2400 Hz carrier at an RMS potential of about 5V to excite the transducers in pressure measuring amplifiers. Either a resistance Wheatstone bridge of the type used with dc amplifiers previously covered, or an inductive transducer may be used with carrier amplifiers.

HP's own 1280-series medical pressure transducer is actually an inductive Wheatstone bridge. It uses two fixed resistors and two pressure-variable inductances to produce a very sensitive and quite linear ac Wheatstone bridge transducer system. A core common to both inductors is connected to the pressure sensing diaphragm. At a pressure of 0 torr, the core affects both coils equally and the result is zero output from the bridge. Applying a pressure to the diaphragm displaces the core, causing it to affect one coil more than the other. When this occurs, of course, the bridge is unbalanced and an output is generated.

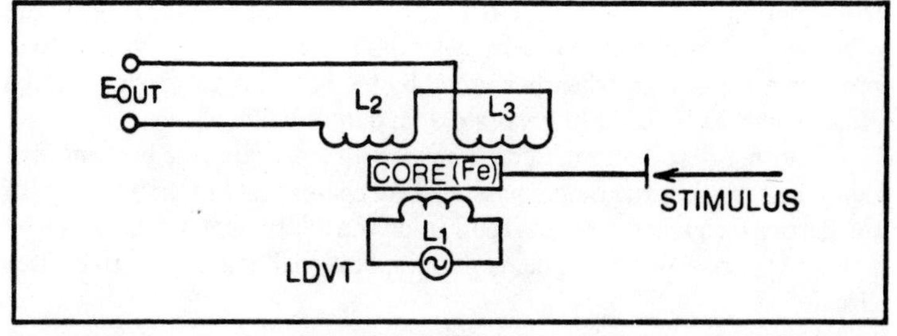

Fig. 12-13. Circuit of the *linear differential voltage transformer* (LDVT) type of transducer.

Another form of reactive transducer is one which uses two fixed resistors and a pair of variable capacitors in a similar arrangement. A rotor plate shaped like butterfly wings is equally common to both. When a perturbing influence rotates the plate, one capacitor will have a higher capacitance and the other has a lower. This results in the same sort of imbalance as in the inductive case. Still other types of transducers are found which use various other phenomena to generate an output voltage. Among these are the Hall effect and piezoelectric (crystal) types.

Figure 12-13 shows another form of inductive transducer which has proven itself: the linear differential voltage transformer (LDVT). When the common core is at rest, it equally affects both secondary coils L_2 and L_3. An ac carrier is needed to excite primary coil L_1. When both secondary coils have equal inductance, currents flowing in the load are equal but of opposite polarity and tend to cancel each other. Displacing the core causes one coil to have an increased inductance while the other takes on a decreased inductance. This causes the currents to be unequal, thereby causing less than total cancellation, and an output voltage results.

CARRIER AMPLIFIER SYSTEMS

Alternating signals can be used to excite a bridge in exactly the same manner as a dc voltage. The processing is then much like the dc version of the circuit if an RMS-to-dc converter is used following the instrument amplifier. The ac carrier systems, though, can offer the user much more than simple dc systems.

Besides the method just described, either envelope (amplitude) detection or phase detection schemes can be used to generate a dc output voltage, as required by the indicating and readout instruments.

In the envelope system, we depend upon the fact that a slightly unbalanced bridge will produce a steady carrier signal at the output of the instrumentation amplifier. Variations in the stimulus parameter will cause amplitude fluctuations in this signal. These fluctuations can be rectified and filtered (to remove any residual carrier) to produce a dc level which can be used to drive the readout instruments.

In the phase-sensitive system, a sample of the excitation carrier is fed to one port of a phase detector circuit, while the output voltage is fed to the other port. This circuit works because the reactances, usually inductive, produce a phase shift when perturbed by the stimulus parameter. Such a phase shift can be used to generate a dc output voltage.

In either case, some method is needed for restricting the bandwidth of the circuit to a narrow range, passing frequencies that are ±10 percent of the carrier frequency. For this application the instrument amplifier can be followed by one or more stages of an operational amplifier active filter circuit.

INTEGRATE-AND-HOLD CIRCUIT

There are a number of instrumentation applications where long time constants or other factors conspire to reduce the meaning of the output of the usual operational amplifier integrator circuit. The main culprit here is output droop due to minute discharge currents which tend to affect the integrator capacitor.

Figure 12-14 shows a circuit which will continuously integrate an input waveform and deliver the resultant to a peak-holding circuit. Amplifier A_1

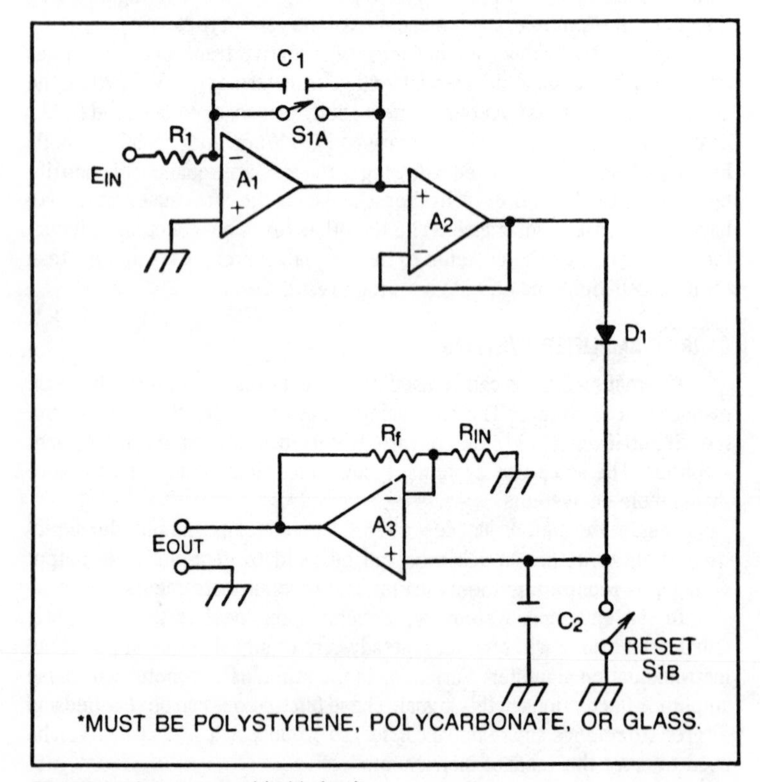

Fig. 12-14. Integrate-and-hold circuit.

operates as an integrator with a time constant R_1C_1. Amplifier A_2 is a unity-gain follower used to buffer the input of the peak-holding circuit. Capacitor C_2 is charged by the integrated signal, which is passed through amplifier A_2 and a diode. This capacitor will hold its value until discharged by reset switch S_{1B}. Amplifier A_3 isolates the capacitor from the low-impedance loads presented by devices which might be used to indicate the output level.

If no gain is required in this latter stage, R_F and R_{IN} are deleted and is connected as a unity-gain follower.

All three operational amplifiers in this circuit must be devices which have very high input impedances and very low input bias currents. Types featuring picoampere-level input bias currents should not be wasted in these circuits. Such quality operational amplifiers are needed in order to maintain the accuracy of integration and the integrity of the peak value of the charge across capacitor C_2.

High bias currents in amplifiers A_1 and A_2 will tend to discharge capacitor C_1, thereby disturbing the tracking accuracy of the integrator. If, on the other hand, amplifier A_3 has an excessive input current, peak-holding capacitor C_2 will be discharged, causing the very output droop symptom we are trying to avoid.

Although such currents appear tiny and can easily be neglected in short-time-constant applications, they tend to accumulate over long periods, and ruin accuracy if the circuit must hold its charge over hours or even minutes. Both capacitors C_1 and C_2 must be high-quality types for the very same reason: avoidance of output voltage droop. It is necessary to use a polystyrene, polycarbonate, or glass capacitor for either C_1 or C_2.

Diode D_1 must be custom selected from a batch of lower grade types, be purchased especially from a batch of lower grade types, or be purchased especially for its extremely low normal reverse leakage currents. Otherwise, the charge on capacitor C_2 will tend to leak off through the almost zero impedance of the output terminal of amplifier A_2.

Switches S_{1A} and S_{1B} will be ganged together in most cases, but can be separate if the peak reading is to be held for some period of time after the integration has stopped. Keeping the integrator shorted out may also be required if a noisy environment is anticipated. Noise components passing through the system can tend to affect the charge state of capacitor C_2. As in other forms of electronic integrators, this switch can be either a JFET electronic type, a set of relay contacts, a regular old-fashioned panel switch, or one of the new types of *analog switch* ICs. If one of the analog switches or a JFET switch is used, the specification should be checked for which indicates the resistance across the terminals in the off condition; otherwise another spurious discharge path may be added which can foul up the results. Proper attention to matters of quality component and amplifier selection should yield accuracies up to 0.3 percent.

Figure 12-15 shows the block diagram of a portable geiger counter which can be made using standard, low-cost operational amplifier circuitry.

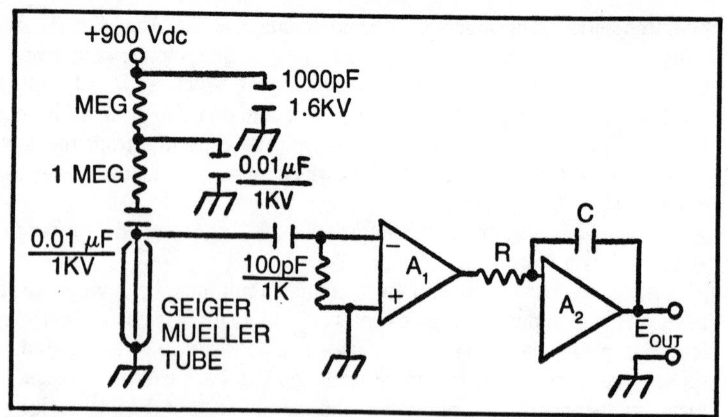

Fig. 12-15. Simple geiger counter.

The heart of the instrument is a sensor called a *Geiger-Mueller* tube. Such tubes will generate pulses in response to radiation. They can be purchased for relatively low cost from any of several amateur and professional electronic and scientific supply houses, and from certain electronic surplus dealers.

A high-voltage, low-current dc supply delivering 450—900V is needed to bias the G-M tube. In most portable instruments this potential is generated by an astable multivibrator driving a stepup transformer and a rectifier/filter network. When radioactive particles strike the G-M tube, they ionize a low-density gas on the inside of the tube chamber for a brief instant. This causes a sharp, sudden decrease in the resistance of the tube.

The voltage-divider action of the G-M tube's internal resistance and the power-supply impedance causes a sharp drop in the applied potential when this occurs. This is reflected through the coupling capacitor as a series of sharp pulses, with a repetition rate on the order of several hundred pulses per second. These are differentiated by a 1M resistor and a 100 pF capacitor before being applied to the input of some operational amplifier circuitry. The first stage can be either a Schmitt trigger or a monostable multivibrator.

In the case where the first stage is a Schmitt trigger, it will be necessary to follow this stage with an astable multivibrator. The purpose of the trigger, in that instance, is to "clean up" the pulses and make them into a series of nice rectangular pulses which can easily trigger a one-shot. The monostable multivibrator is used to generate one regular pulse of constant duration and amplitude for each pulse generated by the G-M tube.

Pulses from the monostable vary only in repetition rate. Because of this they can be integrated to provide a dc output which is proportional to the number of particles per second impinging on the G-M tube.

The meter is calibrated in pulses per unit of time (second or minute).

In fancier systems, one might want to feed the pulses to a digital counter and actually count the number per unit of time, of some submultiple, and then extrapolate. This does, however, result in some highly variable readings, because the count will change from one measuring period to another.

An experiment found in some freshman physics laboratories involves just such a scheme. When I performed the experiment, the 1-second counts varied from a low of 22 to a high of 68, using the same sample and apparatus over a period of only a few minutes.

Calibration of an instrument such as this can be done using the power-line ac as a 60 Hz frequency standard. Such a method will produce a reading of 60 pps, yet is easily generated using a filament transformer (to reduce voltage) and a half-wave rectifier. The pulses are then applied to the input of the differentiator network and the scale is calibrated.

A popular wrinkle in the design of such instruments is to add a loudspeaker at the output of the pulse amplifier to allow the user to hear the ticks as particles impinge on the tube and cause pulses.

PHOTOTACHOMETERS

This class of instrument measures the rotating speed of many types of machinery without need for any sort of mechanical coupling. The sensor is a phototransistor mounted in a suitable probe which can be aimed at the device under test. Most phototransistors are npn devices and are manufactured with a light-sensitive base region. The package of the transistor is, or contains, a clear plastic lens so that light from the outside world can be used to illuminate the base region.

Figure 12-16 shows a method for making a simple phototachometer using low-cost operational amplifiers and a low-cost phototransistor. The transistor can be purchased from any of several hobby electronic suppliers, or in quantity from professional suppliers. There are few bargains if top-grade semiconductors are offered (see the Motorola HEP line), but the

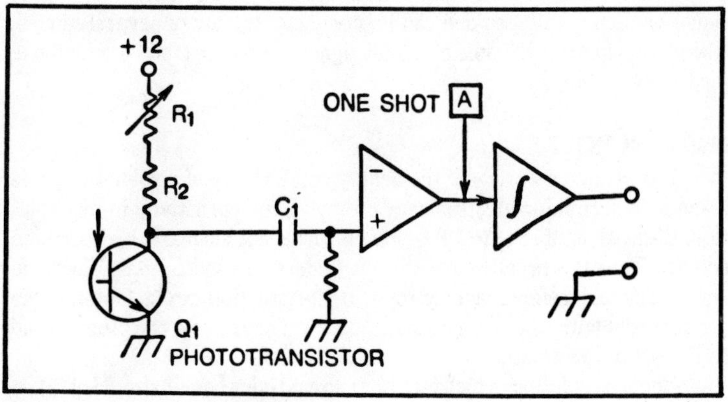

Fig. 12-16. Simple phototachometer.

price of buying in low quantities, singly packaged, is small compared with having to generate a 25—50 dollar minimum order to an industrial supply house.

When a sensor probe containing Q_1 is aimed at a rotating object, it picks up light pulses reflected from the object. These excite the base of Q_1 and generate pulses at the collector terminal. To prevent slow variations in ambient lighting conditions from affecting this circuit, it is necessary to differentiate the pulses in network R_3/C_1.

The output of the differentiator is used to trigger an operational amplifier multivibrator or Schmitt trigger in much the same manner as in the geiger counter of the previous section. The monostable multivibrator produces constant-amplitude, constant-duration pulses which can be integrated to produce a dc level proportional to the short-term average rotational speed.

Interestingly, in both the geiger counter and phototachometer, sufficient integration to generate a reasonably stable meter reading can be realized simply by placing a 5 to 25 μF capacitor across the meter movement. This technique, which is used in a variety of scientific and engineering instruments, relies upon the mechanical damping of the meter movement and the RC time constant of the capacitor and the resistance in the coil of the meter for integration.

If superior tracking and accuracy is required, an operational amplifier integrator using a high-quality capacitor is indicated. If the contrast between ambient and reflected light proves to be too low, the system can still be of use provided that it is possible to paint a light colored spot on some part of the rotating surface.

In a multiblade-fan arrangement, paint a dot on each blade and divide the reading by the number of blades. One popular hobby electronics periodical once published a circuit for an instrument such as this using an op amp Schmitt trigger feeding a 555 timer IC connected as a monostable multivibrator.

This IC, and its dual timer cousin, the 556, can be used over a wide range of supply voltages and can be connected in any of several modes. These facts make it valuable for the designer to become familiar with these inexpensive chips.

DIGITAL pH METER

The pH is a measure of the acidity or alkalinity of a solution, and is made by determining electronically the hydrogen ion activity in that solution. Each pH number (1 to 14) represents a decade change in hydrogen ion activity. The pH is usually measured by immersing a special glass electrode and a Calomel reference electrode in the solution being tested. This arrangement will generate a voltage output which is linear and proportional to the pH of the solution.

A neutral solution, which is neither an acid nor a base, has a pH of 7, and this corresponds to an output of zero. An acidic solution, on the other hand,

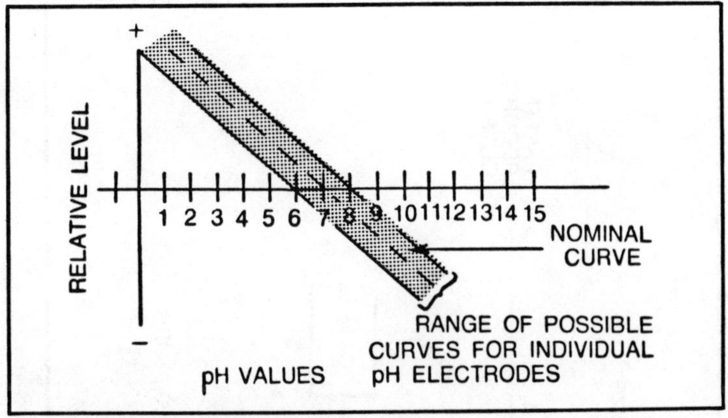

Fig. 12-17. pH electrode characteristic curve.

will have a lower pH number and generates a + output voltage. An alkaline (basic) solution has a higher pH and generates a minus voltage across the electrode pair.

The output voltage curve of a typical pH electrode is shown in Fig. 12-17. The dotted line represents the nominal or design curve, while the shaded region shows how far off a real electrode might be from the ideal.

The slope of the curve varies substantially with temperature and this must be taken into account when designing pH meter circuitry.

A single gain control will be used for both calibration of the instrument and temperature compensation (see Fig. 12-18). The basic design of any pH meter is pretty straightforward, as it is merely a high-impedance dc voltmeter capable of measuring in the millivolts range. The output indicator is calibrated in pH number from 1 to 14 on a linear scale.

If the voltmeter contains an inverting amplifier, so that the slope of the output voltage function increases with increasing pH, we can scale the output voltage of the instrument to read out directly in pH numbers on a digital voltmeter. A scale factor of 100 mV per pH number works out nicely. With this scale factor, the maximum pH number, about 14, will produce 1.4V. This figure fits nicely into the 0—2V range of the usual low-cost digital panel meter.

Since the slope of the electrode output function will vary from about 50 mV per pH unit to over 70 mV per pH unit as the temperature varies from 0°C to 100°C, we will require some means for changing the slope of the output function to compensate for this factor. That is the purpose of the gain control in the first stage of the circuit in Fig. 12-18. This control, labeled resistor R_9, is panel-mounted with a dial calibrated in temperature degrees.

The output voltage of most pH electrodes is reasonably linear over the range of interest (25°C ± 10°C) so we can feel free to calibrate the control at only two or three points, then interpolate the rest of the scale markings.

Resistor R_{14} is a summation current offset adjustment and is used here

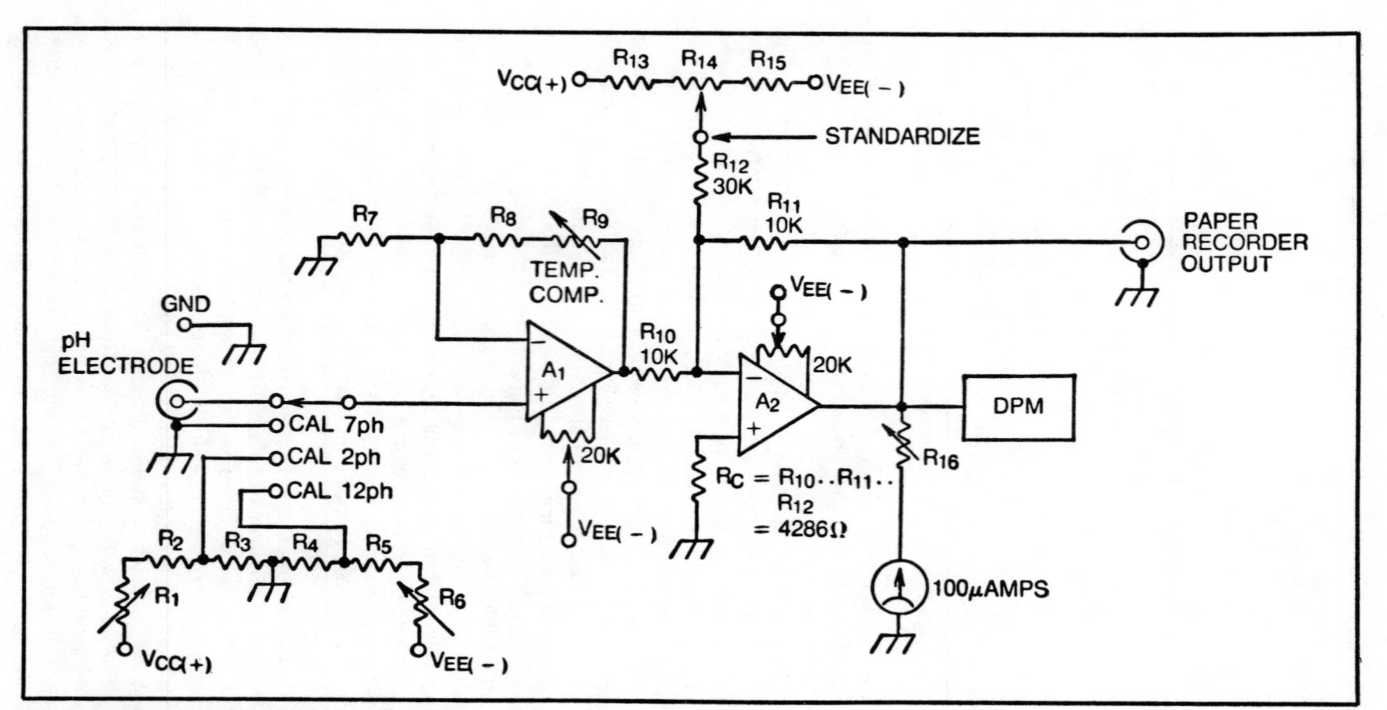

Fig. 12-18. Simple digital or analog pH meter.

as a standardization control. It should be capable of swinging the output voltage over the entire anticipated output range of ±1.40V. The operator uses this control to calibrate the instrument to specific pH values just before each use. Standard pH test solutions are used or the built-in calibration points can be used if a slight error can be tolerated and/or the standard solutions are either unavailable or suspected of being contaminated.

A function switch selects from four possible inputs to the voltmeter: the electrodes, a short to ground (calibrate position for pH 7), and two special calibrate points (one at pH 2 and the other at pH 12). These last two calibration points were selected because they generate equal, but opposite polarity output voltages in most standard electrodes made for pH testing. They are also reasonably nice points for making calibrations.

The choice of which operational amplifier to use in the two stages of the pH meter is determined by the accuracy and quality demanded of the instrument. For low-cost *student* grade instruments, a device from the 741 family for A_2 and a low-input-current FET for A_1 can be used. If a higher accuracy is demanded, however, A_1 must be a varactor bridge or chopper-stabilized device offering an input impedance of 10^{12} to $10^{14}\Omega$. This is necessary because most typical pH electrode pairs have impedances on the order of 10^8 to $10^{10}\Omega$. A low-impedance operational amplifier would tend to load the electrode, reducing the output voltage by a factor which can be calculated from the standard voltage-divider equation.

Chapter 13

IC Instrumentation Amplifiers

The three-op-amp instrumentation amplifier was introduced in a previous chapter. It is reintroduced here for review purposes. Some of the principal integrated circuit instrumentation amplifiers (ICIA) are little more than IC versions of that previous circuit.

The instrumentation amplifier has found extensive use because of several advantages. Principal among these are that high gain is possible (with only a few problems) and extremely high input impedance is the rule rather than the exception. As you can tell from Fig. 13-1, the input stages of the instrumentation amplifier are noninverting followers. The input impedance, therefore, is the input impedance of an operational amplifier. For low-cost, garbage-grade operational amplifiers the input impedance will be at least 500 kohms. For most it will exceed 1 megohms. Devices from the BiMOS, BiFET and some "super-beta" families offer much higher input impedance figures. RCA advertises their BiMOS series (i.e., CA-3140, CA-3160 etc.) as having an input impedance of 1.5 terraohms; that's 1.5×10^{12} ohms!

A requirement for extremely high input impedance exists wherever the "internal" or "source" impedance of the signal source is very high. In medicine, biology, chemistry, and physics applications there are many transducers and electrodes that have a high source impedance. A human electrocardiograph electrode will exhibit 10 kohms to 100 kohms under some conditions. Chemical pH or oxygen electrodes may have source impedance of 1 to 10 megohms.

Engineers often use a "10×" rule regarding input impedance. The input of an amplifier or display device should have an input impedance of at least *10 times* the source impedance of the device or electrode that provides the signal. If a glass 0_2 electrode has a 100 megohm impedance, then the

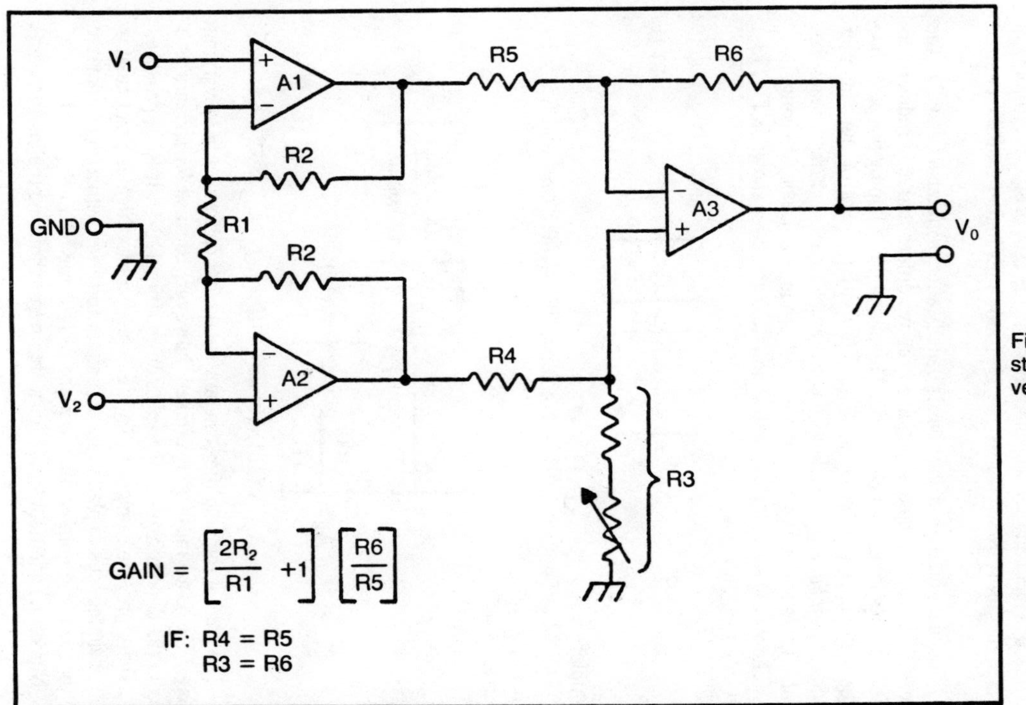

Fig. 13-1. Input stages of the instrumentation amplifier are noninverting followers.

minimum input impedance for the associated amplifier would be 10 × 100 megohms or 1000 megohms (10^9 ohms). In that case, a BiFET or BiMOS input operational amplifier or instrumentation amplifier is required.

The input of the instrumentation amplifier is *differential.* That means the output voltage is proportional to the differential gain of the amplifier and the *difference* between the voltages applied to the two inputs.

There are many situations where a differential IA is very desirable. In medical/biological applications, for example, we find it necessary to acquire minute (i.e., microvolt or millivolt) signals in the presence of high intensity interference fields. Most notorious of these fields is the ubiquitous 60 Hz fields generated by the ac power lines (touch an amplifier or oscilloscope input and see what happens!). In the case of electrocardiograph signals, the interference signal may be 1000 times higher than the desired signal!

Fortunately, interfering signals usually affect *both* inputs equally. The human ECG, for example, is acquired via two differential electrodes referenced against a common electrode. The signal picked up by the electrode wires will therefore be equal. The differential inputs of the amplifier produce *equal but opposite* affects on the output signal. This fact means that *equal* signals applied to both inputs will produce *zero* output change!

The voltage gain for the instrumentation amplifier shown in Fig. 13-1 is set by the following equation:

$$A_v = \left[\frac{2\,R_2}{R_1} + 1\right]\left[\frac{R_6}{R_5}\right] \qquad (13\text{-}1)$$

Example:

Let R2 = 50 kohms, R1 = 1 kohms, R6 = 100 kohms and R5 = 10 kohms

Solution:

$$A_v = \left[\frac{12\ (50\text{ kohms})}{(1\text{ kohms})} + 1\right]\left[\frac{(100\text{ kohms})}{10\text{ kohms}}\right]$$

$$A_v = \left[\frac{(100)}{(1)} + 1\right] \times (10)$$

$$(101)(10) = 1010$$

The gain of the amplifier can be varied most conveniently by varying resistor R1. Care must be exercised, however, because R1 appears as a term in the denominator of the transfer equation (13-1). If R1 approaches zero, therefore, the gain goes very high—perhaps too high. In practice, it is often advantageous to place a fixed resistor in series with a potentiometer and then use the combination in place of resistor R1 in Fig. 13-1.

Numerous additional amplifiers obtain from building the instrumentation amplifier in integrated circuit (IC) form. For one thing, drift is better controlled because all three operational amplifiers and all resistors share a common silicon substrate. Hence, all stages drift in the same manner and often cancel each other's effects. Drift is not zero, but it is reduced significantly over that of the discrete component IA design.

A second advantage is that of component density. An IA built from IC operational amplifiers and discrete resistors will require at least 2 to 3 square inches of printed circuit board. In IC form, however, the same amplifier might require less than 1 square inch!

Still another advantage is cost. While the unit cost of the single ICIA might be greater than the total unit cost of discrete components, the aggregate cost of the final product is often lower, design is simpler, assembly is easier, PC board layout is less involved, and the general overall hassle factor is reduced. The advantages of the ICIA are sufficiently interesting that these chips might someday eclipse (but not replace) the conventional IC operational amplifier.

The size advantages of the ICIA are not always of primary interest. In some cases, however, the size is of concern or it can make an existing product better. In the case of a transducer or electrode, in a noisy environment for example, it becomes possible to install an amplifier on or in the transducer. This method allows us to send a higher amplitude on or in the transducer. This method allows us to send a higher amplitude signal through the noisy environment to improve the signal-to-noise ratio. In one example, a pressure transducer had a built-in ×100 ICIA so it could produce an output signal of 100 mV to 1 Volt instead of 100 to 1000 microvolts. Obviously, if you expect to pick up 10 mV of noise from the 60 Hz power lines (a function of line length), you are better off to send a 1000 mV signal than a 100 μV signal. The result is a lot higher SNR: 1000/1 instead of 1/10!

In the section to follow, we will examine two basic commercial ICIA devices: Burr-Brown's INA-101 and the National Semiconductor LM-363 series (four versions of two basic LM-363-family items). Following our discussion of these products will be examples. Some of them may parallel Chapter nine circuits. Other projects will be instrumentation applications useful to physical and life sciences, enthusiasts engineers, technicians, hobbyists, and other users of electronic circuits.

COMMERCIAL ICIA DEVICES

The typical ICIA device will contain a circuit similar to the one shown in Fig. 13-1. An exception is that "R1" will be external (and will probably be labelled "R_g" or something similar) to the IC package. This external resistor is designated R_g, and the pins it connects to are "gain set" pins.

Other ICIA devices might use a different circuit that provides similar results. Therefore, R_g might have a somewhat different function in that circuit.

Typical gain equations for ICIA devices will be of the form:

$$A_v = \frac{50\text{kohms}}{R_g} + 1$$

Which, in the case of circuits such as shown in Fig. 13-1, means that R2 is 25 kohms, and that R3 = R4 = R5 and R6.

We can rearrange such a transfer equation to find a value of R_g to achieve a desired voltage gain. After all, it is usually the *gain* that we know, not the resistor value. The equation is:

$$R_g = \frac{50 \text{ kohms}}{A_v - 1}$$

Example:

Design an amplifier using an ICIA to produce a gain of 100.

Solution:

R_g = (50 kohms)/(A_v − 1)
R_g = (50 kohms)/(100−1)
R_g = 50 kohms/99 = 0.51 kohms = 510 ohms

The design of the amplifier is obviously a lot easier with this equation!

The ICIA may come in any of several packages. There are several examples in 8- or 10-pin round metal cans that are similar, but not identical, to the T0-5 transistor case. There are also 8-, 14-, and 16-pin dual inline package (DIP) devices around. In a few cases, there are also hybrid instrumentation amplifiers that are sufficiently like ICIA devices to be considered with the ICIAs. Even though they are very much larger, they are essentially the same devices.

The National Semiconductor LM-363 device is actually a family of related devices in round metal cans or 16-pin DIPs. The three devices in metal cans are fixed-gain models. The three editions are:

Model	*Gain*
LM-363-10	×10
LM-363-100	×100
LM-363-500	×500

The purpose of these devices is to provide fixed, standard gains in small packages. The gains selected (×10, ×100, and ×500) are among the most commonly encountered in actual practice. Consider an example where a fixed gain LM-363 device might be used. Recall earlier that we discussed a low-output level transducer in a noisy environment. The idea was to place an ×10 or ×100 amplifier at the transducer in order to improve the signal-to-noise ratio. The LM-363-10 and LM-363-100 devices offer the opportunity to perform this function with minimum parts count. In the late seventies, I built such a transducer amplifier around 741-family operational amplifiers and it required several outboard resistors and a potentiometer (see TAB book No. 1012, *How to Design and Build Electronic Instrumentation*). That ×10 amplifier had to be built in a 1½-by-2¼ inch Pomona die-cast aluminum box mounted on a Grass FT-3 transducer. That gain-of-10 preamplifier can now be built inside of the *ITT-Cannon* connector used by the Grass transducer. The solution might be an LM-363-10 in the connector.

Figure 13-2 shows the LM-363-X device. The device is in an 8-pin metal can and it has an open-loop voltage gain of 10,000,000 so it will very nearly approximate the behavior of an ideal operational amplifier as found in textbooks. The LM-363-X had a gain-bandwidth product of 30 megahertz.

Pin no. 8 of the LM-363-X is used for frequency compensation, so the values of *R* and *C* are determined by your design bandwidth requirements. Direct current power is applied to pins nos. 1 and 4 of the LM-363-X such that V+ is applied to pin no. 1 and V− is applied to pin no. 4.

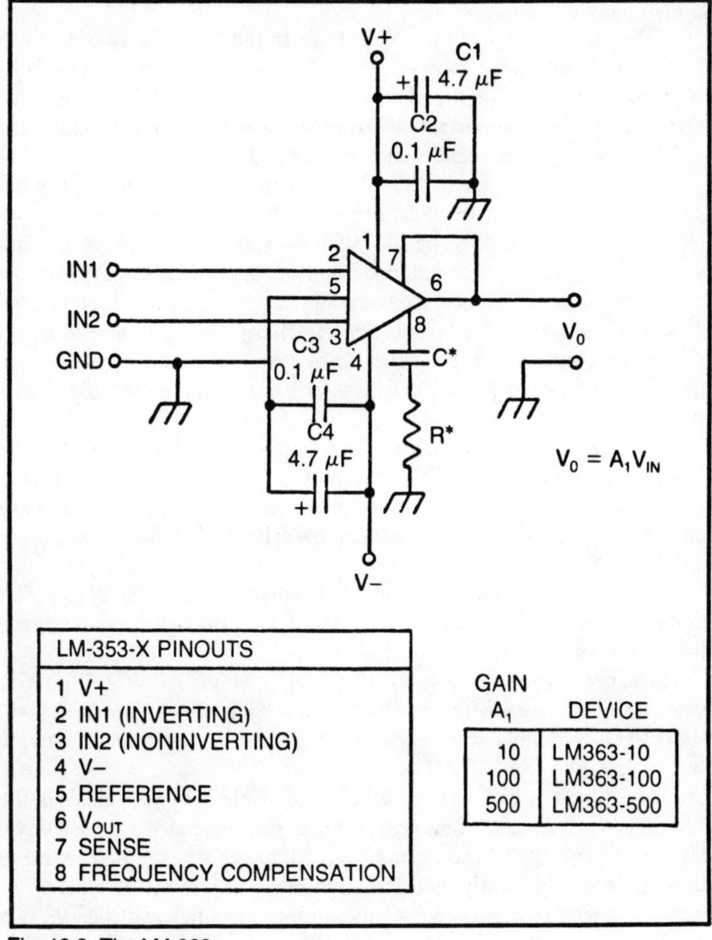

GAIN A_1	DEVICE
10	LM363-10
100	LM363-100
500	LM363-500

Fig. 13-2. The LM-363.

The decoupling capacitors that are attached to these pins are needed, as in regular operational amplifiers, to prevent oscillation or instability of the amplifier in a practical circuit. Two capacitors are used on each power supply line because of the high bandwidth of the amplifier. The 4.7 μF capacitors are used for lower frequencies. These capacitors are usually tantalum electrolytics so they are polarity sensitive. The 0.1 μF units are intended to de-couple high frequency signals. They should be disc ceramics or their equivalent. The reason for using both types of capacitors is that the high-value tantanlum capacitors will not work too well at high frequencies and the disc ceramic has a value too low to handle low frequencies.

The capacitors used for decoupling must be mounted as close as possible to the body of the LM-363-X. Otherwise, oscillation may occur despite the capacitors. The mounting of the 0.1 μF disc ceramic capacitors is especially crucial.

The other version of the LM-363 is a 16-pin DIP (Fig. 13-3) that will provide step-selectable gains of ×10, ×100, or ×1000. The gain is set by shorting specific pins (2, 3, and 4). To obtain a gain of ×10, for example, all three pins are left open circuited. To obtain a gain of ×100, short pins 3 and 4. To obtain a gain of ×1000, short pins 2 and 4.

The 16-pin version of the LM-363 has a number of features not available on the 8-pin fixed-gain models. There are, for example, two frequency compensation terminals rather than just one. There are also two voltage offset pins as opposed to zero on the 8-pin versions. Perhaps the most significant difference for some applications is the "+shield" and "−shield" pins (9 and 8, respectively). These pins are used to easily implement guard shield techniques to overcome degradation of common mode rejection ratio (CMRR) and loss of bandwidth due to cable capacitances.

The LM-363 will operate with dc voltages from ± 5 volts dc to ± 18 volts dc. The "raw" CMRR is 130 dB and the bias current is two nanoamperes. The 7 nV/(HZ)$^{1/2}$ noise figure makes the LM-363 applicable as a low noise amplifier. If you also require very low drift, the LM-363 is available in a 0.5 μV/°C version.

Figure 13-3 shows the circuit for a "universal" differential amplifier that provides variable gains of 0 to 10, 0 to 100, or 0 to 1000 depending upon the setting of switch *S1*.

The heart of the circuit is the 16-pin DIP LM-363-AD, *IC1*. This IC is connected such that switch *S1* will either leave pins 2, 3, and 4 open or will short the gain pin (no. 4) to either ×100 (pin no. 2) or ×1000 (pin no. 3) terminals of the LM-363-AD.

The circuit of Fig. 13-3 uses the guard shield driver terminals of the LM-363-AD. Their use is optional, but *highly* recommended when low-level signals are anticipated (i.e., gain of ×1000, most commonly). The use of these pins should greatly increase the performance of the amplifier.

The second stage is essentially a utility amplifier and consists of a single operational amplifier connected in the inverting follower configura-

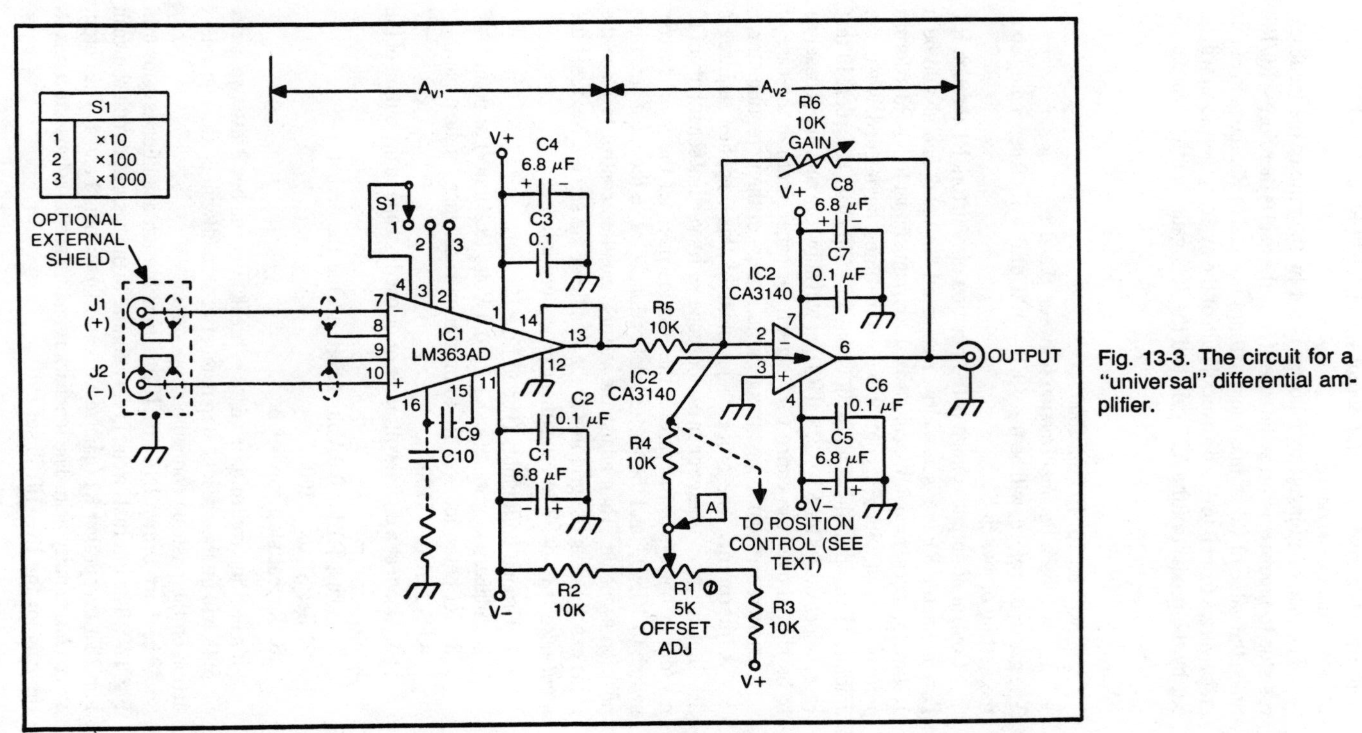

Fig. 13-3. The circuit for a "universal" differential amplifier.

tion. Since *IC2* inverts the *IC1* output signal, the "(+)" and "(−)" labelling of inputs must be *reversed.*

The gain of an inverting follower is set by the ratio of the feedback-resistor-to-input-resistor. In the case of *IC2,* the gain is therefore −R6/R5. Since the value of R6 (at maximum setting) is equal to R5, the gain of this stage varies from 0 to 1. The overall gain of the system, therefore, will be set by the product of the *IC1* gain and the *IC2* gain. In other words:

$$A_v = A_{V1} \times A_{V2}$$

Where:

A_{V1} will be 10, 100, or 1000

A_{V2} will be a decimal fraction between 0 and 1

The gains, therefore, will be 0 – 10, 0 – 100, or 0 – 1000 depending upon the setting of switch S1.

Control of output voltage is the function of resistors R1 through R3. Potentiometer R1 is a screw-driver adjusted "trimpot" and should be a 10-turn (or more) model. We can also use a circuit similar to R1-R3 to form a *position* control. Such a control will sometimes be needed when the amplifier is used to drive an oscilloscope or strip-chart recorder. In that case, select values for R1, R2, and R3 that will allow the zero-input baseline to be shifted over the entire CRT screen (or paper width in the case of strip-chart recorders) using all but the full range of the potentiometer.

Adjustment. The proper adjustment of this amplifier requires a 3½-digit digital voltmeter or an oscilloscope with a vertical sensitivity of 10 mV/div or better. In the case of the oscilloscope, set the *input selector* switch to "GND," and the vertical deflection factor to the most sensitive position available. Then adjust the vertical position control to place the trace exactly over the grid line in the middle of the screen. Next, set the *input selector* to dc. The adjustment procedure follows:

1. Ground both inputs (J1 and J2).
2. Adjust potentiometer R1 for 0.0 Volts (± 10 mV) at point "A."
3. Set potentiometer R6 to maximum resistance (highest gain).
4. Set S1 to "X100."

4. Connect a digital voltmeter or dc oscilloscope to the output of the amplifier.

6. Adjust R1 for 0.0 Volts (± 10 mV) at the output.
7. Set S1 to "X1000."
8. Repeat step number 6.

If a position control is used, then break step number 2 into two parts. Step 2A will be the present step number 2; step 2B will be the equivalent action on the position control potentiometer.

The Burr-Brown INA-101 IC instrumentation amplifier is shown in Fig. 13-4. The internal circuit is very similar to the basic IA circuit shown in Fig. 13-1 except that R1 (gain set) is external via pins 1 and 4. The output stage (A3) is unity gain. The feedback resistors are 20 kohms. As a result, the gain for the INA-101 is set by:

$$A_v = \frac{40 \text{ kohms}}{R_g} + 1$$

Where:

R_g is the external resistor (in kohms)

The INA-101 device is a low-noise (13 nV/(Hz)½ at 10 kHz) amplifier that sports a minimum 60 Hz CMRR of 106 dB and a 10^{10} ohm input impedance (that's *10 billion ohms!*). The drift specification is 25 μV/°C.

The INA-101 will operate over a range of dc power supplies of ± 5 volts to ± 20 volts, with ± 15 volts being the intended operating potentials. The current packaging for the INA-101 is the 10-pin metal can that is usually described as "similar to T0-5."

A representative circuit using the INA-101 is shown in Fig. 13-5. This circuit can be used in a wide variety of applications that require a differential amplifier. This is especially true where an extremely high input impedance and small size are desired. The adjustment of offset potential is similar to that given above for Fig. 13-3:

1. Set R1 to approximately the middle of its range.
2. Short together the three input terminals: (+), (−) and COM.
3. Connect a 3½-digit digital voltmeter to the output terminal.
4. Adjust potentiometer R1 for 0.0 volts (± 10 mV) at the output.
5. Disconnect the input shorts and the voltmeter.
6. The amplifier is now ready for use.

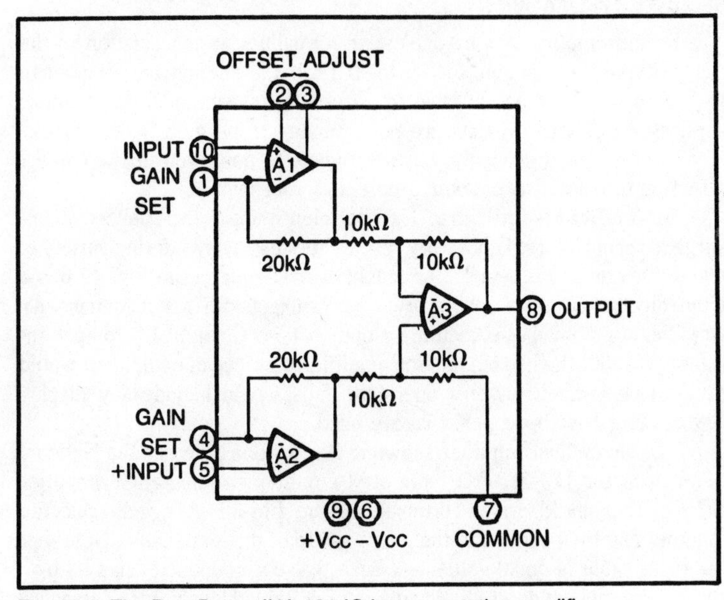

Fig. 13-4. The Burr-Brown INA-101 IC instrumentation amplifier.

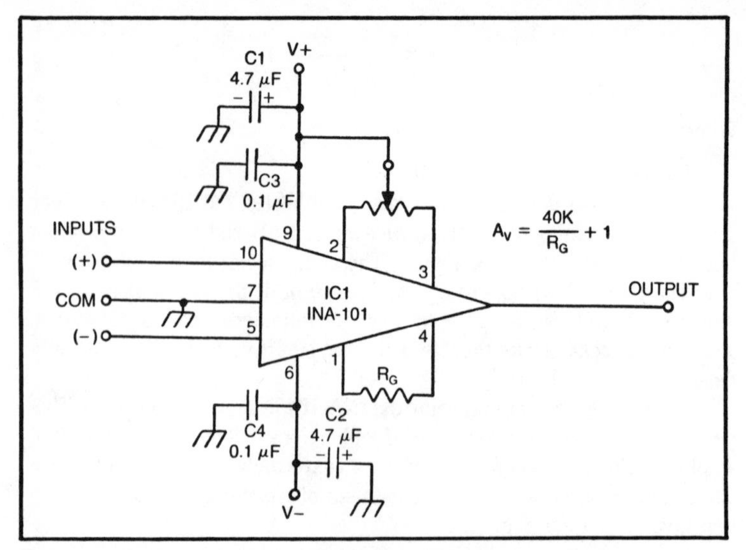

Fig. 13-5. A representative circuit using the INA-101.

The cost of ICIA devices might seem high when compared with IC operational amplifiers, but the cost difference tends to diminish in light of performance improvements and convenience.

SELECTED APPLICATIONS

Specific applications are one means for gaining an appreciation for the capabilities of a component such as the ICIA. In this section, we are going to look at a small collection (two or three) IC instrumentation amplifier applications. These projects are not intended to be merely "cookbook" ideas to be copied slavishly, but seed ideas to point you in the correct direction to a solution of some problem of your own.

Biomedical Amplifiers. The life sciences have experienced an upsurge in recent years. Laboratory researchers use a bewildering variety of electronic equipment—including amplifiers. The project in Fig. 13-6 is a biomedical amplifier for laboratory use on subjects other than humans. An amplifier for human use requires isolation (see Chapter 14) for patient safety. Without the use of isolation amplifiers, a piece of equipment would have to be entirely battery operated. This would include any display devices (e.g., oscilloscopes) that are used.

The biomedical amplifier shown in Fig. 13-6 is based on the National Semiconductor LM-363-AD integrated circuit instrumentation amplifier (ICIA). The shield driver terminals of the LM-363-AD are connected together and then applied to the guard shield of the input cable. Note that the input cable is double-shielded, such that each conductor has its own shield, and then an outer shield covers both individual shields. The guard

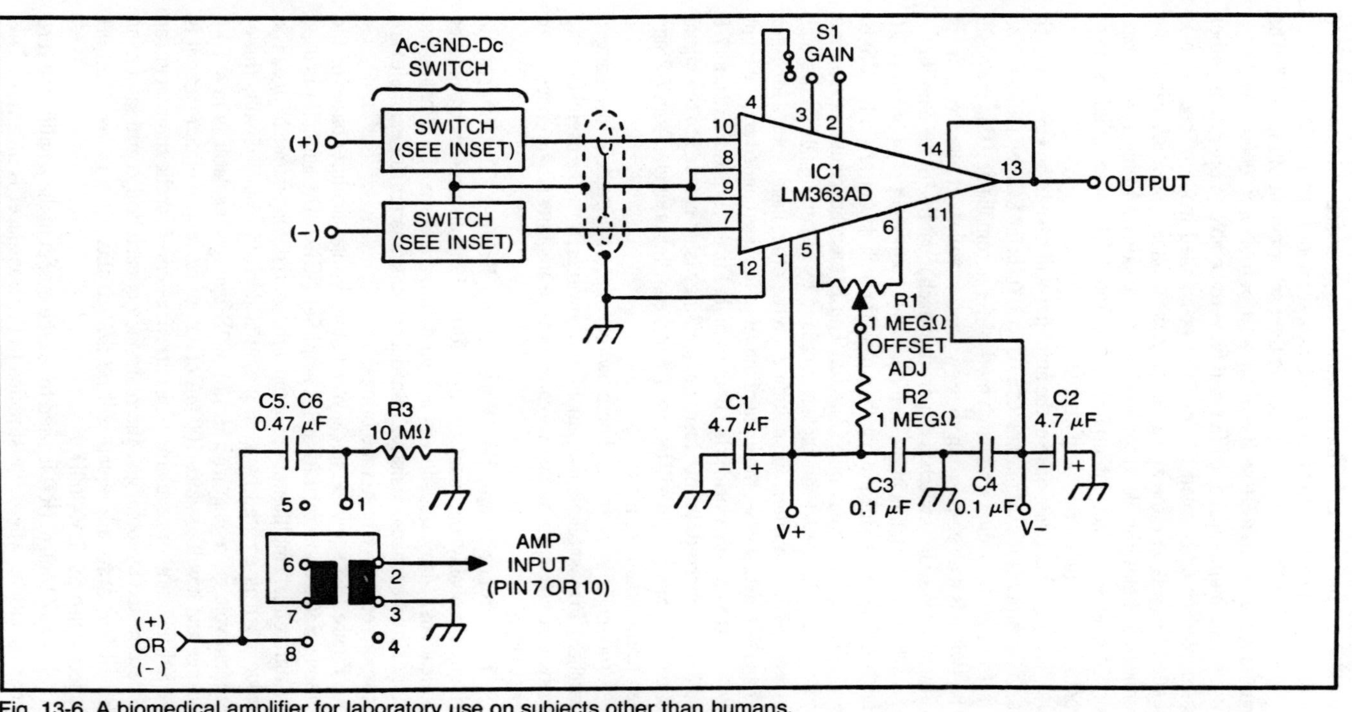

Fig. 13-6. A biomedical amplifier for laboratory use on subjects other than humans.

shield is the *inner* shield. The outer shield is grounded and also connected to the reference terminal (used here as a common) of the LM-363-AD.

Note that this circuit is based on the earlier circuit of Fig. 13-3. The gain is set by switch S1 so it will be ×10, ×100, or ×1000.

A true biomedical amplifier will have to be able to operate in either ac-coupled or dc-coupled modes. The ac-coupled mode of operation is needed to overcome the small direct current offset potentials caused by connecting a metallic electrode to electrolytic skins, forming a small "battery" from the contact potential thus generated. The ac-coupled mode of operation will block this dc potential.

The frequency response of the amplifier will have to be very low such as on the order (for example) of 0.05 Hz to 100 Hz for ECG amplifiers. The inset in Fig. 13-6 shows a switch method for accomplishing this purpose. The switch is a three-position slide switch that will short together pairs of terminals. One such switch is required on each input line of the amplifier.

When the switch is in the first position, it will short together pins 5-6 and 1-2. The input signal must then pass through capacitor C5 (or C6) to reach the amplifier input pins (7 or 10). The 10 megohm resistors are used to drain any charge on the capacitor caused by either signals or the bias currents of the amplifier. In position 2, on the other hand, shorts together 6-7 and 2-3. In that case, the input of the amplifier is grounded and the input line from the outside world is left floating high. Finally, in position 3 pins 7-8 and 3-4 are shorted. In that case, the amplifier is dc-coupled to the signal source. The signal path will be pins 7-8 of the switch, a jumper from 7-2, and then to the amplifier input.

You might want to build both switches into one control (use ganged switches). In most biomedical amplifiers, however, it will be useful to make the switches separate so that we can make the amplifier single ended when necessary.

Transducer Amplifier (Wheatstone Bridge). The Wheatstone bridge is probably the most common form of circuit used in transducer applications. Many transducers are built into the form of a Wheatstone bridge. In other cases, resistive transducers (thermistors, for example) are incorporated into Wheatstone bridges.

Figure 13-7 shows a typical Wheatstone bridge amplifier based on the National Semiconductor LM-363-X amplifier (ICIA). The amplifier is used as a differential amplifier at the output arms of the Wheatstone bridge. The bridge itself is excited by a dc potential derived from a 5-volt, three-terminal voltage regulator. The LM-309H voltage regulator is in a T0-5 package and it will produce 100 mA of output current. If higher current is needed, use another regulator. The current required for the transducer can be determined by looking at the resistance of each bridge arm (assuming that all four arms are equal) will be $5/R$. If this value is less than 0.1 amperes, use the LM-309H.

The null control (R1) is used to set the output of the amplifier to zero under conditions where the stimulus to the transducer is also zero. This

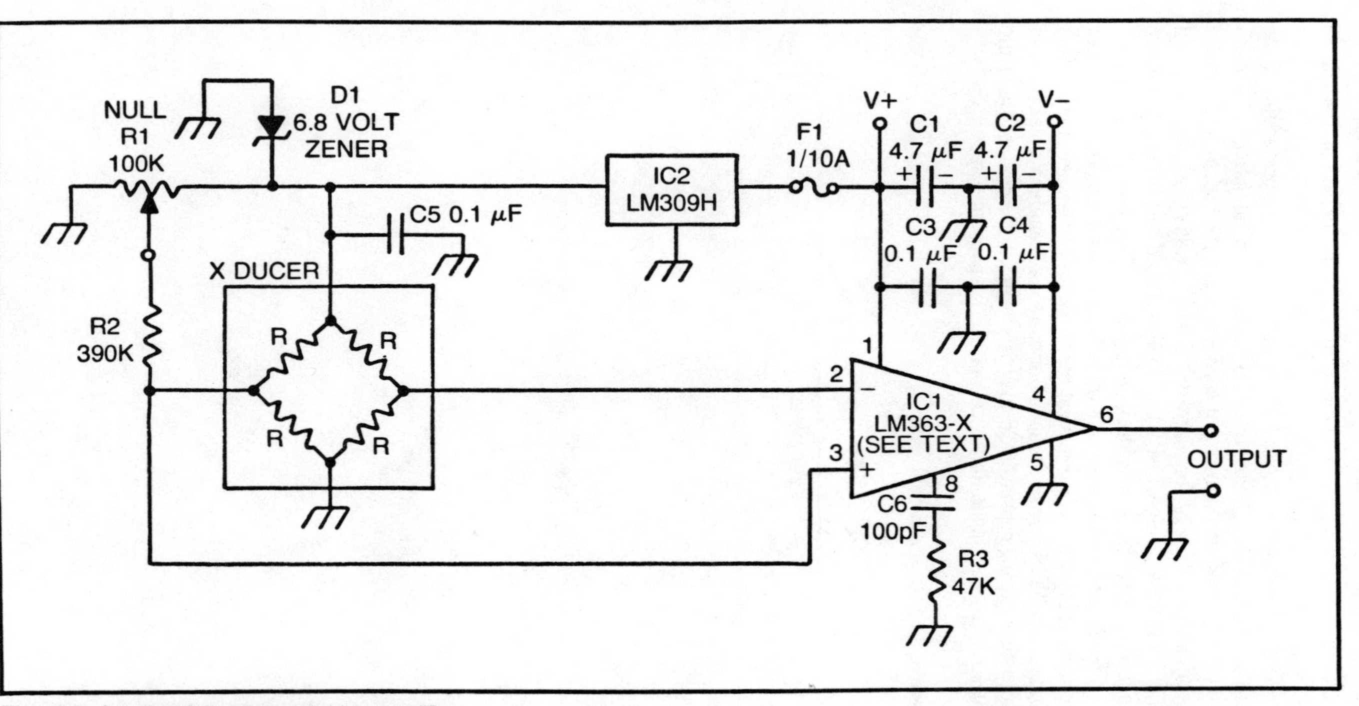

Fig. 13-7. A typical Wheatstone bridge amplifier.

control is not used so much to eliminate amplifier offsets as transducer offsets.

The 6.8 volt zener diode (D1) is used strictly for protection of the transducer. Most Wheatstone bridge transducers are sensitive to the excitation voltage and will burn out if connected to a too high voltage. If IC2 shorts out, placing +12 (or more) volts on the transducer, then D1 will conduct and thereby blow fuse F1. This fuse should be 1/10 or 1/5 ampere unless a low resistance transducer is used.

The frequency response of a transducer is low compared with other electronic applications. The typical response for transducer amplifiers is 100 Hz or so. We can make the amplifier more stable under a wider range of conditions by using capacitor C6 and resistor R3 in the circuit. Tailor the values of these components to produce the response needed.

Chapter 14

Isolation Amplifiers

An isolation amplifier is one in which the impedance between the inputs and both the output and the power supply terminals is maximized. A typical isolation amplifier symbol is shown in Fig. 14-1. Note that the input side of the amplifier has its own dc power supply terminals, separate from the main power supply terminals. This *isolated* power supply is isolated from the ac power lines by a very high impedance (10^{12} ohms in many models). Thus the isolated power supplies tend to be batteries or they are derived from a ultrasonic oscillator.

There are numerous applications for the isolation amplifier. In certain applications, the signal source can be derived from a high voltage circuit that could possibly (perhaps easily) damage the electronic circuitry. That type of application features a signal-source environment that is incompatible with the health and well-being of the electronic instrumentation circuit.

Medical electronic instrumentation applications have a similar need, but for the opposite reason: the signal-source (you, if you are a hospital patient) is incompatible with the possibly dangerous electronic circuit environment. See *Servicing Medical & Bioelectronic Equipment,* TAB book No. 930, and *Introduction to Biomedical Equipment Technology,* John Wiley & Sons. It is believed that hospital patients who do not have intact skin can be killed by 60 Hz currents in low microampere range (i.e., under 100 μA). In certain laboratory experiments performed on dogs, 60 Hz currents as low as 20 μA, introduced directly into the heart, proved fatal. As a result of that experiment, clinical engineers set the standard chassis-to-ground leakage current at a maximum of 10 microamperes.

Certain electronic instruments used in medicine have a potential for introducing current into a patient's body. Obviously, the electrocardiograph (ECG), which displays the heart's electrical waveforms, and the elec-

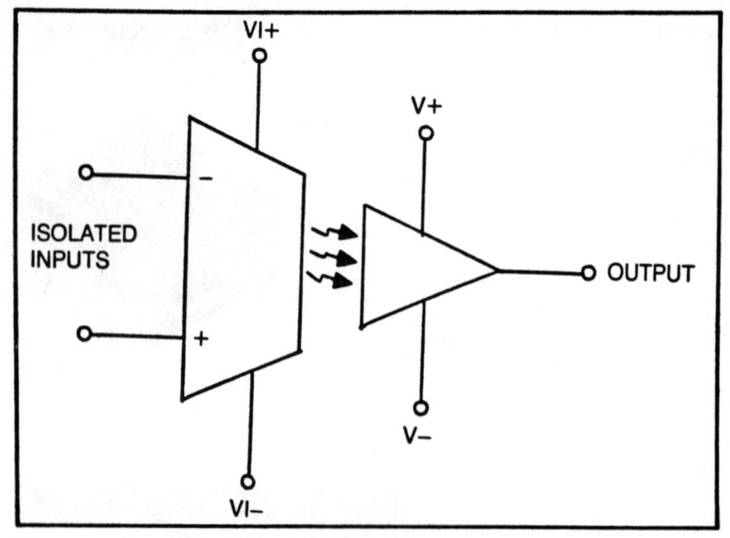

Fig. 14-1. A typical isolation amplifier circuit.

troencephalograph (EEG), which displays the brain's electrical waveforms, are potential current sources. The electrodes from the inputs of these instruments represent a low impedance path (i.e., under 10 kohms) to the patient's body. If the EEG or ECG common electrode is grounded to the same point as the ac power line ground (or neutral), then an open-circuited chassis-ground wire can have serious consequences for the patient. The isolation amplifier solves that problem and protects the patient.

Another hospital instrument with a potential for electrical harm is the cardiac output computer. This instrument measures the amount of blood pumped from the heart in unit time (liters per minute). The measurement technique involves threading a special multilumen, thermistor-tipped, catheter through the patient's veins into the right side of the heart. The catheter tip is passed, via the blood vessels, into the *vena cava* (large vein entering the right atrium of the heart), through the right atrium and right ventricle of the heart until the thermistor tip rests in the pulmonary artery.

In this position the thermistor is able to measure the temperature of the blood as it exits the right side of the heart on its way to the lungs. There is an exit port from one of the catheter lumens that will rest just outside of the right atrium (i.e., in the vena cava, at the input side of the heart). The doctor making the measurement will inject into this lumen a fixed amount of iced or room temperature saline solution (usually 5 or 10 milliliters). The iced saline mixes with the blood going into the right atrium and thereby lowers the local blood temperature a small amount. By looking at the temperature change at the output of the heart, we can calculate cardiac output. The computer integrates the temperature curve and plugs it into an equation that yields cardiac output.

The thermistor tip must be electrically isolated from the ac power lines or the patient will be at risk of electrocution. In most cases, the thermistor will be part of a Wheatstone bridge circuit that uses a differential amplifier to boost the output to a usable level. For purposes of patient safety, the bridge excitation voltage and amplifier inputs must be isolated. For this application, an isolation amplifier is indicated.

Medical applications sometimes require special models of isolation amplifier that have high voltage-protected inputs. A medical machine called a *defibrillator* is used to correct certain potentially fatal heart arrhythmias. The defibrillator dumps a capacitor charge into the patient's body. This charge can reach several thousand volts for 5 to 15 milliseconds. As a result, it is necessary to specify isolation amplifiers that have protected input circuitry that will withstand those short, but often repeated, bursts of high voltage.

TRANSFORMER COUPLING

There are several methods used to implement isolation amplifier techniques, but all can be classified as either *transformer-coupled* or *optically-coupled.*

The transformer-coupled version uses an external ultrasonic oscillator (20 kHz to 500 kHz) to provide power to the isolated input amplifier stages and to provide a *carrier signal* to a modulator stage. A simplified block diagram of such an isolation amplifier is shown in Fig. 14-2.

The power transformer (T1) and the signal transformer (T2) are designed to operate at high "ultrasonic" frequencies, in this case 200 kHz. They are specially designed to be extremely efficient at 60 hertz while remaining very efficient at 200 kilohertz. These transformers will not pass either 60 Hz leakage currents from the ac power mains or 120 Hz ripple signals from the dc power supply rectifiers. The inability of the transformers to pass 60 to 120 Hz signals is the reason why the amplifier provided such high isolation from the power mains.

The isolated preamplifier stage (A1) derives its power (VI– and VI+) from the 200 kHz ac signal. This signal is rectified and filtered to provide a few milliamperes of current at some potential between ± 5 volts and ± 15 volts. Because of the low current levels required by the preamplifier, it is often the case that silicon or germanium signal diodes are used for rectification. Because of the high frequencies involved in this circuit, ripple filtering is a lot easier than it is at 60 Hz. The filtering function can be accomplished with 0.01 to 0.1 microfarad capacitors instead of 100 μF typically used at power line frequencies. Of course, lower capacitor values imply small physical size.

The "ground," or common, terminal for the isolated stage is separate from the main ground. Under no circumstances should the isolated ground be a chassis ground.

The 200 kHz is also used as a *carrier* that is amplitude modulated (AM)

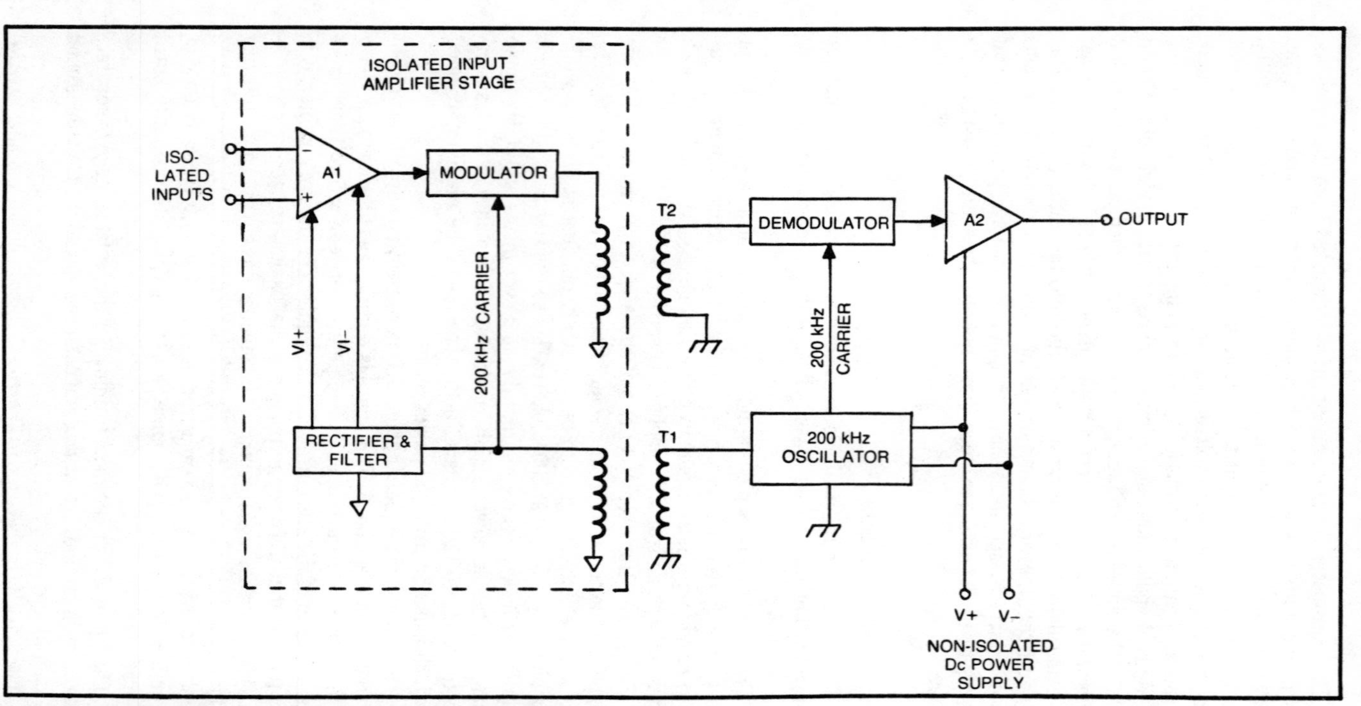

Fig. 14-2. A simplified block diagram of an isolation amplifier.

by the input signal. The resultant AM signal is passed through transformer T2 to the nonisolated side of the circuit. Like the power transformer (T1), the signal transformer T2 is very inefficient at 60 Hz, but passes 200 kHz very easily.

The AM signal from the secondary winding of T2 is fed to a synchronous demodulator. There it is compared with a sample of the 200 kHz carrier in a detector circuit and the original modulating signal waveform is recovered. The transformer-type isolation amplifier is also sometimes called a *carrier amplifier* because of the AM modulation/demodulation process. The recovered signal is further amplified in A2, and then passed from the output to nonisolated electronic circuitry.

OPTICAL COUPLING

The other type of isolation amplifier uses optical coupling between the isolated and nonisolated sides of the circuit (see Fig. 14-3). In this type of device, transformer T2 is replaced with an optoisolator (a device in which a light-emitting diode (LED) is juxtaposed with a phototransistor). Light from the LED impinges on the base of the phototransistor, thereby causing the transistor to conduct. If the signal from the output of the isolated amplifier input stage(s) is used to modulate the LED, then it will be passed onto the phototransistor and then to the output amplifier, A2.

Some optically coupled isolation amplifiers use a transformer/oscillator arrangement to provide power to the isolated stages. In other cases, the VI– and VI+ lines are brought out of the package pins and an isolated power source must be provided. The isolated supply might be a

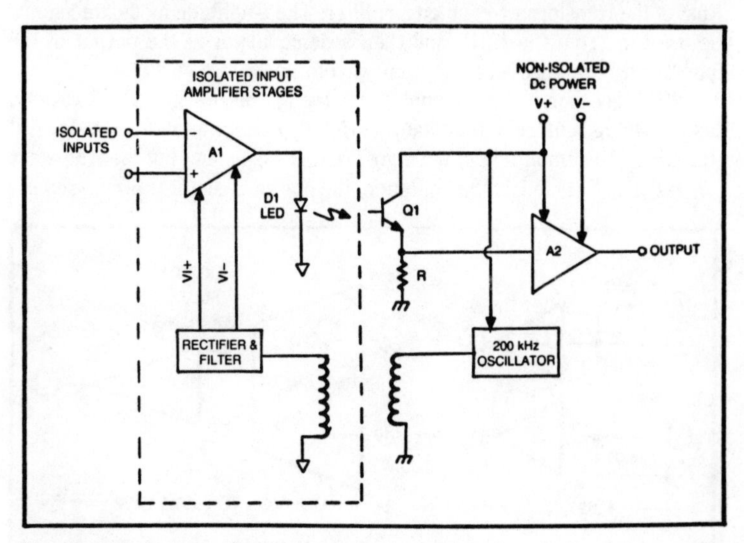

Fig. 14-3. Optical coupling between the isolated and nonisolated sides of the circuit.

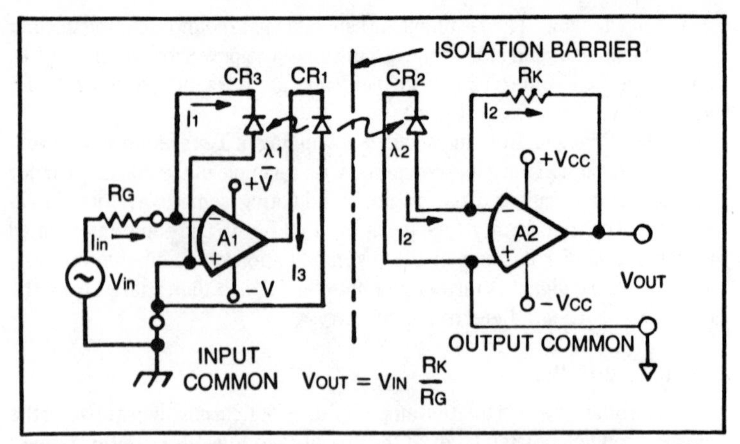

Fig. 14-4. The block diagram of a Burr-Brown 3650/3652 isolation amplifier.

battery or some form of dc-to-dc converter that is based on the same principals as the dc power supplies in other isolated amplifiers. The Burr-Brown Corporation offers isolated power supplies with two or four output ports to power their nonpowered isolation amplifiers. In that type of arrangement, several different isolation amplifiers will be driven by a single isolated power supply.

Optically coupled isolation amplifiers have, until recently, been subject to drift and nonlinearity because of the properties of the LED. In some cases, the manufacturer uses a modulator/demodulator method similar to that of the transformer-coupled amplifier. The amplitude modulated signal is used to drive the LED, and then a demodulator at the output of the phototransistor recovers the input waveform.

Still another isolation amplifier, although not of the hybrid variety, used a voltage controlled oscillator (VCO) to produce an audio FM signal at the LED. The amplitude of the signal remains constant, but the frequency varies. The FM signal at the output of the phototransistor is processed in a

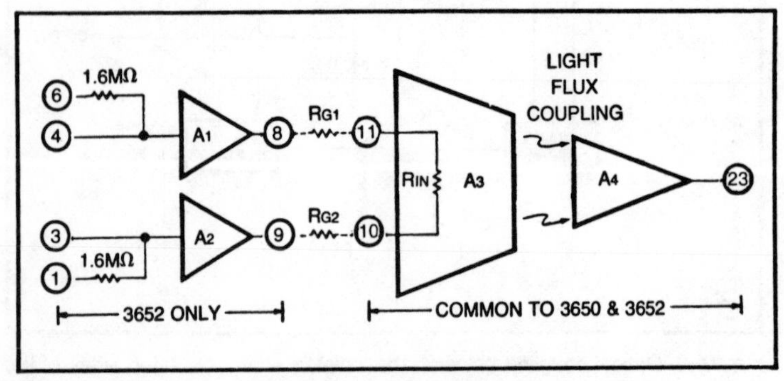

Fig. 14-5. The block diagram of the 3650/3652 device.

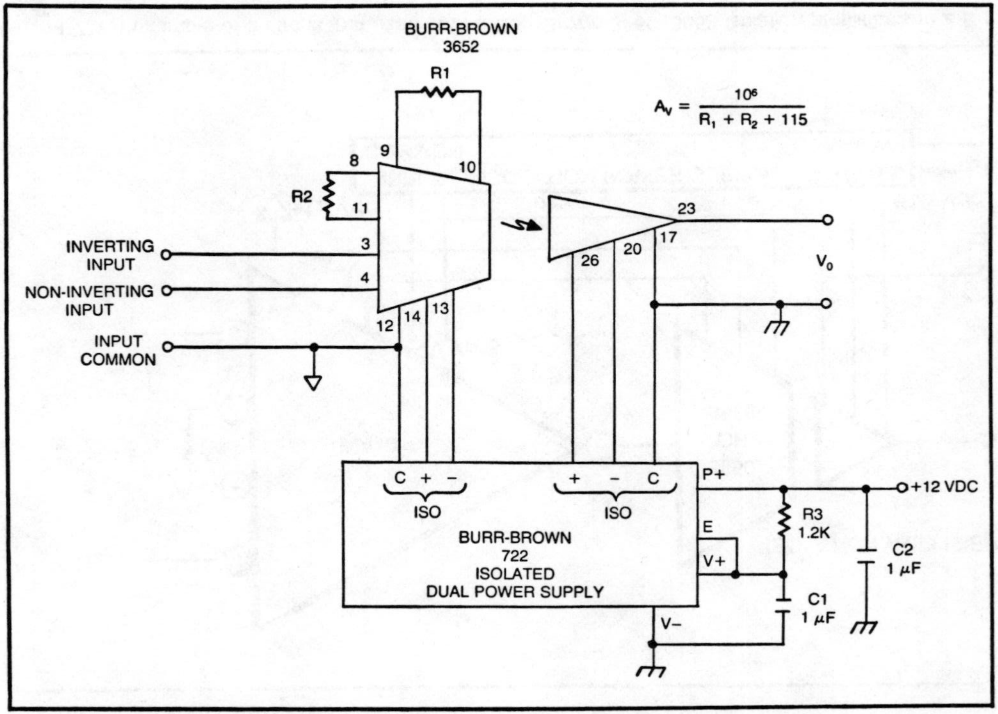

$$A_V = \frac{10^6}{R_1 + R_2 + 115}$$

Fig. 14-6. A typical circuit using the 3652 isolation amplifier.

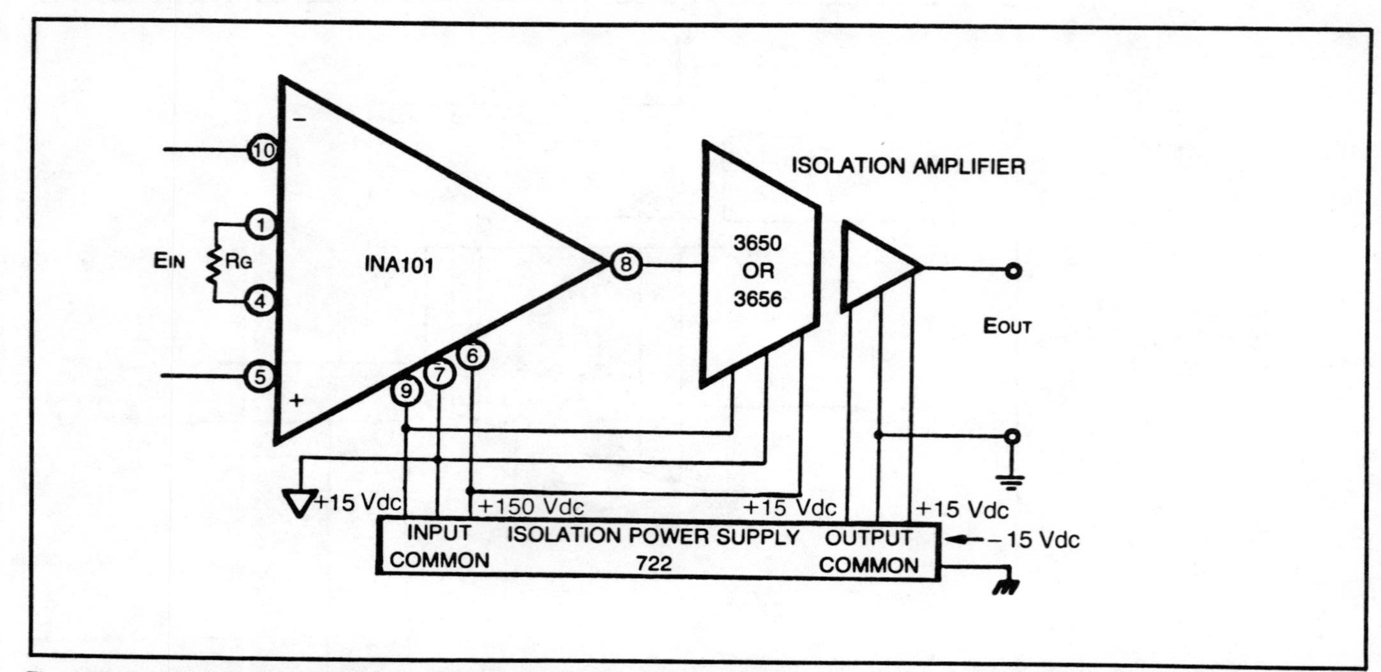

Fig. 14-7. An example of a circuit that uses both a Burr-Brown 3650 /3652 isolation amplifier and a Burr-Brown INA-101 IC instrumentation amplifier.

"coilless" FM demodulator (PLL or pulse-counting/integrator) and the input signal is thereby recovered.

Figure 14-4 shows the block diagram of a Burr-Brown 3650 or 3652 isolation amplifier. This device uses a special circuit that will provide improved linearity for optically coupled isolation, without the use of a carrier method. The circuit is based on a pair of matched photodiodes, *CR2* and *CR3*. Diode *CR2* is in the input circuit of the output amplifier (A2). The CR3 is across the input circuit of the input amplifier A1. This circuit uses negative feedback methods to cancel some of the errors that normally creep into optically coupled isolation amplifiers.

In later sections, we will examine the B-B 3650 and 3652 devices a little closer and provide design examples of typical applications. Note that the 3650 and 3652 devices do not have their own isolated power supplies so they must have external isolated power supplies. The Burr-Brown 722 device will provide two isolated power supplies; the 724 will provide four.

The 3650 and 3652 isolation amplifiers are optically coupled devices, and are constructed as hybrids. These devices will survive high continuous common-mode voltages (i.e., as in medical applications) of ± 2000 volts. The common-mode rejection is 140 decibels. The 3650/3652 devices provide only 0.25 microamperes of leakage at 240 volts ac (60 Hz); the leakage capacitance is only 1.8 picofarads. The linearity specification is 0.05 percent with a linearity specification of 0.05 %/1000 Hrs. A 15 kHz (± 3 dB) bandwidth is provided with a 1.2 V/μsec slew rate.

Figure 14-5 shows the block diagram of the 3650/3652 devices. The 3650 is a current-input device. The 3652 can be either (amplifiers A1 and A2 are voltage amplifiers) current or voltage input. A typical circuit using the 3652 isolation amplifier is shown in Fig. 14-6. Power is supplied by a Burr-Brown 722 dc-to-dc converter.

An example of a circuit that uses both a Burr-Brown 3650/3652 isolation amplifier and a Burr-Brown INA-101 IC instrumentation amplifier (ICIA) (see Chapter 13) is shown in Fig. 14-7. In this circuit, the Burr-Brown INA-101 ICIA is used as an input preamplifier to provide all of the benefits normally associated with instrumentation amplifiers: high input impedance, easily controlled gain, and so forth. The INA-101 and the isolated portions of the 3650/3652 device are powered from a single Burr-Brown 722 dc-to-dc converter. Note that the isolated and nonisolated grounds are represented by separate symbols. These grounds should be kept separate (not connected).

Chapter 15

Instrumentation Applications

Electronic instrumentation can be a major expense in scientific and engineering research efforts, as well as in practical industrial situations. Often there is little that can be done to alleviate the cost because "homebrew" equipment is simply not sufficient. In other cases, however, purchasing commercial amplifiers is a gross waste of money. In one case, for example, I built a relatively simple amplifier project for a physiologist at an East Coast medical school. When he wanted to "write it up" for a physiology journal (another case of publish or perish in the academic world), I thought it was silly to write an article for a scientific journal on so simple a project. He claimed, however, that what was simple for me as an electronic technician and an engineering student was terribly complex for the working scientist whose expertise was in fields other than electronics. The physiologist would have to pay close to $900 for such an amplifier, yet I had built it for pennies.

Earlier in this book I mentioned another project called a "transducer amplifier" (see Chapter 13 on IC Instrumentation Amplifiers). In that case, the two options open to my physiologist "client" were both expensive (more than $500) and would take 13 weeks or even longer to obtain if the year's research budget did not contain funds for buying of "extra" amplifiers. We were able to deliver an adequate amplifier (no excess capability) in two days for $25 in parts and three hours of electronic shop time.

The average reader who possesses a moderate sophistication in electronics can, without either an engineering degree (heresy! heresy!) or a mountain of money, provide himself with decent electronic equipment. Only the usual "hobbyist" level of knowledge is required.

The ability of the average experimenter to design and build devices has increased dramatically over the years. Design is, and should be, the domain of professional engineers. But there is a wide range of design or quasi-design chores that can be handled by people on other levels. In the days when transistors and vacuum tubes were king, however, this statement would not generally be true. In those bygone days, even minor design jobs required either a professionally trained electronic engineer or an extremely competent electronics technician (often with a technical school degree). With the introduction of the integrated circuit operational amplifier, however, the situation began to change. Gain setting, for example, reduced to a matter of selecting a couple of resistors—a little 9th-grade algebra. In the words of John Smith's early op-amp book, *Operational Circuit Design,* "the contriving of contrivances becomes a game for all."

The IC operational amplifier is still with us and versions are available today in extremely high quality form that approach the textbook ideal. There are IC and "hybrid" devices that perform wonderful functions with little outside assistance. There is one Burr-Brown hybrid, for example, that offers a transfer function of the form:

$$V_o = V_x(V_y/V_z)^m$$

where the "X,Y,Z" terms are input voltages, and the exponent "m" is a factor from 0.2 to 5 (and is set by a simple resistor network!). The design of a squarer (m = 2) or a squarerooter (m = 0.5) then becomes easy to accomplish!

ANALOG VERSUS DIGITAL?

The main thrust of the electronics instrumentation industry these days is towards microcomputer-based methods. We are able to replace many analog functions and discrete digital logic functions with computer software. The advantage is that hardware can be simplified, can be "universalized," and is often a lot more flexible. Assuming that neither additional memory capacity nor additional I/O ports are needed, changes in software and capability become a matter of reprogramming the computer. A new tape or a new Read Only Memory (ROM) and—presto!—a new instrument from the same analytic engine. One could conceivably adopt the "mainframe" concept that is used so successfully in oscilloscopes and strip-chart recorders in order to fashion a wide variety of instruments. The mainframe instrument would contain the computer circuitry, a selection of I/O ports, some random access memory (RAM) and the power supply. The plug-in would contain analog circuitry needed to interfere with the specific type of experiment or signal source, A/D-D/A converters, and sufficient ROM to contain the operating program for the specific application at hand.

The world of digital instrumentation is exciting, but one must be admonished to not forget the analog world. So why analog if digital is so good? There are times when the analog approach is superior to digital methods or may be more economical. In some cases, for example, the instrument resolution is better using analog than digital techniques. One major manufacturer of IC and hybrid amplifiers, for example, makes a device with a current-resolution to low-level signals that would require a 20-bit (expensive!) analog-to-digital converter to equal.

Although few electronics professionals can afford to ignore computers these days, one is advised to know analog as well. It may be that an analog circuit may be the better choice in some situations. Remember, the job of the instrumentation engineer is to solve the problem in the best manner possible and that doesn't necessarily mean in the most modern or sophisticated manner possible.

INSTRUMENTATION TECHNIQUES

The purpose of electronic instrumentation is to measure or control some parameter from the physical world. Signals can be acquired from electrodes (as in biopotentials) or from *transducers.* A transducer is a device that converts physical parameters (e.g., displacement, temperature, force/pressure, speed, etc.) into an electrical signal that is analogous to that parameter. Fox example, a pressure transducer will produce a voltage output that is proportional to the applied pressure. Other transducers will change some electrical property, e.g., resistance, in response to the physical parameter being measured. A thermistor, for example, changes electrical resistance in response to changes in temperature. The thermistor, unlike certain other transducers, requires an external *excitation voltage.* In order to use such a transducer most rationally, one must use a circuit such as the Wheatstone bridge or a half-bridge.

Wheatstone Bridge

As mentioned above, certain resistive transducers require a Wheatstone bridge circuit for proper operation. The classic Wheatstone bridge circuit is shown in A of Fig. 15-1 and a redrawn version is shown in B of Fig. 15-1. The redrawn version is provided to aid our analysis of the circuit. In this version of the circuit, we can see that it consists of two series resistive voltage dividers (R1/R2 and R3/R4) connected in parallel with each other.

Output voltage V_o in B of Fig. 15-1 can be shown to be the difference between individual drops E2 and E4:

$$V_o = E2 - E4$$

We can write the respective voltage divider equations for E2 and E4 as follows:

$$E2 = \frac{V R_2}{R_1 + R_2} \qquad (15\text{-}2)$$

and,

$$E4 = \frac{V R_4}{R_3 + R_4} \quad (15\text{-}3)$$

By substituting Eqs. (15-3) and (15-2) into Eq. (15-1):

$$V_o = \frac{V R_2}{(R_1 + R_2)} - \frac{V R_4}{(R_3 + R_4)} \quad (15\text{-}4)$$

In the null condition the output voltage V_o is zero, so:

$$\frac{V R_2}{(R_1 + R_2)} - \frac{V R_4}{(R_3 + R_4)} = 0 \quad (15\text{-}5)$$

Therefore:

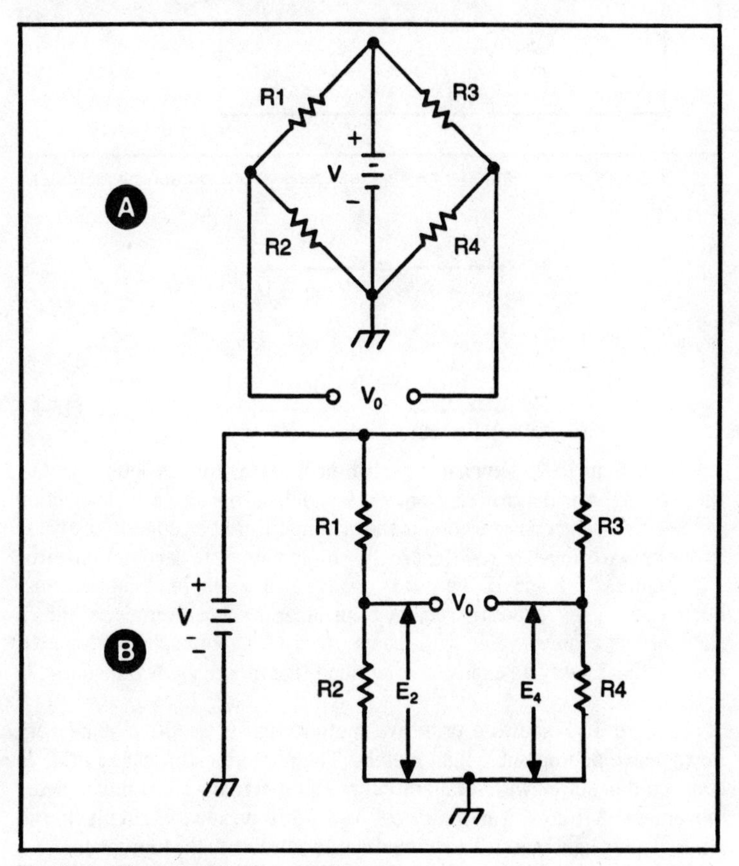

Fig. 15-1. Wheatstone bridge circuits.

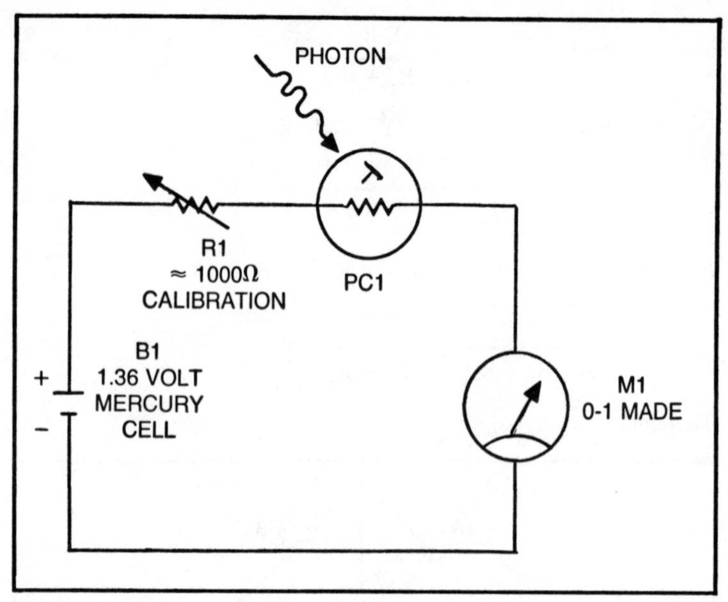

Fig. 15-2. A primitive method for a very inexpensive photographic light meter.

$$\frac{V R_2}{(R_1 + R_2)} = \frac{V R_4}{(R_3 + R_4)} \tag{15-6}$$

or,

$$\frac{R2}{R1 + R2} = \frac{R4}{R3 + R4} \tag{15-7}$$

Equation (15-7) demonstrates that the null condition is determined by the *ratio* of the bridge arm resistances. It should be obvious from inspection of the circuit, and consideration of the arithmetic, that changes in the value of one or two bridge arms will cause the output voltage to become non-zero.

Figures 15-2 and 15-3 show two ways that a simple resistive transducer can be used. In both cases, the transducer is a *photoresistive cell,* i.e., a resistor that changes value with changes in the level of impinging light. Of course, this is only an example so assume that *any* resistor transducer is usable.

Figure 15-2 shows a primitive method that is used for some very inexpensive photographic light meters. The photoresistor, called *PC1,* is connected in series with a calibration resistor, R1, and a dc milliammeter movement. A 1.36-volt mercury cell is used to power the circuit. In the photographic light meter, R1 can be varied according to the film speed (ASA or DIN rating) and the meter calibrated in *f*-stop numbers or in *f*-stop/shutter speed combinations.

The circuit shown in Fig. 15-2, although used in some commercial applications, is too crude for most serious work. A significant problem with this circuit is gross nonlinearity with most transducers and that the meter reading does not drop to zero. A superior photographic light meter can be made with a Wheatstone bridge; an example is shown in Fig. 15-3. Although the example is photographic, the same ideas can be used in almost any circuit that requires a resistive transducer. Since this circuit is so "universal," let's generalize a little on the topic of Wheatstone bridges.

There are several ways to use a bridge circuit. First, let's consider the situation where R1 and R2 are fixed and R4 is variable. We could apply some standard calibrating condition (darkness for a light meter) to the transducer (R3) and then adjust R4 for a specified meter reading (usually, either null—i.e., zero center—or positive full-scale deflection or negative full-scale deflection). When the adjustment is completed, and R3 is exposed to the nonstandard circumstance, the meter pointer will deflect to a position that indicates the value of the measured parameter.

In another scenario, we do not calibrate the meter at all, but use it to indicate the null condition to denote bridge balance. In that type of circuit, one of the other resistors (R1 or R2, maybe both) may be variable. Let's pick R2. The transducer is exposed to a standard calibrating condition and R4 is set to a standard point that corresponds to a reading on its dial that

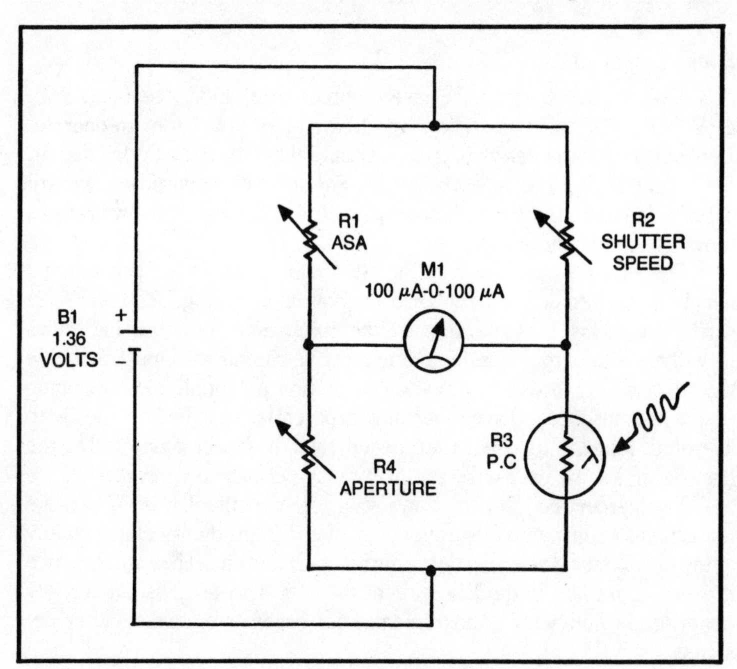

Fig. 15-3. A superior photographic light meter can be made with a Wheatstone bridge.

denotes the standard condition. Resistor R2 would then be used to balance the bridge; it is adjusted for a zero reading on the meter. When the transducer is exposed to another condition (when it is making a real measurement), the resistance of R3 changes. This unbalances the bridge and deflects the meter. Resistor R4 is then varied to rebalance the bridge. When the meter is brought back to null (zero), then the resistance of R4 denotes the value of the measured parameter. If a calibrated dial is used on R4, then the dial reading will yield the parameter value.

Finally, we have our photographic light meter (the actual subject of Fig. 15-3). In ordinary photography, there are four variables that affect getting a good exposure: film speed (ASA/DIN), shutter speed, aperture (f-stop) and the amount of available light.

In Fig. 15-3, the photosensitive cell (R3) measures the amount of light available to take the picture; R1 is used to indicate the ASA/DIN rating of the film being used; R2 indicates the camera shutter speed; and R4 indicates the aperture (opening) of the lens. Normally, R1 will be set once when the camera is loaded with a specific type of film. The bridge will be balanced when the exposure is correct. Because resistance R3 is set by available light, the camera operator will juggle R2 and R4 to obtain the balance condition. For internal thru-the-lens meters, the camera controls and film speed indicator will be ganged with R1, R2 and R4.

Bridge Excitation

A Wheatstone bridge must have a source of excitation potential (shown as V in Fig. 15-1 and as B1 in Figs. 15-2 and 15-3) in order to operate. Depending upon the design of the electronics that follow the bridge output, the excitation could be ac, dc, or pulses. For our present purposes, we will assume dc excitation of the bridge. Figure 15-4 (A through F) shows various forms of the excitation scheme.

The scheme shown in A of Fig. 15-4 uses a simple battery. Often a simple 1.36-volts dc mercury "instrumentation cell" (e.g., *HG1* or *HG2*) can be used. Most bridges will use either microammeter output indicators or will have an output amplifier. One must be careful with most resistive transducers not to use too high an excitation potential. Most common resistive transducers have a maximum potential specified in the 5- to 15-volt dc range. If this limit is exceeded, then the power dissipated by the transducer will be excessive and may cause permanent damage.

The mercury cell has a certain advantage over other batteries because it maintains a constant voltage over most of its life and then declines rapidly at the end. Zinc-carbon cells decay during their lifetime. They will produce greater errors late in the life cycle of the cell. This error is not terribly important in null-seeking instruments, but becomes crucial in other designs.

The principal disadvantage of battery excitation is that the battery goes dead (so it must be renewed). The answer is to use an electronic regulated power supply for the excitation potential. A *regulated* supply is needed to guard the excitation supply against variations in the applied voltage. Referring to Eq. (15-4), you should note that V_o, the output voltage, is proportional to V, the excitation potential. In other words, changes in V causes changes in V_o, hence represent error in the data!

Figure 15-4 (B) shows the circuit using a *zener diode* voltage regulator. The zener diode will keep the excitation voltage relatively constant. This is especially true if the ambient temperature remains constant despite changes in the external supply voltage V+.

The series resistor (R1) is used to limit the zener current to a safe level. We must calculate the value of this resistor from equations given below. First, though, we must establish the following:

- Value of V_z.
- The minimum and maximum values of V+.
- The effective load resistance presented by the bridge.
- The total bridge current.

In order to illustrate the process, C of Fig. 15-4 is a redrawn equivalent of B of Fig. 15-4. The resistance R_L represents the load resistance presented to the zener diode by the Wheatstone bridge. In other words, it is the "looking back" resistance or the "Thevinin's equivalent" resistance measured across points A-B (in B of Fig. 15-4) with D1 and R1 disconnected. If all four resistances in the bridge are equal to each other, then R_L is the same as the resistance of any one resistor in the bridge:

If: R1 = R2 = R3 = R4 = R

Then: $R_L = R$

If the four resistors in the bridge are not equal to each other, then R_L is the series-parallel value of the bridge:

$$(R1 + R3) \parallel (R2 + R4)$$

Which is calculated by:

$$R_L = \frac{(R1 + R3)(R2 + R4)}{R1 + R2 + R3 + R4}$$

Let's assume a value of R_L = 1000 ohms for the purposes of our example. This resistance is close to the upper range of many physical transducers that use resistive-strain gauge elements in a Wheatstone configuration.

The value of V_z must be a "standard" zener diode value and less than the maximum voltage that the transducer will tolerate. Because 7.5 volts is a common specification for Wheatstone transducers, we can select 4.7 Vdc, 5.6 Vdc, 6.2 Vdc, or 6.8 Vdc. For the sake of example, select 4.7 volts dc (generally, lower excitation potentials mean less self-heating, hence less drift).

So now we know R_L = 1000 ohms and V_z = 4.7 volts dc. The total bridge current is, by Ohm's law:

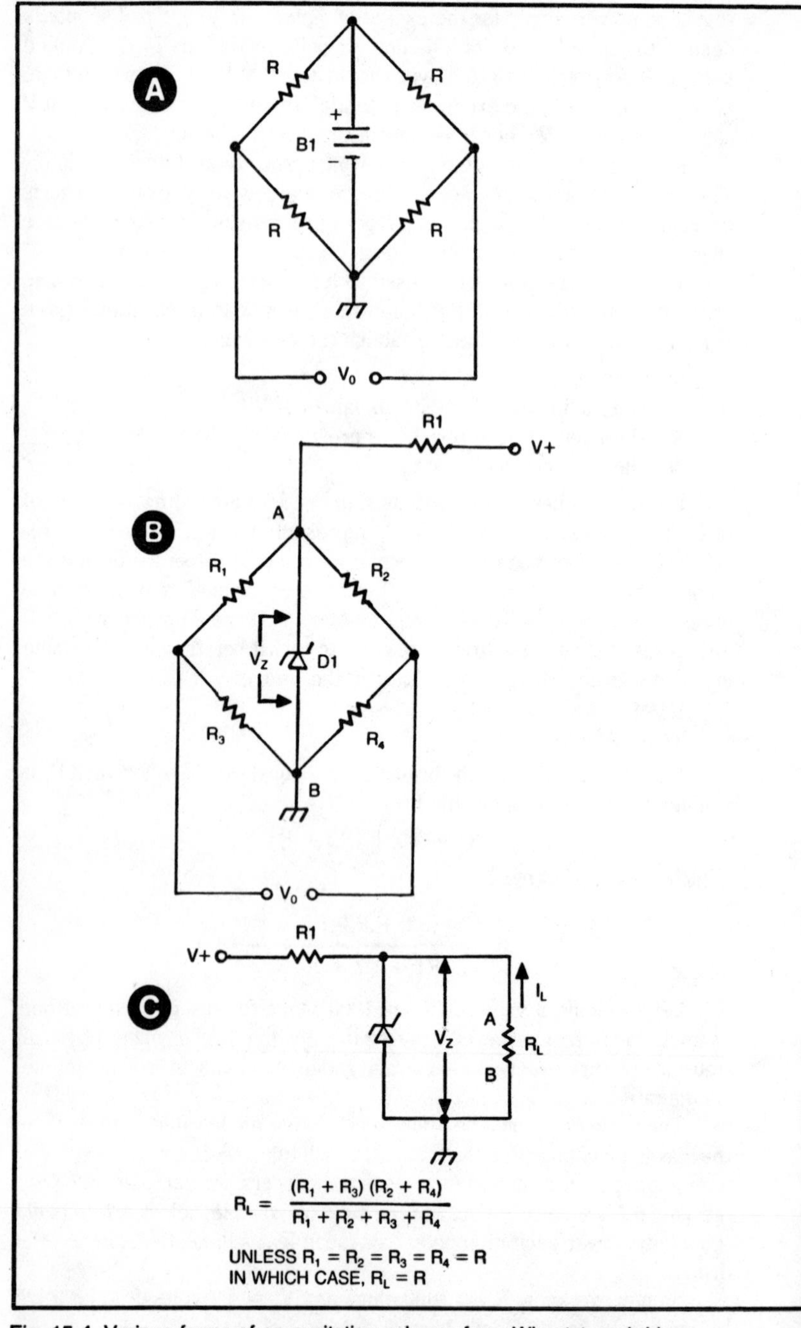

Fig. 15-4. Various forms of an excitation scheme for a Wheatstone bridge.

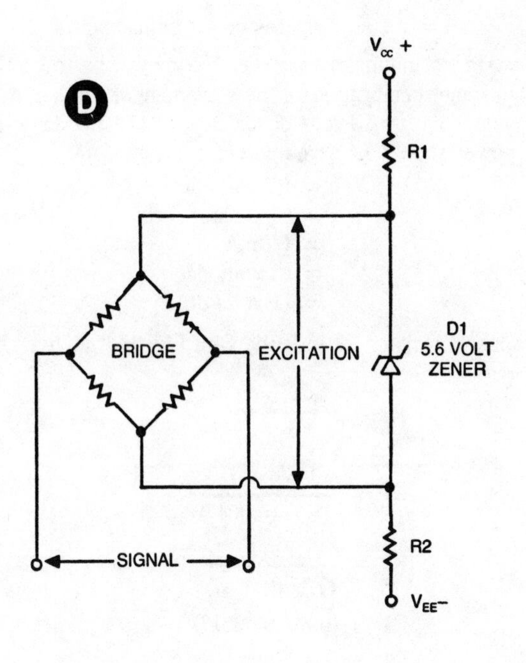
D
V_{cc} +
R1
BRIDGE
EXCITATION
D1
5.6 VOLT
ZENER
R2
SIGNAL
V_{EE}−

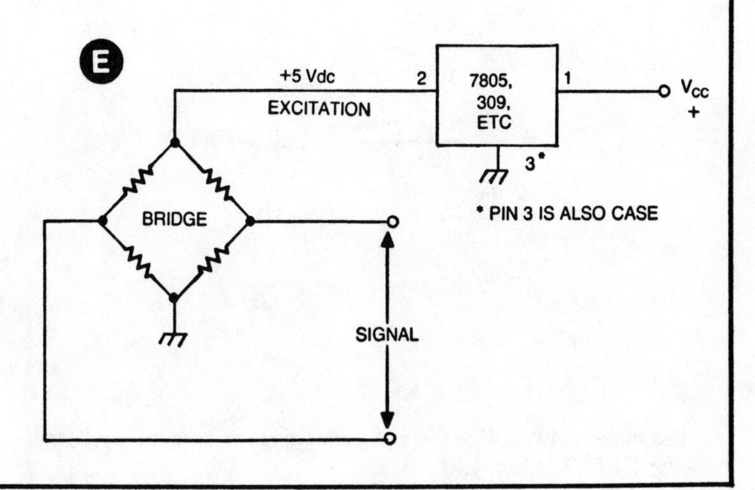
E
+5 Vdc
EXCITATION
2
7805,
309,
ETC
1
V_{CC}
+
3*
* PIN 3 IS ALSO CASE
BRIDGE
SIGNAL

$I_L = V_z/R_L$
$I_L = (4.7V)/(1000 \text{ ohms})$
$I_L = 0.0047$ amperes or 4.7 milliamperes

The maximum/minimum values of V+ may have to be measured, derived from some specification for the equipment or another, or guessed. We will "guess." $V_{max} = 13$ volts dc and $V_{min} = 11$ volts dc for a nominal 12-volt dc power supply. Our parameters are, therefore:

$V_z = 4.7$ volts dc
$R_L = 1000$ ohms
$I_L = 4.7$ mA
$V_{max} = 13$ volts dc
$V_{min} = 11$ volts dc

The value of resistor R1 in B and C of Fig. 15-4 is given by:

$$R1 = \frac{V_{min} - V_2}{1.1\ I_L}$$

$$R1 = \frac{(11V - 4.7V)}{(1.1)\ (0.0047)}$$

$$R1 = \frac{(6.3)}{(1.1)\ (0.0047)}$$

$$R1 = (6.3)/(0.00517)$$

$$R1 = 1{,}218 \text{ ohms}$$

R1 need not be precise so use 1.2 kohms. This is the nearest "standard" resistance value that will normally be available. The wattage rating of the zener diode (D1) is found from:

$$P_{D1} = \frac{(E_{max} - V_z)^2}{R1} - I_L V_z$$

$$P_{D1} = \frac{(13 - 4.7 \text{ volts})^2}{1200} - ((0.0047)(4.7))$$

$$P_{D1} = \frac{(8.3)^2}{(1200)} - ((0.0047)(4.7))$$

$$P_{D1} = \frac{69}{1200} - 0.022$$

$$R_{D1} = 0.056 - 0.022$$

$$P_{D1} = 0.04 \text{ watts}$$

Use either a 400 mW or 500 mW zener diode or even a 1-watt zener diode for D1 in B of Fig. 15-4.

The wattage rating of the resistor is found from:

$$P_{R1} = P_{D1} + I_L V_z$$
$$P_{R1} = (0.04 \text{ watts}) + (0.0047)(4.7)$$
$$P_{R1} = (0.04 \text{ watts}) + (0.022 \text{ watts})$$
$$P_{R1} = 0.062 \text{ watts}$$

Use a ¼-watt resistor, or larger, for R1.

Figure 15-4 (D) shows the method for using a zener diode for producing a bipolar reference source. The total voltage applied will be $V_{cc+} - V_{ee-}$ or, if V_{ee} and V_{cc} are equal, twice one of them. This method will produce the same voltage across the Wheatstone bridge as the monopolar method, but in some cases—depending upon the design of the V_{ee} and V_{cc} power supplies—will tend to reduce drift of the zener potential with temperature.

The circuit shown in E of Fig. 15-4 uses a three-terminal IC voltage regulator to produce the Wheatstone bridge excitation voltage. These devices are housed in transistor packages or in certain special plastic packages. For the most part, let's consider only those "universal" types in transistor packages. There are three basic package styles in use. Each package style has its own unheatsinked current rating. The "H" package (LM-309H) is a 100-milliampere regulator and is the T0-5 transistor package. This style can only be used on certain high resistance transducer or the current rating will be exceeded. The "T" package (LM-340T-05) is a plastic power transistor package. This type of case uses an end-tab with a hole in it to mount the power transistor/regulator to the heatsink.

In the positive voltage regulators of this style, the end-tab is the common terminal. It can be bolted directly to a grounded heatsink or chassis without worry of blowing it (not so with the negative versions, however!). The "T" regulators are capable of delivering 750 milliamperes so they are usable for almost all transducers. The "K" package (LM-309K) is a diamond-shaped T0-3 power transistor package. The K-package devices are capable of delivering 1 ampere (that's 1000 mA) so they will also handle any transducer.

You will also find K-package devices with larger current ratings. The LM-323K device, for example, will deliver 5 volts at 3 amperes. The Lambda Electronics LAS-1905 will provide 5 volts at 5 amperes. At least one 10-ampere device is on the market, but it is all but irrelevant to transducer applications.

The voltage designation of the three-terminal IC regulator is often given as part of its part number. The 78xx series, for example, will replace the "xx" with the voltage rating. Hence, the 7805 is a 5-volt device. The 7812 is a 12-volt device. The 78xx devices are positive voltage regulators. The LM-340(   )-xx devices are also found using the voltage as part of the type number. The parenthesis ( ) will contain the package style (K or T). The "xx" is the voltage. An LM-340K-05 is a 5-volt regulator with a T0-3 package (rating 1-ampere). The LM-309 device is outside of this neat system (it was an early type, so what the heck). The LM-309 is always a 5-volt regulator: LM-309H is 100 mA, LM-309K is 1000 mA.

The supply voltage applied to the input of the three-terminal IC regulator should be 2.5 volts higher than the rated output voltage. Hence, the 5-volt regulator needs not less than +7.5 volts applied to the input terminal. The input voltage should not be too much higher than this or the regulator will dissipate higher amounts of heat. The life expectancy will be lowered and the output voltage will tend to drift a bit. This drift is not crucial in TTL digital circuits, but introduces an error term when the regulator is used for transducer excitation purposes.

The three-terminal IC regulator represents one of the better methods for supplying excitation potential to the transducer. One must be cautioned, however, against the use of the regulator with other circuits. The regulator that serves the Wheatstone bridge must serve only the bridge or dynamic situations in the other circuits will cause artifacts in the output signal from the bridge. It is sometimes the case that the regulator will be mounted in the same environment with the transducer and preamplifier. That is acceptable provided that the heat generated by the voltage regulator does not cause the transducer or the amplifier to drift.

The bridge used in electronic instrumentation applications often must be balanced (or nulled) at the outset. There are several ways that this can be accomplished. First, we could adjust the bridge elements in order to achieve the null condition. This is done in many cases. In still other cases, we will have to use an external null circuit. The reason for this is that the transducer may not normally be balanced because of errors in the construction (normal tolerances).

A typical example might be the pressure transducer used in medical electronics. The device is a Wheatstone bridge strain gauge in which all four bridge elements are of equal value when the transducer is at rest. When a pressure is applied to the "diaphragm" of the transducer, then the resistances change value (all four of them change in that type of bridge) according to the applied pressure.

There might be manufacturing differences between each strain gauge element. There might also be a "static head" of pressure against the diaphragm that will keep the transducer reading a small positive or negative pressure when, in fact, it is open to atmosphere and should read zero. This problem is especially prevalent in medical blood pressure transducers because the transducer or its plumbing to the patient tends to be moved inappropriately. The circuits in Fig. 15-5 show three methods (well, 2½) for zeroing the transducer bridge. As usual, these methods are also appropriate to other Wheatstone bridge circuits.

In A of Fig. 15-5, we see the traditional method in which a small value potentiometer, R5, is used to balance the bridge. The value of R5 should be approximately 10 to 25 percent the value of R1 and R3 (assuming R1 = R3). The excitation voltage V is applied to the wiper of the potentiometer. The position of the wiper therefore adds resistance to one arm while subtracting it from the other. The bridge is placed in a condition where it is supposed to

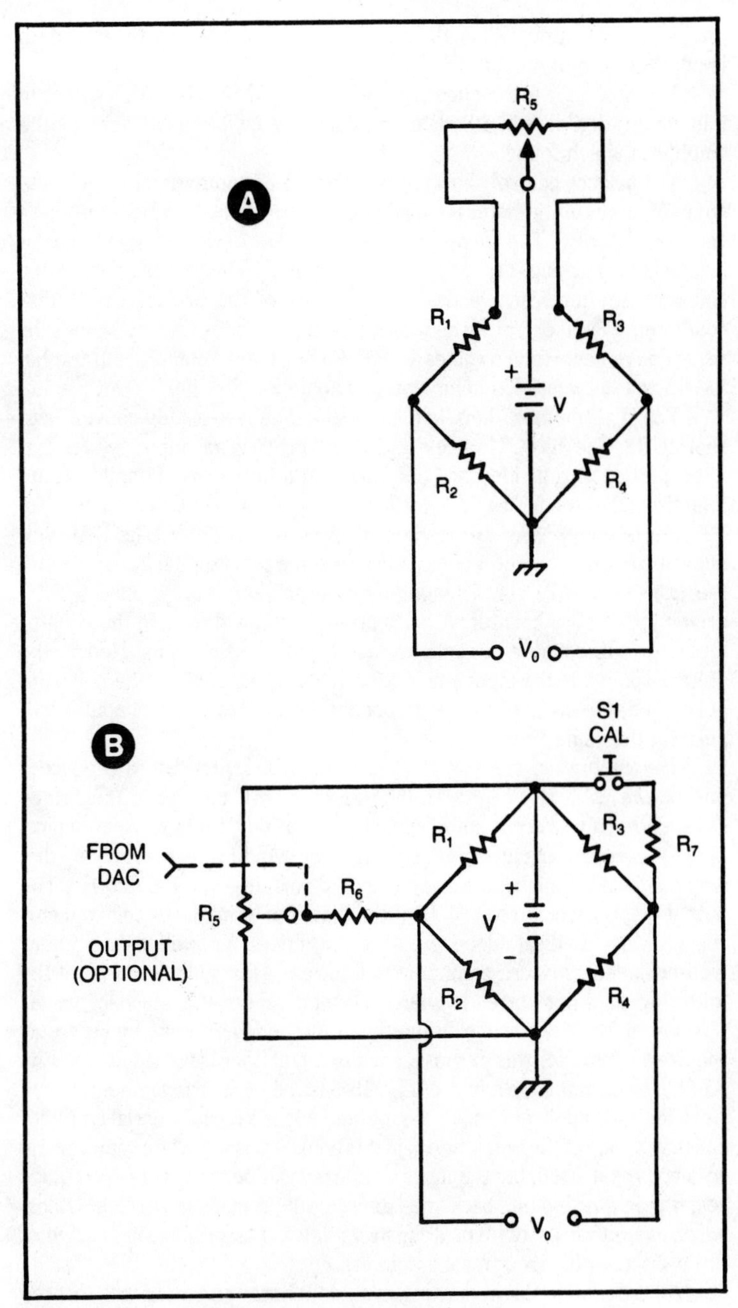

Fig. 15-5. Methods for zeroing the transducer bridge.

produce a zero output. When the pressure transducer is open to air, and R5 is adjusted to null output.

The other 1½ techniques are shown in B of Fig. 15-5. Also shown in this illustration is a method for producing a calibration signal to the amplifiers which follow.

The balance control shown in B of Fig. 15-5 is potentiometer R5. The wiper of this potentiometer is connected to one node of the bridge through a series resistor R6. The voltage at the wiper will introduce a current into the bridge node, causing it to produce an offset in V_o. The idea is to produce a counteroffset that cancels the natural offset of the bridge. Under that condition, V_o will be zero when it supposed to be zero. Typical values for these components (given values for R1 - R4 of under 2 kohms) are 100 kohm for R5 and between 220 kohm and 680 kohm for R6.

The "half method" here is the use of a digital-to-analog converter to replace R5. The "DAC" is a device that will produce an output voltage that is proportional to a reference potential and a binary word applied to its digital inputs (see *Microcomputer Interfacing A/D - D/A,* TAB book No. 1271, or *Microprocessor Interfacing,* TAB book No. 1396). The DAC will allow us to use a computer output port, or some other digital circuit, to null the transducer. We can arrange "pushbutton" zeroing by using a DAC driven by a binary counter. A pushbutton switch will turn on the counter clock. As the counter increments, its output state changes. Hence, the voltage applied to the input end of R6 will also change. When the null point is reached, the counter can be stopped. Of course, a microcomputer will perform the same trick.

The calibration resistor (R7) is used with switch S1 to produce a pushbutton calibration system. The resistor will unbalance the bridge sufficiently to represent some standard condition. If this were a medical blood pressure transducer, for example, we would select a resistor that would unbalance the bridge some standard amount—say 100 mm Hg. The output display would read "100" if the amplifier gains were adjusted correctly. Most medical blood pressure amplifiers (as well as any other well-designed pressure amplifier) will have a gain control on one of the following amplifier stages to adjust the total gain to this standard value.

For most Wheatstone bridge applications, the output voltage may require a boost. For this purpose, an output amplifier is provided (see Fig. 15-6). The circuit shown in A of Fig. 15-6 is the usual arrangement. It will work for most applications. The amplifier (A1) is a dc differential amplifier and may be any of the types shown in this book. Typically, the simple, single op-amp type is used, but the input resistors must be not less than 10 times larger than the "looking back" resistance of the transducer/bridge. Otherwise, use either an ICIA or an instrumentation amplifier constructed of three discrete IC operational amplifiers.

A perpetual problem existing in all dc Wheatstone bridges is that the output voltage V_o is a function of the supply voltage, V. As long as V remains

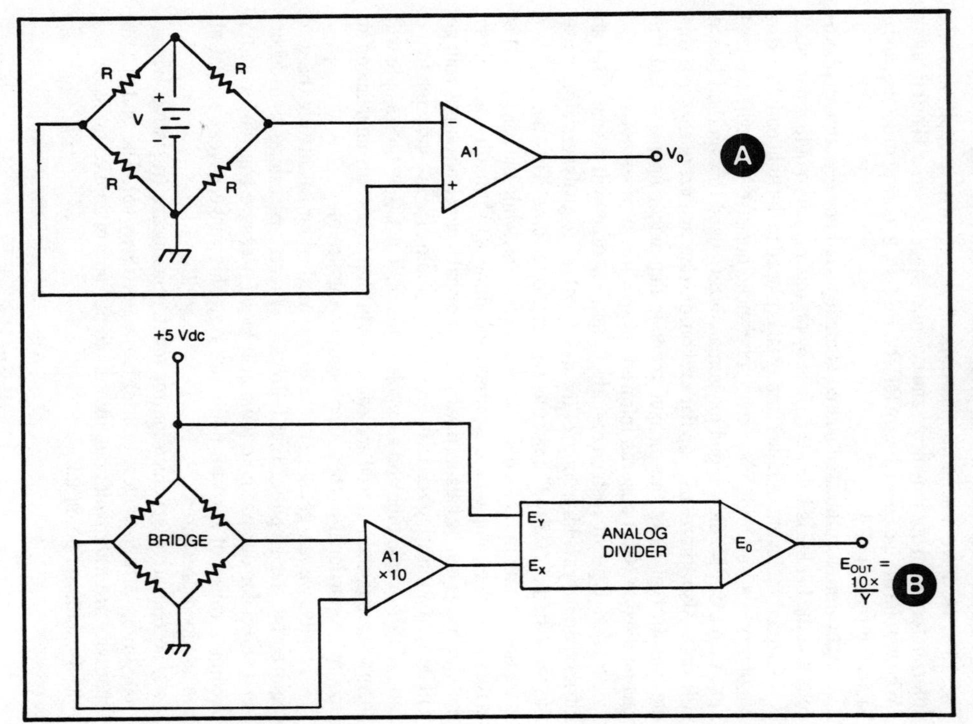

Fig. 15-6. An output amplifier (A) and a ratiometric circuit (B).

constant there is no problem, because the only changes in V_o will be real changes in the applied parameter. But if the excitation potential tends to change a little bit, then the changes in the output voltage will contain an error term caused by changes in V. The solution to this situation, if the problem is significant in any given application, is to use a *ratiometric* circuit such as shown in B of Fig. 15-6.

In this case, the bridge output voltage is applied first to a gain of ×10 differential amplifier and then to the E_x input of an analog voltage divider. The E_y input of the voltage divider sees the excitation voltage. The output of the analog divider will be equal to kE_x/E_y (in this case K = 10). Changes in the excitation potential will be servoed out of the output voltage, E_o.

Until now, we have been using photographic light meters and transducers in which the Wheatstone bridge was internal for our examples. In Fig. 15-7, we have a scientific instrument that sees wide application (in different forms) in both medicine and science: the *colorimeter.* The circuit is a Wheatstone bridge consisting of R1, R2, PC1, PC2 (both photocells), and a balancing resistor R3.

Light from a collimated source is made to fall equally on both photocells and the bridge is balanced, thereby producing a zero output potential V_o. When a translucent sample of material is placed in the light path to one of the photocells, the bridge becomes unbalanced because PC2 will see less light than PC1. Medical blood oxygen analyzers used this method (some still do!). Also, there are popular carbon dioxide analyzers that use this method. In that case, the measurement is dependent upon the fact the carbon dioxide ($C0_2$) absorbs infrared rays, while air does not.

In that type of instrument, the "light" source will actually be an infrared emitter. Oddly, some of the most costly $C0_2$ analyzers simply use the same kind of "Calrod" heater as electric coffee pots! The "sample" is a glass tube containing the exhaled air from a patient, while the path to PC1 is in room air. The sample tube is purged and allowed to "breath" room air so that the bridge can be balanced with R3. After balancing (the output voltage will be zero, indicating zero $C0_2$ level), the sample tube is connected to the patient's air exhale tube and a sample is taken. The $C0_2$ in the sample will absorb some of the infrared and cause the bridge to become unbalanced an amount proportional to the $C0_2$ content of the sample.

Finally, we are going to consider the method for calculating the gain required for the amplifier that follows a Wheatstone bridge transducer. Let's select for our example a medical blood pressure transducer with a maximum range of zero to +400 mm Hg. This range covers almost all human blood pressures.

The operative specification for most transducers (resistive Wheatstone bridge strain gauges, that is) is the *sensitivity* (ψ). The units of the sensitivity are microvolts output voltage per unit of applied pressure per volt of excitation potential:

$$\psi = \frac{\mu V}{V \text{ mm Hg}}$$

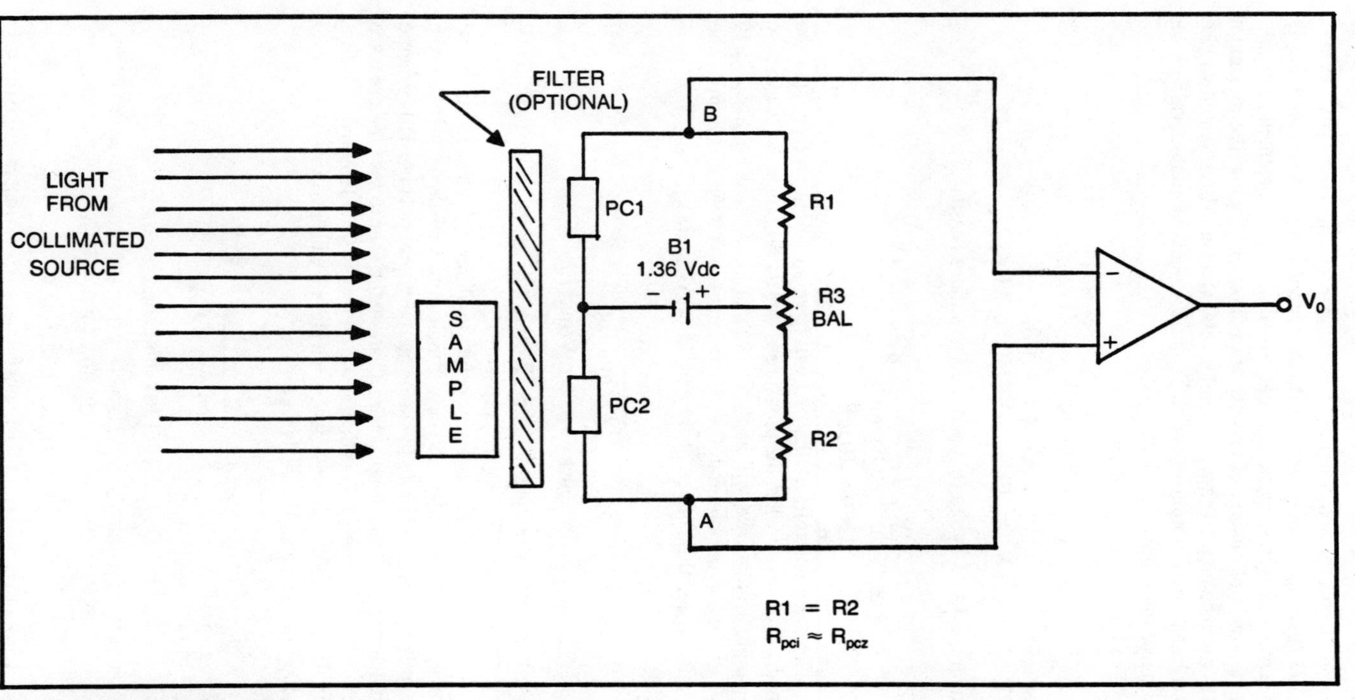

Fig. 15-7. A colorimeter circuit.

For many typical blood pressure transducers, this sensitivity figure is 5 μV/V/mm Hg. In order to compute the output voltage, we must multiply the sensitivity by the applied excitation voltage and the applied pressure. For purposes of design, of course, we will want to know the maximum pressure to be applied so we will select 400 mm Hg. Also selected will be +5 volts as the excitation potential. To find the maximum output voltage we will make the following calculation:

$$V_o = \frac{5\ \mu V}{V\ mm\ Hg} \times 5V \times 400\ mm\ Hg$$

$$V_o = (5\ \mu V \times 5 \times 400)$$

$$V_o = 10{,}000\ \mu V @ 400\ mm\ Hg$$

Converting to millivolts to make the units more reasonable:

$$V_o = \frac{1\ mV}{1000\ \mu V} \times 10{,}000\ \mu V$$

$$V_o = 10\ mV$$

The foregoing tells us that we will have an output voltage from the transducer of 10 mV when the pressure is 400 mm Hg. In order to increase the output voltage, we will apply a National Semiconductor LM-363-10 ICIA to the output potential, thereby raising the voltage to 100 mV. The scale factor for the voltage at the output of A1 (i.e., V_{A1}) is:

$$SF1 = \frac{100\ mV}{400\ mm\ Hg}$$

$$SF1 = 0.25\ mV/mm\ Hg$$

We will produce an output potential at other pressures scales to 0.25 mV per millimeter mercury applied pressure.

We must now select the gain for amplifier A2. Because a digital voltmeter is being used for the output indicator, it would be wise to make the scale factor numerically the same as the digital reading. That scheme would eliminate any look-up factor and allow the user to read the pressure directly from the meter. This digital voltmeter is a 0-to-1999-mV-3½-digit affair. If we let 400 mV represent 400 mm Hg, we will have a properly scaled reading. In this case, the scale factor is:

$$SF2 = \frac{400\ mV}{400\ mm\ Hg}$$

$$SF2 = 1\ mV/mm\ Hg$$

The gain of the final amplifier A2 is merely the ratio of the two scale factors:

$$A_{V2} = SF2/SF1$$

$$A_{V2} = 1/0.25 = 4$$

In order to provide an adjustment range, we will want to make the gain of amplifier A2 variable from 4 to plus or minus ×1. In other words, approximately 3 to 5. We can do this by making the feedback resistor from the series conbination R4 and R5. When the potentiometer R5 is at zero resistance, the gain of A2 is

$$A = R4/R3$$
$$A = 33\ k/10\ k$$
$$A = 3.3$$

At the other end of the extreme, the total resistance will be 33 kohm plus 20 kohms (or 53 kohms). The gain in that condition is:

$$A = (R4 + R5)/R3$$
$$A = (33\ k + 20\ k)/(10\ k)$$
$$A = 53\ k/10\ k$$
$$A = 5.3$$

The gain of the circuit, therefore, will vary from 3.3 up to 5.3, covering the required gain of 4. We will then be able to adjust potentiometer R5 for the standard gain. In operation, the user will open the transducer to atmospheric pressure (our zero reference) and adjust potentiometer R2 for a zero reading. In actual practice, medical people sometimes adjust to "+1" rather than zero because some instruments do not measure vacuums. It is thus impossible to tell whether or not the amplifier is truly zeroed. A vacuum of −100 mm Hg would produce the same reading as 0 mm Hg! In either event, the amplifier is then nulled. We are ready to proceed to the gain adjustment.

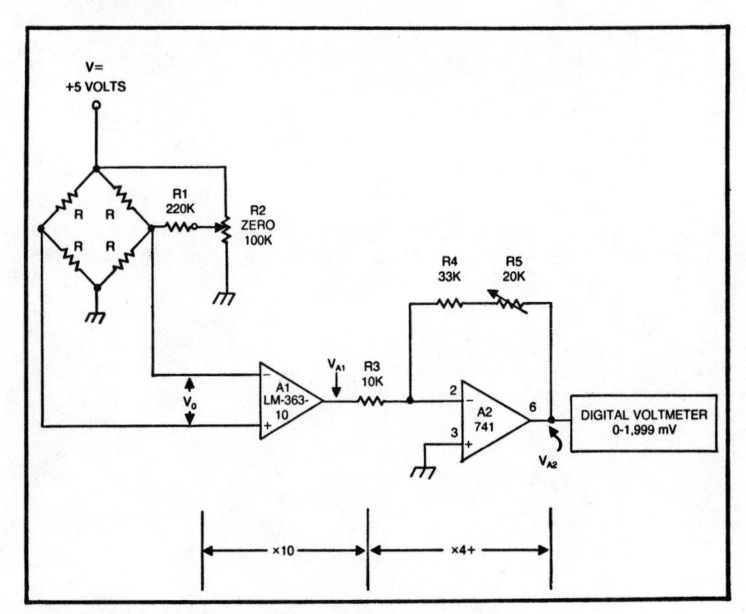

Fig. 15-8. A Wheatstone bridge transducer with amplifier.

The operator will next apply a standard pressure (100 mm Hg is a good idea) with a *sphygmomanometer* (see the texts cited earlier on medical electronics). With the 100 mm Hg pressure being held constant, adjust R5 for a reading of 100 on the digital voltmeter (Fig. 15-8). The amplifier is now ready for use.

Note: This is not a project in the strictest sense because it is not intended for use on real medical instruments—like the kind used on people. The circuit is somewhat simplified and would not provide the degree of protection human subjects require. It is presented FOR EXAMPLE ONLY.

Although this chapter digresses a little from the main subject of the book, it is included in order to make you aware of some applications of these devices. This chapter also provides you with some idea of the techniques used in real electronic instrumentation as used in chemistry, physics, medicine, and the life sciences (that about covers the waterfront). Sufficient design information is provided to allow you to make some of these instruments. I know that many readers like to regard engineers as some kind of loathsome, demonic, slug-like creatures of wholly regrettable parentage who must, alas, be called in whenever the slightest, tiniest little design problem is encountered. With this text, some other of the world's sophisticates will be able to become slug-like themselves.

Chapter 16

Additional Projects

The first edition of this book, (*OP-AMP Circuit Design & Applications,* TAB book No. 787), had only a few projects, and several of my friends have told me about that! At least one of those friends continuously insists that projects be provided for "12-volt applications." I suppose his reason is that he is engaged in mobile amateur radio operations rather than the types of activities that lend themselves to the use of an operational amplifier. While some of these projects operate from 12 volts, I still must say "sorry Norman."

A few of the projects in this book have appeared elsewhere (but not in the original edition of this book). In some cases, I have lifted the project directly and simply reprinted it. The reason for this is that they were extremely popular with users and readers and they still have a wide applicability. There are also some updated versions of the projects. The transducer amplifier in this chapter has been discussed in preceding chapters and it is given here in detail sufficient for you to build your own version. The transducer amplifier uses an updated IC instrumentation amplifier rather than the older op amp that was used in the earlier version. This new IC allows us to reduce the size of the preamplifier, if appropriate.

All of the projects in this chapter have actually been built and tested. There are no "applications notes guesses" in this chapter so you can build with some confidence. It might surprise you that not all applications notes from semiconductor manufacturers have built and tested circuits. I have been burned a few times on this score. I am now a little wary. So wary, in fact, that I refuse to use a circuit from a manufacturer where I have detected such shenanigans!

Most of the components used in projects described in this chapter are readily available from electronics hobbyists suppliers. The only exception is the National Semiconductor LM-363-100 device. Although I suspect it will become popular enough for leading suppliers to stock it, you will have to obtain this chip from an industrial semiconductor distributor such as Schweber Electronics, Hamilton-Avnet, Pioneer-Standard, or some other company. They are usually listed under "electronic equipment and supplies" in local directories. Make sure that they carry National Semiconductor components before you order.

Most of these distributers will sell individual components, but require a minimum order of $10 to $25. In that event, you might want to order other supplies from the same source. You will also find that these companies often have no showroom or pick-up counter (some do, some don't). They do all of their business by telephone. The reason for this is that they are geared toward the industrial user of semiconductors, not the radio-TV-mobile-radio service trade or hobbyist trade as are other distributors. In most cases, however, a money order or bank tellers check will obtain the component you need by United Parcel Service or some similar service if you can't walk in and pick it up.

While I am on the subject, please allow me to digress on my "favorite" gripe with small electronics model shops and small service companies, as well as some advanced hobbyists, who seem to use a large quantity of components. Very few of these people really buy electronic supplies wholesale, despite what they tell you. Take the Radio-TV-HiFi-Mobile-radio service trade. They tend to buy components on an individual basis. In fact, I remember one person who actually bought Mylar capacitors for television service on an as-needed basis. He then had the chutzpah to complain about the wholesaler's prices. He complained that the wholesaler charged him nearly $1 for the component, yet ol' Joe got it for 42 cents. The difference, of course, was quantity. The lower price given to "ol' Joe" was because ol' Joe bought 50 at a time. In most cases, small shops store capacitors in plastic parts cabinets that have little drawers for each value. It takes about as much room to store 20 or 30 capacitors as 1!

The situation in semiconductors is even worse. The typical small operation will buy semiconductors from "replacement" lines, and then cross-reference the device to its semiuniversal replacement. Of course, one number in the replacement line will suffice to replace a large number of part numbers—especially *set* manufacturer (as opposed to semiconductor manufacturer) part numbers.

I have another proposal. The proper way to save money on semiconductor purchases is to use cross-reference guides. When faced with a semiconductor to replace or to use in a project, look in all of the available cross-reference guides such as TAB book No. 1470, *The Master Semiconductor Replacement Handbook–Listed by Industry Standard Number* or TAB book No. 1471, *The Master Semiconductor Replacement Handbook–Listed by Manufacturer's Number.* You can get an idea what type of transistor is used to replace the device under consideration.

The reference guides generally print the main, pertinent specifications of their line in the catalog. Next, look for standard "2N" type numbers being crossed over to the *same* replacement type. With a little effort, you will find the correct replacement device! Those replacement devices are not generally specially made for the replacement trade, but are little more than selected devices from the regular industrial lines. The replacement line people merely order the same industrial type with his own type number printed on the case rather than the "2N" type number.

The cost of these industrial transistors and diodes is a lot lower than the devices in replacement lines. The same is true of integrated circuits. Let's take a few examples. The TV service industry uses 1000 volt PIV, 1-ampere diodes as replacements for the rectifiers in television sets. The "industrial" type with this rating is the 1N4007 device. Most of the replacement diodes are nothing more than 1N4007 devices in an expensive blister pack display carton. The price is a lot different. The 1N4007 and some replacement diodes were compared. Prices were obtained for the same quantity on the same day from distributors in the same city. The price for 100-type 1N4007 devices was $13 (that's 13 cents each!). The replacement line devices were all in the $45 to $70 range! The 2N3904 and 2N3906 devices are pnp and npn plastic transistors used commonly in audio and TV applications. I found the prices for these devices in the $20/100 range (packed in bags, not blister packs). The replacement devices cost an average of $156/200 . . . and that's the quantity prices! The average person could save a lot of money with a little forethought.

When you examine projects and products that use electronic components, you will find only a few types in use despite the large number of different OEM part numbers. One manufacturer of American automobile radios used a special IC device for the audio power amplifier and preamplifier stages in their products. The semiconductor division of the same company made the device. Yet, the car radio division charged (wholesale) four times more money than the 1-to-9 quantity price from the industrial division. I obtained the IC devices from an ordinary industrial distributor and showed them to the person who ran the wholesale operation (along with a car radio repair facility). He couldn't believe that I had obtained the "xx-x" device so inexpensively. We installed it in a car radio and—it worked!

WHEATSTONE BRIDGE TRANSDUCER PREAMPLIFIER

Many scientific and engineering people use resistive Wheatstone bridge strain gauge transducers to make measurements. Some parameter (such as force, pressure, displacement, and so forth) is caused to move the strain gauge diaphragm and thereby change the resistance of the elements to the applied stress parameter.

Some transducers have a relatively low output potential. Sensitivity factors such as 5 to 50 *microvolts* per unit of applied parameters are common. This means a 1 millivolt or so output voltage for relatively high applied stress values. If the transducer output signal is transmitted through a long cable to the instrument used to display the output, then noise is likely. The physiologist who used the transducers I built the amplifier for was experiencing 60 hertz interference. The transducer output was being transmitted through a 6-foot cable to a Tektronix oscilloscope that had a 200-μV/cm deflection factor. All measurements displayed 60 Hz noise. Although the doctor was able to use the data, it was second-best data because of the 60-Hz noise.

I recommended an amplifier at the output of the transducer, but my friend rolled his eyes and mentioned something about funds. The amplifier cost more than $500 (in one version, up to $1500 in others) and the research grant did not include funds for buying amplifiers—at least not in that year. As a result, I built a transducer preamplifier based on the simple IC operational amplifier.

In the paragraphs to follow, we will discuss the original design that used either the RCA CA-3140 device or selected 741 devices and the updated version that uses the newer National Semiconductor LM-363-100 device.

The original circuit for the transducer preamplifier is shown in A of Fig. 16-1. This circuit is based on a low-cost operational amplifier. A1 can be either the RCA CA3140 BiMOS device or a 741 device that is selected for low offset voltage. In most cases, an output offset of less than 150 millivolts (unnulled) is tolerable and can be eliminated in the stage to follow. With some modification, the circuit can be configured to provide null offset, but that was deemed unnecessary.

The circuit shown in Fig. A of 16-1 is the simple dc differential amplifier discussed in a previous chapter. The gain of such an amplifier is given by the expression:

$$A_{vd} = \frac{R3}{R1}$$

Provided that:

$$R1 = R2$$

and,

$$R3 = R4$$

In this particular case, the gain of the differential amplifier is

$$A_{vd} = \frac{1{,}000{,}000}{15{,}000}$$

$$A_{vd} = 67$$

Capacitors C3 and C4 are used to improve stability when using the high-frequency CA3140 device. When using the frequency-compensated 741 device, however, the capacitors may not be needed. The gain at frequencies where oscillation could occur is too low on the 741 device.

There are two connectors used on the transducer preamplifier. The input connector J1 is not specified because it will depend upon the type of connector used on the transducer. The usual practice or transducer manufacturers is to provide a cable with a connector on the end of it, but others will mount the connector on the body of the transducer. The original Grass® FT-03 transducer that this amplifier was built to serve is of the latter construction. We used a ITT-Cannon connector for this purpose.

The output connector (J2) is one of the small blue Amphenol 126-series connectors used in many instrumentation applications. Almost any of these connectors can be used in this application because only a few wires are needed. I recommend either the 7-pin or 9-pin versions so that future expansion can be accommodated.

Wheatstone bridge transducers require external excitation potentials. The resistive strain gauge Wheatstone bridge usually requires a dc potential (or RMS ac potential) with a maximum value of 5 to 10 volts. The Grass transducer, for example, is specified at 7.5 volts dc maximum. A popular medical arterial blood pressure transducer, on the other hand, is specified at 5 volts dc maximum.

There are several ways to provide the excitation potential. We could, for example, place the excitation power supply in the electronics (if any) external to the transducer preamplifier. Or, as we did in this project, we could place the excitation power supply inside the transducer preamplifier. The +5 volt dc excitation potential is provided by a 100-milliampere, LM-309H three-terminal IC regulator. This device is available in a T0-5 transistor package. It will readily fit inside a small metal package housing the amplifier.

The zener diode (Z1) shown in A of Fig. 16-1 is not used for voltage regulation, but for protection of the transducer. The LM-309H input potential is derived from the +12-volt dc power supply to the operational amplifier. Because the transducer will burn out at that potential, a shorted LM-309H would destroy the expensive transducer (sigh!). The zener potential is selected to be above the excitation potential (5 volts in this case), but less than the maximum voltage allowed to the transducer. In the version of the preamplifier that I built, the diode was rated at 7.5 volts. That is maximum rating of the transducer. If the LM-309H shorts out, then the diode will conduct and either clamp the voltage or blow fuse F1 (preferably the latter).

The two capacitors shunted across the zener diode are used to reduce the random noise produced by the regulator and the zener diode. A reverse-biased avalanche diode, such as the zener, will produce a large amount of noise. These two capacitors are used to reduce the noise applied to the transducer, hence to the amplifier. The reason for the use of two capacitors is that the 10 μF unit is needed for low-frequency components, while the 0.1 μF unit is used for higher frequencies. The 10 μF capacitor is an electrolytic so it is almost useless at higher frequencies.

Note the parts list for the transducer preamplifier of Fig. 16-1. The resistors are 1-percent types in order to keep the common mode rejection

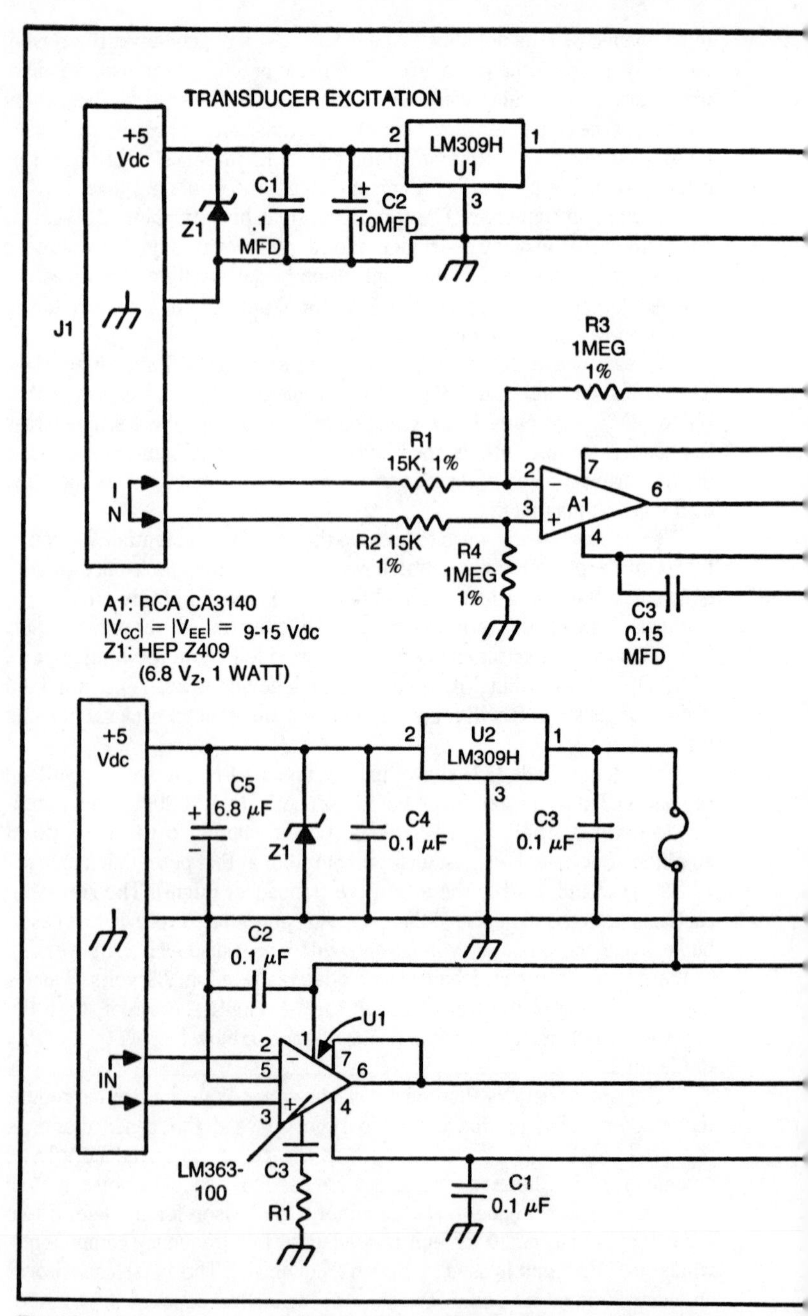

Fig. 16-1. A transducer preamplifier circuit (A) and an updated version of the circuit (B).

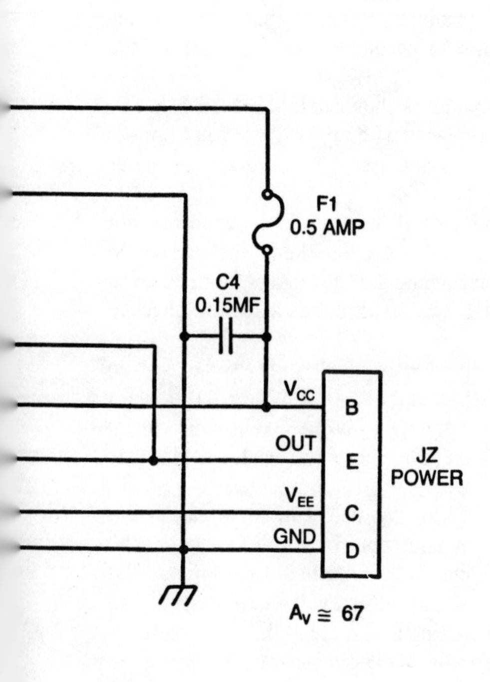

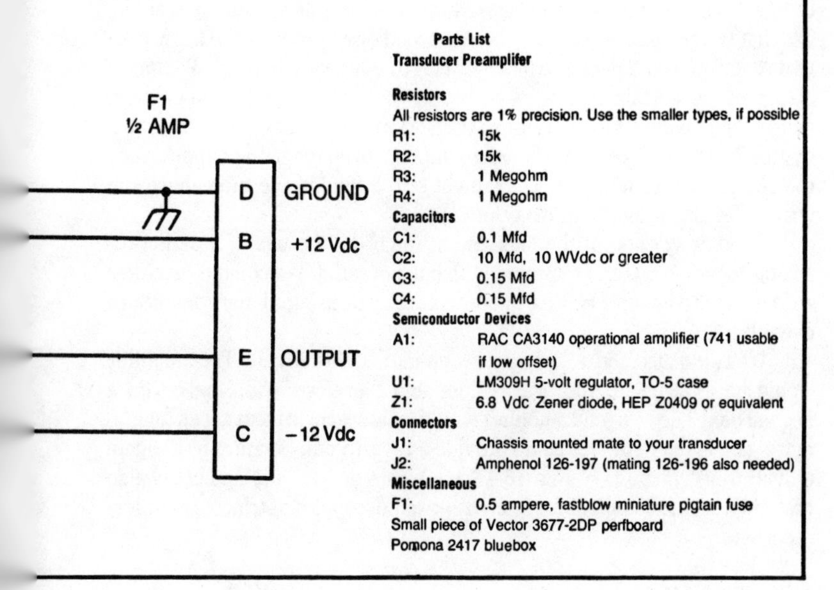

Parts List
Transducer Preamplifer

Resistors

All resistors are 1% precision. Use the smaller types, if possible

R1:	15k
R2:	15k
R3:	1 Megohm
R4:	1 Megohm

Capacitors

C1:	0.1 Mfd
C2:	10 Mfd, 10 WVdc or greater
C3:	0.15 Mfd
C4:	0.15 Mfd

Semiconductor Devices

A1:	RAC CA3140 operational amplifier (741 usable if low offset)
U1:	LM309H 5-volt regulator, TO-5 case
Z1:	6.8 Vdc Zener diode, HEP Z0409 or equivalent

Connectors

J1:	Chassis mounted mate to your transducer
J2:	Amphenol 126-197 (mating 126-196 also needed)

Miscellaneous

F1:	0.5 ampere, fastblow miniature pigtain fuse

Small piece of Vector 3677-2DP perfboard
Pomona 2417 bluebox

ratio intact. If some provision is made for adjusting the CMRR, (making R4 variable), then resistors with a looser tolerance are possible. Substitutions of most parts can be made in order to accommodate your own special situations. None are crucial.

The updated version of the amplifier is shown in B of Fig. 16-1. In this circuit, the operational amplifier is replaced with a fixed-gain IC instrumentation amplifier (ICIA). The gain of this amplifier is 100. It is a little higher than the gain of the previous circuit.

The ICIA device requires no external resistors in order to operate properly. The gain-setting circuitry is all internal to the IC package so the external circuit is simplified. This fact confers an advantage for the user in that four fewer resistors are needed. The result is that a smaller physical configuration is possible.

Capacitor C3 and resistor R1 are optional and they are used to custom shape the frequency response of the amplifier. The LM-363-100 has a high-gain bandwidth product. Some shaping may be needed in some crucial applications. I do not recommend using the capacitor/resistor unless it is needed.

Several modifications of this circuit are useful in some cases. We could, for example, provide an external null control. Bring a resistor (100 kohm or so) from one of the unused pins on J2 to one of the input lines of J1. A potentiometer in the external box would select a voltage to be applied to the resistor, hence the offset to be provided. The use of this null control is to cancel any offset present in the transducer. The strain-gauge Wheatstone bridge can sometimes develop a stress offset that is permanent, yet not so bad that the transducer needs to be discarded or returned to the factory. In that case, we would need the offset circuit to eliminate this bias. We might also produce certain situations in the application that biases the strain gauge. The medical blood pressure transducer, for example, can develop a hydrostatic "head" artifact when the plumbing from the patient approaches the transducer from above. The weight of the fluid in the tube above the transducer diaphragm will bias the data.

Another version of the bias circuit might be the use of a digital-to-analog converter (DAC) to provide the null potential. We could then either zero it under computer control or automatically by using a binary counter to drive the DAC.

We could also add a "rear-end" amplifier to this circuit. The amplifier would be external to the preamplifier and therefore would be inside a second box. The rear-end amplifier would be low gain in most cases (unless more gain is needed), but could provide a zero-to-unity feature to the gain (which would make B of Fig. 16-1 have a gain of 0 to 100) and could also provide a *position* control for use with oscilloscopes or stripchart (paper) recorders.

NULL VOLTMETER

A null voltmeter is an instrument that will register voltages plus and minus around zero. In most cases, the idea of the null voltmeter is to find the null in circuits such as discriminators, Wheatstone bridges, and so forth. The null voltmeter shown in A of Fig. 16-2 will perform well for most such applications.

There are two null indicators for this circuit: a dc meter movement and a light emitting diode (LED) indicator. The meter is used in conjunction with potentiometer R15 is used to measure the output voltage from amplifier A3. This same voltage is also monitored by amplifier A4, the LED indicator driver. The feedback path of amplifier A4 has a pair of back-to-back LEDs. Diode D1 will conduct when the voltage at the output of A3 is negative; D2 conducts when it is positive (note that A4 is an inverter).

When the input potential is exactly zero, for example when the external bridge is nulled, both LEDs will be extinguished.

There are three other amplifiers in this circuit. Amplifier A2 is merely a zero to unity stage that controls the output potential. Amplifier A1B has two fixed gains selectable by switch S1. The *low* position is unity gain while the *high* position is X100.

The input amplifier, A1A, is a simple, single-operational differential amplifier. The gain of this stage (follows the equation given earlier in this chapter) is ×10. Potentiometer R5 is used to set the CMRR to null. This potentiometer is adjusted by shorting together the two input terminals and then driving them simultaneously with a signal source. With both inputs seeing the same signal, the equal-but-opposite gains of the two inputs should cause a zero output. Null the voltage to zero using potentiometer R5. If a low frequency ac source is used, then view it on an oscilloscope connected to signal output jack J5.

The power supply for this circuit is a pair of 9-volt dc batteries. This was done in order to make the instrument portable (the original application was to amplify the output of a Wheatstone bridge used to measure amateur radio antenna feedpoint impedance). If you do not need portability, then it might pay to replace these batteries with +12-volt dc-regulated power supplies.

Battery B3 is used to excite the external bridge (if needed). In my original application, the radio transmitter supplied power to the bridge. Battery B3 was not needed. If you use this null voltmeter with some external resistive strain gauge, however, B3 is advisable. Like the main power supplies, B3 can be replaced with a three-terminal IC voltage regulator (see similar circuit in A and B of Fig. 16-1).

Potentiometer R14 is used to provide a null cancellation capability for the null voltmeter. In most cases, this potentiometer is best adjusted by shorting J1/J2 to ground (J4) and then setting R10 to maximum. When this is done, adjust R14 for zero output voltage. This particular adjustment can be done without the use of external instruments as might be used for the CMRR adjustment.

Note the parts list for the null voltmeter is shown in Fig. 16-2. None of the components are crucial in this project. Even the resistors can be lower

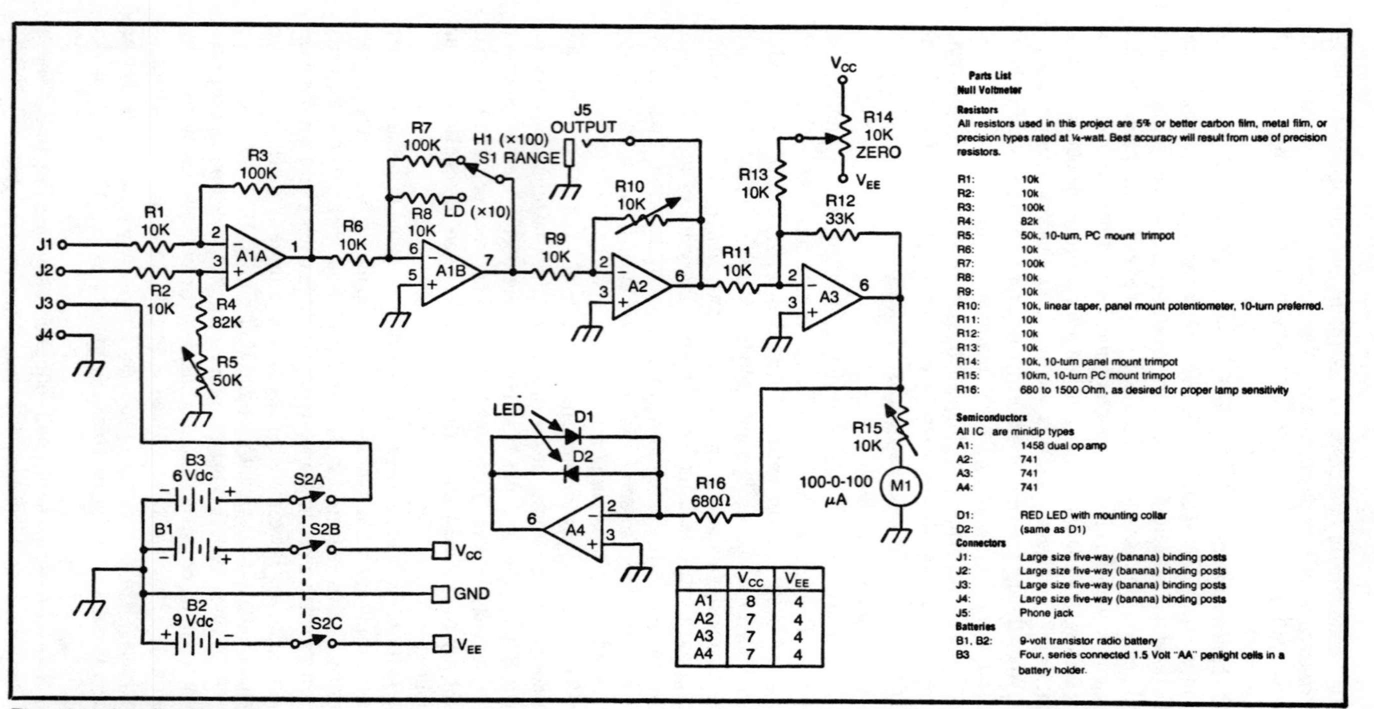

Fig. 16-2. A null voltmeter.

tolerance devices (i.e., 5 percent). The operational amplifiers are all either 741 devices or 1458 devices (which are of the 741 family of devices, being a dual 741 in an 8-pin DIP package).

PROGRAMMABLE-GAIN AMPLIFIER

A programmable-gain amplifier is one in which the gain may be set by some external agency such as a binary word from a computer or a current level applied to a programming pin (and so forth). In this project, the gain of the amplifier is under control of a computer output port.

The heart of the amplifier is an integrated circuit instrumentation amplifier (ICIA) or an equivalent three-op-amp Instrumentation amplifier. In either case, resistor R1 in Fig. 16-3 is the gain setting resistor. If the device selected is an ICIA, then the resistor is that normally connected to pins G1 and G2. If, on the other hand, the amplifier selected is of the three-op-amp variety, then this is the same as R1 in the previous circuits (i.e., the gain setting resistor between the two feedback resistors of the input amplifier stages).

In most ICIA devices, the gain will be either:

$$A_v = \frac{50}{R1} + 1$$

or,

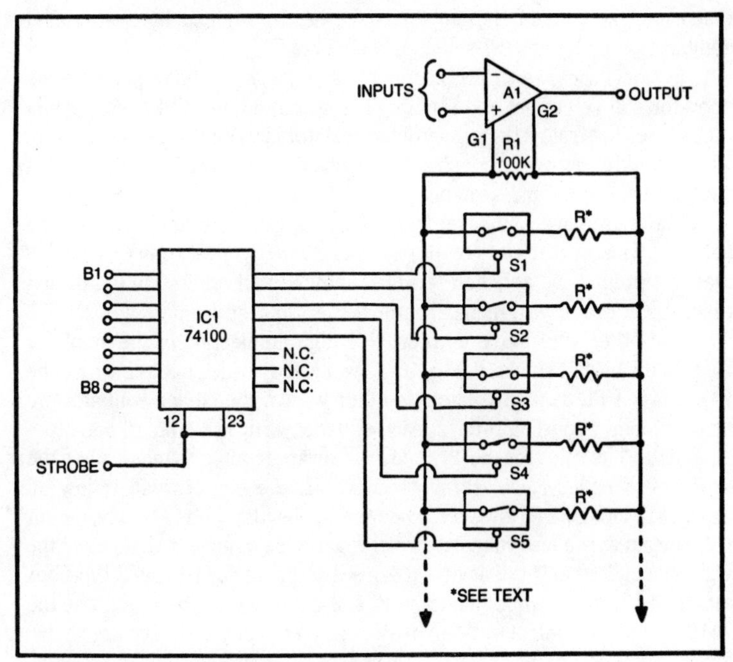

Fig. 16-3. The 74100 controlling switches.

$$A_v = \frac{40}{R1} + 1$$

The preceding equations are predicated upon fixed values for the two feedback resistors; namely 25 kohm and 20 kohm, respectively. You should recall that the equation then drops out to the very equation given for the three-op-amp instrumentation amplifier in a previous chapter.

The gain of our amplifier is modified by the fact that we now have external resistors in parallel with the normal gain-setting resistor. These resistors (designated R in Fig. 16-3) are selected by means of electronic CMOS switches such as the CD-4016 or CD-4066 devices (each a quad CMOS switch). When the control terminal, indicated by the circle, is made LOW then the switch is conducting and had a low forward resistance. In that case, the gain of the amplifier will be set by the parallel combination of R1 and the selected resistor:

$$A_v = \frac{50}{\left[\dfrac{R_1 \times R}{R_1 + R}\right]} + 1$$

The preceding equation holds true only so long as only one external resistor is selected to be placed in parallel with R1. If we want a gain that is somewhat odd, it is possible to select more than one parallel resistor. In that case, the gain of the amplifier will be determined by the parallel combination of R1 and *all* selected resistors.

In most cases, I suspect that only unique gains will be required so the operator will select but one shunting resistor at a time. But it may pay in other cases to arrange the values of the resistors in a kind of 1-2-4-8 system which would allow one to construct any gain between 1 and 10 or 1 and 100 if sufficient resistors and switches are provided.

There are several different ways that the gain-setting resistor can be selected. One neat trick is to simply provide mechanical rotary switching that will ground the selected terminal and keep all others HIGH. In that case, the operator will manually select the required gain.

The other alternative is to provide digital selection of the amplifier gain. In the circuit shown in Fig. 16-3, we have provided such control. The 74100 is a TTL dual quad-latch. In other words, the device contains two banks of four Type-D flip-flops, each of which will "remember" one bit of input data. The rules for the Type-D flip-flop are familiar to most: when the *strobe* (also called *clock*) terminal is HIGH, the outputs will follow all changes of input data. However, when the strobe line goes LOW, the output will remain at the last valid data level regardless of further changes of the input signal. In the 74100 device, there are a total of eight Type-D flip-flops arranged four to a strobe line (pins 12 and 23). We can, therefore, use the 74100 device to control up to eight switches (of which, only five are shown for the sake of simplicity).

The inputs of the 74100 device are connected to the bit lines of the computer output ports, B1 through B8. The idea is to write a LOW to the bit that corresponds to the desired gain. We do this neat trick by placing the correct word on the computer port. For example, if we want to turn on switch S3, then we will make B3 LOW and all others HIGH. This is done by writing the word 11111011 to the output port.

The 74100 will not automatically accept the word written to its inputs unless the strobe lines are HIGH. We can accomplish this trick in at least three different ways. We could, if we had access to the bus inside of the computer, create a logic circuit that would decode the port address (and the fact that an output operation is taking place) and then issue an OUT command to the strobe line. The HIGH level of the OUT command would then tell the 74100 to accept the data written at that time to the data bus. In that case, of course, the B1 through B8 lines of the 74100 would be connected to bits B0 through B7 of the data bus (note numbering offset). This method can be seen in greater detail in TAB book No. 1396, *Microprocessor Interfacing.*

Another technique would be to dedicate one bit of a second output port to become the strobe signal. We could, for example, designate port-Ø as the data port to be connected to the inputs of the 74100, and port-1 as the control port. Let's assume that the strobe lines from the 74100 are connected to bit-8 of port-1. We would write a program that would accomplish the following steps:

1. Write 11111011 to port-Ø
2. Write 1ØØØØØØØ to port-1
3. Write ØØØØØØØØ to port-1

The last step is necessary to prevent the 74100 from following additional changes at its inputs. We could then write the next value to output port-Ø when the time comes.

Still another method for handling the strobe is allowable when the system does not require all eight switches. In that case, we could leave bit B8 of the 74100 unused. The corresponding bit of the output port then becomes the strobe signal. A typical scenario might be to write 11111011 to the output port for a brief period (say 1 millisecond). The "1" in the B8 position would serve to turn on the strobe. This operation is then followed immediately by writing 01111011 to the port. Because the data bit is still LOW, and the control bit dropped LOW, the 74100 will remember the correct code to turn on switch S3.

The digitally programmable amplifier has many uses and it is especially powerful where either automatic or remote control of gain is needed. One application that I find useful is automatic scaling of the amplifier gain. We could, for example, create a special calibration signal for the amplifier. Of course, this signal would have to be turned on and off by the computer. The computer program would then scale the amplifier to the optimum gain by comparing the output response to the calibration signal with some value stored in memory somewhere. We could, for example, A/D convert the

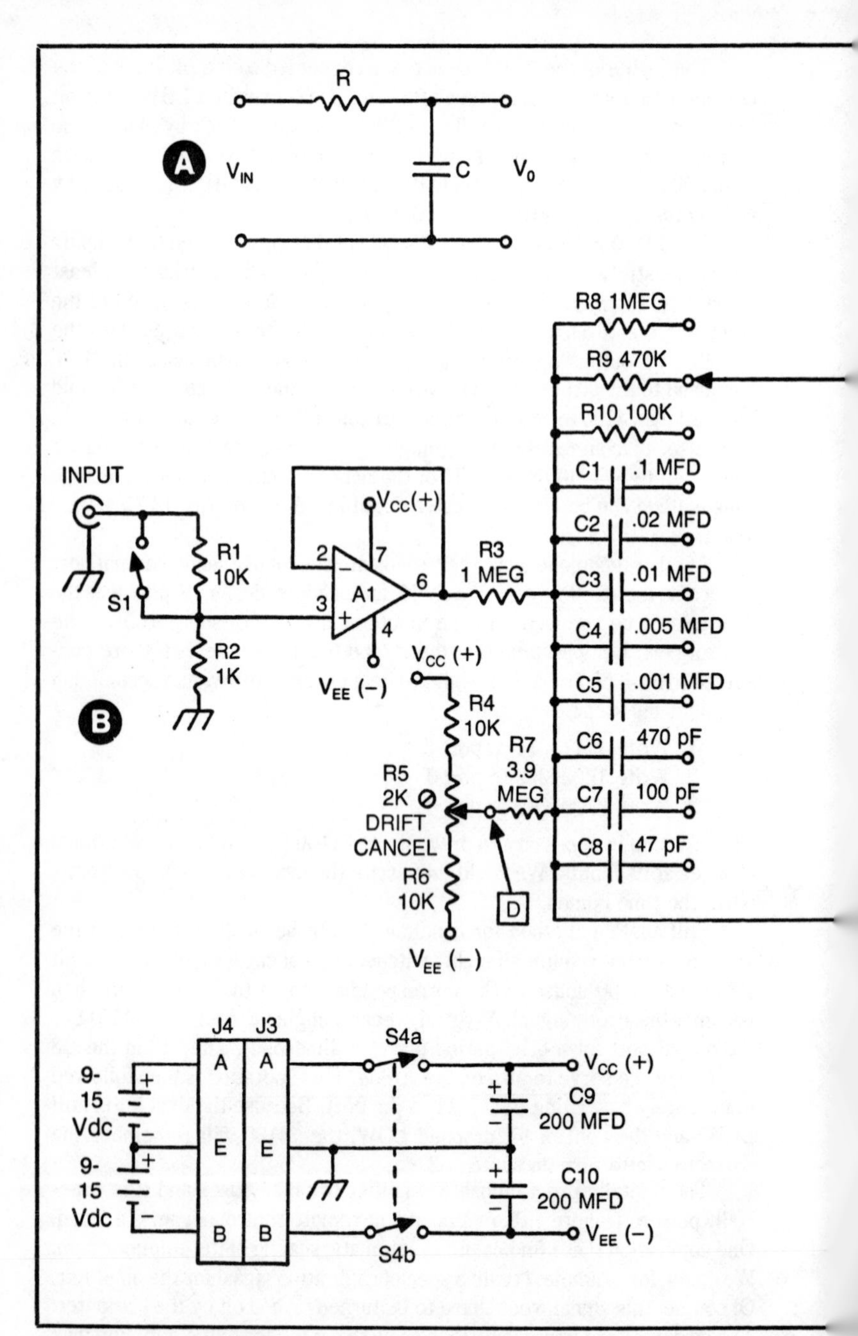

Fig. 16-4. The RC network (A), the Miller integrator (B), and the circuit for a practical, multi-time-constant operational amplifier integrator.

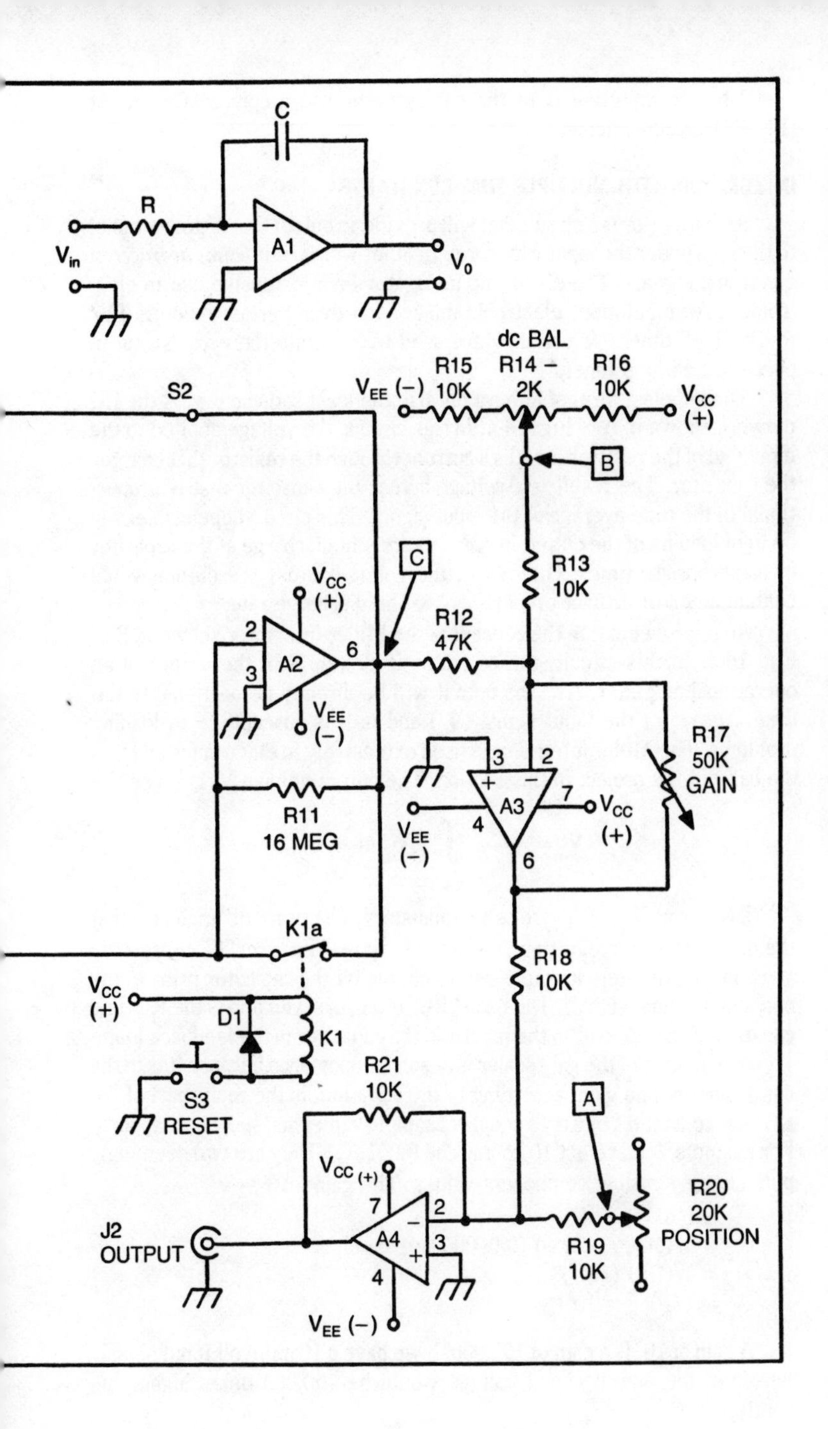
C
R
A1
V_in
V_0
dc BAL
R15 10K
R14 – 2K
R16 10K
V_EE (–)
V_CC (+)
S2
B
C
R13 10K
V_CC (+)
2
3
A2
6
V_EE (–)
R12 47K
R17 50K GAIN
3
2
A3
7
4
6
V_EE (–)
V_CC (+)
R11 16 MEG
K1a
V_CC (+)
D1
K1
R18 10K
S3 RESET
R21 10K
A
V_CC (+)
7
2
A4
3
4
J2 OUTPUT
R19 10K
R20 20K POSITION
V_EE (–)

signal before inputting it to the computer or use a comparator circuit (LM-311 or equivalent).

INTEGRATOR WITH MULTIPLE TIME-CONSTANTS

An integrator is a circuit that will provide an output that is proportional to the area under the input waveform. In other words, it is a *time averager* of electronic signals. The electronic integrator finds extensive use in electronic instrumentation, electronic music, and even certain modern TV/Radio/Hi-Fi tuners where they are used to integrate the error signal in phase locked loop tuners.

The simplest form of integrator, also the least satisfactory, is the RC network shown in A of Fig. 16-4. In this circuit, the voltage applied to the input end of the resistor creates a current through the resistor that charges the capacitor. The result is a voltage across the capacitor that is proportional to the time average of the input signal. This circuit depends heavily on light loading of the output in order to prevent discharge of the capacitor at inappropriate times. Otherwise, the voltage across the output would contain an error artifact proportional to the discharge rate.

An improvement in the concept is the Miller integrator shown in B of Fig. 16-4. In this circuit, the capacitor is driven from the output of an operational amplifier, A1. The output will be directly proportional to the time average of the input signal (V_{in}) and is less susceptible to loading problems. The Miller integrator is used extensively in electronics and it is the basis of the project in this section. The output voltage V_o is given by:

$$V_o = \frac{1}{RC} \int_{t_o}^{t_1} V_{in}\, dt + C$$

The terms V_{in} and V_o are self-explanatory. The term "dt" indicates that the mathematical integration is made over time. The term "C" represents any constant of integration present (a charge on the capacitor prior to the onset of the input signal). The term "RC" is a gain scaler and is the RC time constant of the resistor in the input and the capacitor in the feedback loop.

The matter of the gain scaler is of some importance because it is in the denominator. The gain, according to the equation, is the reciprocal of the RC time constant. Let's try a couple of sample values and see what happens. For example, let's select 10 kohms and 0.001 μF. They are two seemingly imminently sensible component values. The gain is:

$A_v = I/RC$
$A_v = 1/(10{,}000 \text{ ohms})\ (0.000000001 \text{ farads})$
$A_v = 1/(10^4)\ (10^{-9})$
$A_v = 1/10^{-5} = 10^5$

A gain of 10^5 is a gain of 100,000! If we have a 10 millivolt input signal, therefore, the output signal voltage would be 100,000 times higher instantly:

$V_o = (10\ mV)(100{,}000)$
$V_o = 1{,}000{,}000\ mV$
$V_o = 1000$ volts!

Clearly, because the operational amplifier operates on less than 20 volts (most less than 15 volts), the output will never rise to the correct level. The amplifier output will saturate, becoming useless, after only a few milliseconds no matter how little input signal is realized.

One major aspect of the gain problem is that all real operational amplifiers have some input offset current. These will tend to charge the feedback capacitor and cause the output signal to creep upward from the instant the circuit is turned on. If the RC time constant is small enough, the output will snap to saturation immediately. The gain is simply too high for practical use. This is especially true with low-cost operational amplifiers with bipolar input stages.

Regardless of the input impedance of the operational amplifier, however, it is necessary to regard the gain scaler with some trepidation. If an input signal is truly ac (has no dc component), then the output may well follow the input with little trouble. If there is any dc component on the input signal, it will most surely charge the capacitor at a rate determined by its value and the value of the gain scaler.

Figure 16-4(C) shows the circuit for a practical, multi-time constant operational amplifier integrator. With the exception of amplifier A2, all of the operational amplifier devices in this circuit can be 741-family devices or better. For most applications, there will be nothing crucial about these components. Amplifier A2, however, must be an RCA CA3140 BiMOS device or equivalent. The reasons for this restriction will become apparent in a moment.

The actual Miller integrator in this project is A2. The input resistor is R3, which has a value of 1 megohms. A rotary switch is used to select from a bank of feedback capacitors that range in value from 47 picofarads up to 0.1 microfarads. Also selectable are a pair of resistors, R8 and R9, which convert A2 into an amplifier with gains of 1 and ½, respectively. This latter feature is strictly optional and has nothing to do with integration.

The RCA CA3140 device was selected because it uses MOSFET transistors in the input amplifiers, and thereby achieves an immense input impedance (over 10^{12} ohms claimed in the spec sheet!). The high input impedance corresponds to a low bias current supplied from the inputs. Hence there is a lower output offset potential to charge the capacitors. There will still be some minor biasing of the capacitor voltages, however, and this is leaked off by resistor R11. The value of this resistor must be very large (16 megohms) or it will cause the capacitors to leak charge faster than the operational amplifier can supply it. The result would be a large error term. If you prefer, try a higher value resistor at first. I found that 16 megohms worked nicely, but I selected it because of availability in my personal junkbox and not because of some arcane technical reason.

A mechanical switch (S3) is used to provide reset for the integrator. Prior to use, the integrator should be reset in order to eliminate the results of the previous operation (the "C" term in the equation). When S3 is pressed, it will ground one end of relay K1 and thereby cause the contacts of K1 to pull-in and close. When the contacts are closed, the capacitor is shorted out and will discharge.

An alternative to this method might be digital control of the reset function. We could, for example, replace S3 with an open-collector inverter stage such as the 7404 device. When a HIGH is applied to the inverter input terminal, the output will go LOW (thereby grounding the "cold" end of relay coil K1). This last, however, is a frill for most constructors unless they need digital computer control.

The drift problem will exist in all operational amplifier integrators because of imperfections in "real," as opposed to "ideal," operational amplifiers. All such amplifiers will have offset problems, but some more than others. The 741-devices, for example, are all but useless for most integrator applications. The 741 output, when used in prototypes of this circuit, will rise to the supply rail at an extremely fast rate. The "premium" type 725 was almost as bad as the junk 741 devices despite a cost difference of 10:1. I found that the BiMOS RCA device, which cost less than the μA725 device, was far superior in integrator applications. Hence, I selected the now-popular CA3140 device for this project. And it is now less costly than it was at that time.

With the CA3140 device in use, the *drift cancel* control (R5) is capable of overcoming the drift problem. The idea here is to inject a countercurrent into the circuit that will exactly overcome the drift caused by operational amplifier bias currents.

The input amplifier A1 is a unity-gain noninverting follower made from a 741-operational amplifier. The input network, R1/R2, are used to attenuate the input signal to scale it to the integrator (when needed). An alternative method is to replace the noninverting unity gain follower with a zero to unity gain inverting follower stage. This is done by making the input resistor 100 kohms and the feedback resistor a 100-kohm potentiometer.

The two output amplifiers, A3 and A4, are used to control the signal and are the "housekeeping" stages of the project. Amplifier A4 is merely an output buffer, but also serves to accommodate the *position* control. This control would be used to position the trace on the oscilloscope or strip-chart recorder used to display the output waveform (this is, of course, optional).

Amplifier A3 is used both to provide an output gain control (0 to 5) and a dc balance control. The purpose of the dc balance is to reduce any offset of the signal baseline when the gain control is varied from zero to maximum. This control is adjusted until the baseline remains stable as the gain control is varied. It operates by canceling the inherent dc offset created by previous stages. It must be adjusted when the input signal is zero (input terminals are shorted to ground).

Appendix A

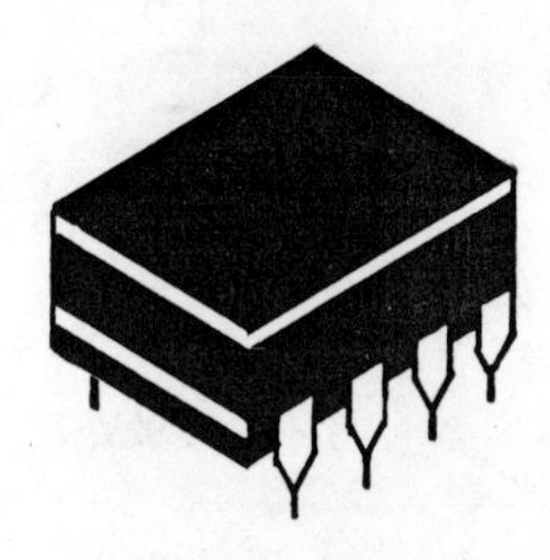

Calculations

Infinite input impedance, infinite open loop gain, and zero output impedance. 1.1

$$E_{OUT} = A_V(E_{IN}) = -(33{,}000/2200)\ (1.5) = -(15)$$
$$(1.5) = 22\tfrac{1}{2}$$ 1.2

$$A_V = 10^6/10^3 = 10^3 = 1000 \text{ or } 60\text{ dB}$$ 1.3

$$A_V = \frac{\dfrac{(20K) + (20K)\ (9K)}{(0.1K)}}{1K} + 9K = \frac{\dfrac{29 + 180}{0.1}}{1} = 1800 + 29 = 1829$$ 1.4

$$E_{OUT} = -[(10K/1K)\ (E_1) + (10/1K)\ (E_2)]$$ 1.5
$$10 = 10E_1 + (10)\ (.1)$$
$$9 = 10E_1$$

Unity 2.1

Impedance transformation 2.2

$$E_{OUT} = E_{IN}\ (1500/100)$$ 2.3
$$= 1.36\ (15)$$
$$= 20.4V$$

Common mode rejection ratio, or CMRR. 3.1

$$A_V = R_1/R_3 = 270K/10K = 27$$ 3.2

$$E_{OUT} = A_V E_{IN} = (27)\ (0.050) = 1.35V$$ 3.3

Amplifying physiological signals, and amplifying Wheatstone bridge output. 3.4

$$A_V = (1 + 2R_5/R_7)\ (R_1/R_3)$$ 3.5
$$= [1 + 2(50K)/1K](10K/5K)$$
$$= (1 + 100)\ (2)$$
$$= 202$$

$$E_{OUT} = -\left[\frac{R_4}{R_1}E_1 + \frac{R_4}{R_2}E_2 + \frac{R_4}{R_3}E_3\right] \quad 5.1$$

$$= -\left[\frac{20}{1}(0.02) + \frac{20}{5}(0.22) + \frac{20}{20}(1.0)\right]$$

$$= -[20(0.02) + 4(0.22) + 1(1.0)]$$

$$= -\ 1.92V$$

$$E_{OUT} = \left(\frac{100}{10}\right)E_1 + \left[-\left(\frac{50}{10}E_2 + \frac{50}{10}E_3\right)\left(\frac{100}{10}\right)\right] \quad 5.2$$

$$= (10)\ (2.2) - [(5(0.05) + 5\ (0.1)\ (10)]$$
$$= 22 - [(0.25 + .5)\ 10]$$
$$= 22 - [(.75)\ (10)]$$
$$= 22 - 7.5$$
$$= 14.5V$$

Analog multiplier 5.3

(2.0) (1.0) = 2.0 volts 5.4

Connect the 10K resistor from the output of A_2 to the noninverting input of A_3. Under these circumstances the output will be $\log E_1 - \log E_2$. Taking the antilog of this is equal to finding E_1/E_2. 5.5

Differentiator 5.6

$E_{OUT} = -de/dt$ 5.7

Cosine A 5.8

Integrator 5.9

Appendix B

Hobbyist Power Supply Designs

One of the most pressing needs for most electronic hobbyists and experimenters is a stable, reliable source of dc power. Needed are bench power supplies, that can be used for many different projects, and dedicated power supplies that are incorporated into specific projects and thereafter remain with the project.

There are a number of sources of well-made commercial power supplies for both bench and service usage. In large quantities, these power supplies are quite low in cost and there would be a serious question of whether any given project or product should have its own custom-designed power supply or one of those so-called "O.E.M." power supplies. For the hobbyist who will build no more than one or two of a kind of any given project, the cost of those commercial power supplies might well be prohibitive.

Another aspect of homebrewing the power supply is the use of junkbox and surplus components. Almost all hobbyists and amateurs will eventually accumulate a respectable supply of electronic components bought at bargain prices or salvaged from electronic equipment. When one uses these sources of components, it becomes possible to reduce the cost of a one-of-a-kind power supply to almost nil.

In the "old days," that is the time before integrated circuits (there *was* such a time, you know!), the design and construction of voltage regulators was a costly affair. Only a few high-quality power supplies would have voltage regulator circuits. Today, any number of manufacturers offer three- and four-terminal integrated circuit voltage regulators that provide the best advantage of voltage regulation and none of the old headaches. In this appendix, the projects use IC voltage regulators.

It would be impossible to select a "universal" set of power supplies that will meet the needs of all electronic hobbyists (too wide is the range of overall interest)! But there are a few different sets of power supply ratings that are common to a large number of users. In this appendix, we will examine designs for the following power supplies:

5-volt dc @ 1-ampere.
5-volt dc @ 5-ampere.
12-volt dc @ 1-ampere.
± 12-volt dc @1-ampere (per voltage).
1 to 25-volt dc @ 5-ampere adjustable.

There are quite a number of other power supply designs we could examine, but they are really outside of the scope of this book. The 5-volt power supplies are intended for those users who experiment with digital electronic projects. The "universal" power supply for small digital projects is the 5-volt @ 1-ampere supply. The 5-ampere version (also at the standard "TTL" voltage of 5 volts) is used for small, single-board computers (i.e., KIM-1, Superboard II AIM-65 or Z80 Starter Kit). Higher-current, 5-volt power supplies are used in larger digital computers, but they are the topic of other books. The 12-volt @ 1-ampere power supply is used for a wide variety of transistor and linear IC applications, and for those CMOS digital projects in which V_{SS} is zero (ground potential).

For most readers who want to work with operational amplifiers and some of the other devices described in this book, the most practical power supply will be the ± 12-volt @ 1-ampere power supply. This circuit will provide up to 1 ampere of current at +12 volts and −12 volts (1 ampere from each).

For those with a wide range of needs there is an adjustable power supply that will output from 1.25 to 25 volts at current levels up to 5-amperes (*Note*: lower current versions can be built by using a smaller transformer).

The author challenges the reader to build their own "super" power supply for bench use by combining several of these projects. Build a supply with ±12-volts @ 1-ampere, +5 volts @ either 1- or 5-amperes and a 1 to 25 volt power supply at 5-amperes or so. None of the projects are extremely difficult to build, nor are any of them critical, so begin work now . . .

5-VOLT DC, 1-AMP POWER SUPPLY

The 5-volt, 1-ampere power supply shown in Fig. B-1 is usable for a large variety of TTL and CMOS digital projects, as well as those analog projects that will operate from this low voltage. The basis for this power supply is a three-terminal IC voltage regulator. The 5-volt type of regulator was one of the earliest available in three-terminal IC form. The LM-309K is now considered the venerable predecessor for all three terminal IC voltage regulator devices. In this application, you can use either the LM-309K, LM-340K-5 or the 7805, all three are approximately equivalent devices.

When selecting a voltage regulator, keep in mind the current rating

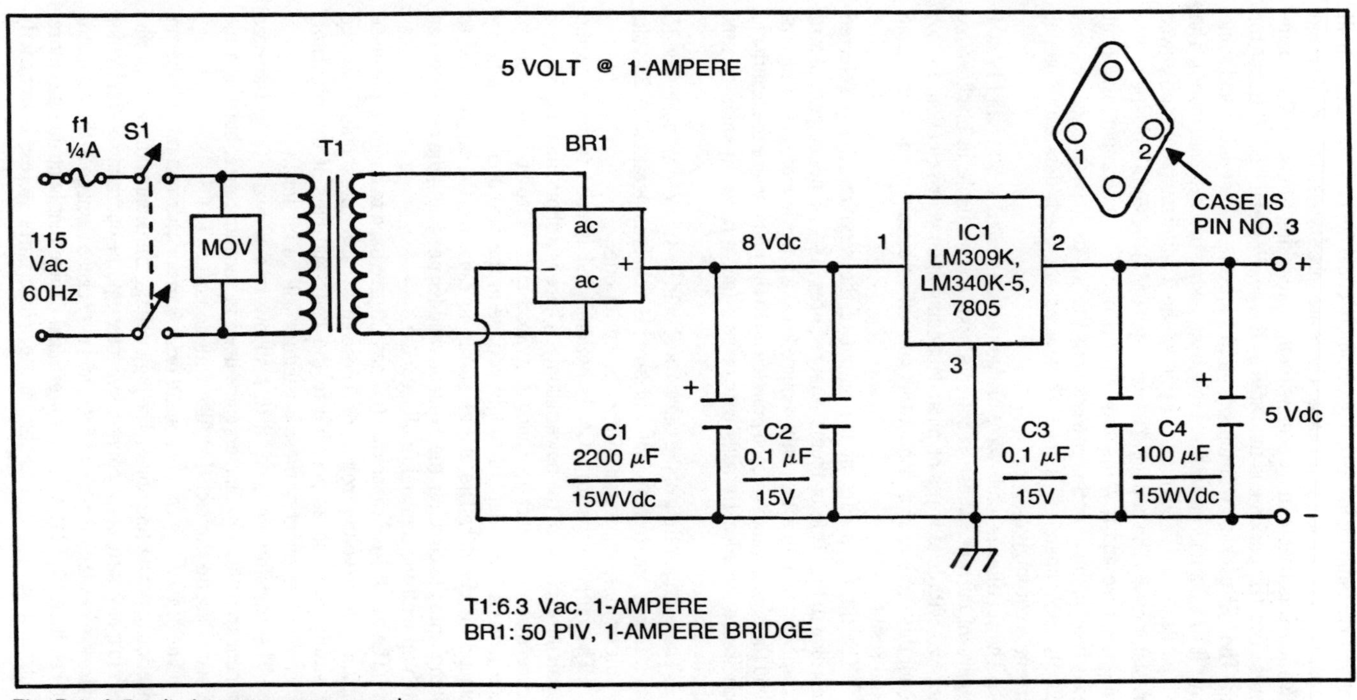

Fig. B-1. A 5-volt, 1-ampere power supply.

that you are building for. Not all seemingly equal devices are usable in all cases. The problem is the package. There are three types. The "H" package (LM-309H) is usable in free-air without heatsinking to only 100 milliamperes. The "H" package is the same as the small, metal "T0-5" transistor can. The "K" package will support up to 1 ampere unheatsinked and some drive it to 1.5 amperes with suitable heatsinking (not recommended). The "K" package (LM-309K) is the same as the T0-3 diamond-shaped power transistor case. The popular "T" package (LM-340T-5) is a plastic power transistor case and it will safely support only 750 milliamperes without heavy heatsinking. For this power supply the "K" package devices are most heartily recommended. If the "T" devices are used, derate the output current accordingly.

The rectifier is a full-wave bridge rectifier rated at 50 volts PIV at 1 ampere of current. These rectifier stacks are available in black epoxy packages with lead wires or pins, depending upon your selection. Do not mount this rectifier in a manner that cuts off air circulation or overheating could result.

The filter capacitor at the output of the rectifier (C1) is selected according to the "rule-of-thumb" that requires 2000 μF per ampere of load current. Some authorities only require 1000 μF per ampere, but I recommend the higher value as good practice up to the point where the additional capacitance significantly adds cost or size (not a factor in small current supplies).

The voltage rating of the capacitor should be 15WVdc or more. The 15 volt rating is the lowest that will provide reliable operation. A 25-volt, 35-volt or more capacitor will not be out of line.

The output capacitor, C4, is optional and is used to improve the transient response of the power supply. There is a short time required for the regulator to react to changes in load current so it is possible to experience a "suck-out" of supply voltage in the face of a sudden heavy demand for current. The charge stored in capacitor C4 can be used to "dump" into the circuit in the event of a sudden need until the regulator can catch up with the demand (milliseconds).

The two 0.1 μF capacitors (C2 and C3) are used to improve the noise immunity of the voltage regulator. These small capacitors should be located physically as close as possible to the body and pins of the regulator. Otherwise, the effect of these capacitors will be minimal.

The transformer used in this supply is a 6-3-volt ac @ 1-ampere filament transformer (filaments are used in vacuum tubes, but the name persists despite the fact that filaments do not).

The "MOV device " is a *metal oxide varistor* that will provide better rejection of power line noise. The high voltage transients normal to power lines in many parts of the country will interrupt the operation of electronics devices, especially digital devices, and may cause damage to the regulator and rectifier. The MOV is a two-terminal device that is made by General Electric. It is readily available in electronic parts stores. It is strictly optional and the power supply will work nicely without it. Do not delete the MOV if you know the power line is noisy or if there is a local history of strange happenings on electronic equipment in your area. When computers just "bomb" for no reason, and do not show any damage to be repaired, is a good indication of power line transient noise.

Make sure that the switch used will support 110 volts ac across the pins. The purpose of the double-pole-single-throw switch is to break both sides of the power line (a safety feature).

5-VOLTS DC 5-AMP POWER SUPPLY

The circuit shown in Fig. B-2 is a 5-ampere version of the first project. This supply is very similar to the 1-ampere version previously described. The principal difference between the supplies is in the ratings of the key components. The bridge rectifier, BR1, for example, must be rated at 5 amperes or more. I recommend that the builder select one of the 25-ampere types normally available to hobbyists. These rectifiers are often overrated, but they will run cool at 5 amperes despite the "real" rating. It is best if the rectifier is either mounted to the metal chassis or to a grounded heatsink. Use silicone heat transfer grease between the rectifier and the mounting surface.

The transformer is rated at 6.3 Vac at not less than 5 amperes with the 8-ampere Triad model preferred. The higher-rated transformer would allow the supply to run cooler (hence more reliably). The filter capacitor is selected according to the same rule as in the previous subject. Because the power supply is rated at 5 amperes, the capacitor should be 10,000 μF. If no single capacitor is available at that rating, then parallel two or more capacitors that add up to the 10,000 μF specified.

The voltage regulator (IC1) is the Lambda Electronics type LAS-1905. This regulator is rated at 5 volts, 5 amperes and is in a T0-3 transistor case. It is preferable that this regulator be mounted on a heatsink in order to reduce the temperature and increase reliability.

+12-VOLTS DC, 1-AMP POWER SUPPLY

Another power supply like the first (refer to the information on the 5-volt, 1-ampere power supply) is the +12-volt, 1-ampere power supply shown in Fig. B-3. This supply differs from the others in the ratings of its components. The transformer, for example, is a 12.6-volt ac, 1-ampere, "filament" transformer. Also, the rectifier has a high PIV voltage rating.

The integrated circuit voltage regulator (IC1) is a LM-340K-12 or a 7812 device. Again, the "K" package is preferred if a full 1 ampere of current is required. Otherwise, this power supply is the same as the other.

±12-VOLT DC, 1-AMP POWER SUPPLY

If we connect two single-polarity power supplies "back-to-back," we can make the form of dual-polarity power supply needed by operational

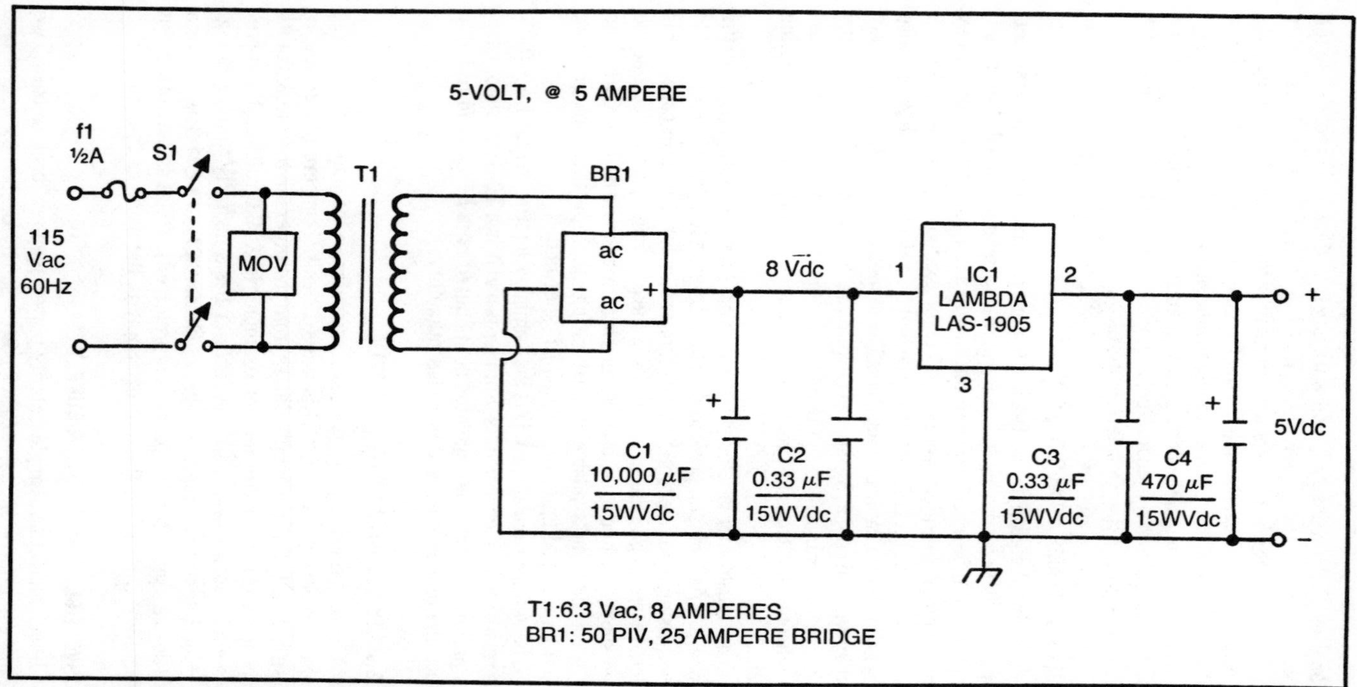

Fig. B-2. A 5-volt, 5-ampere power supply.

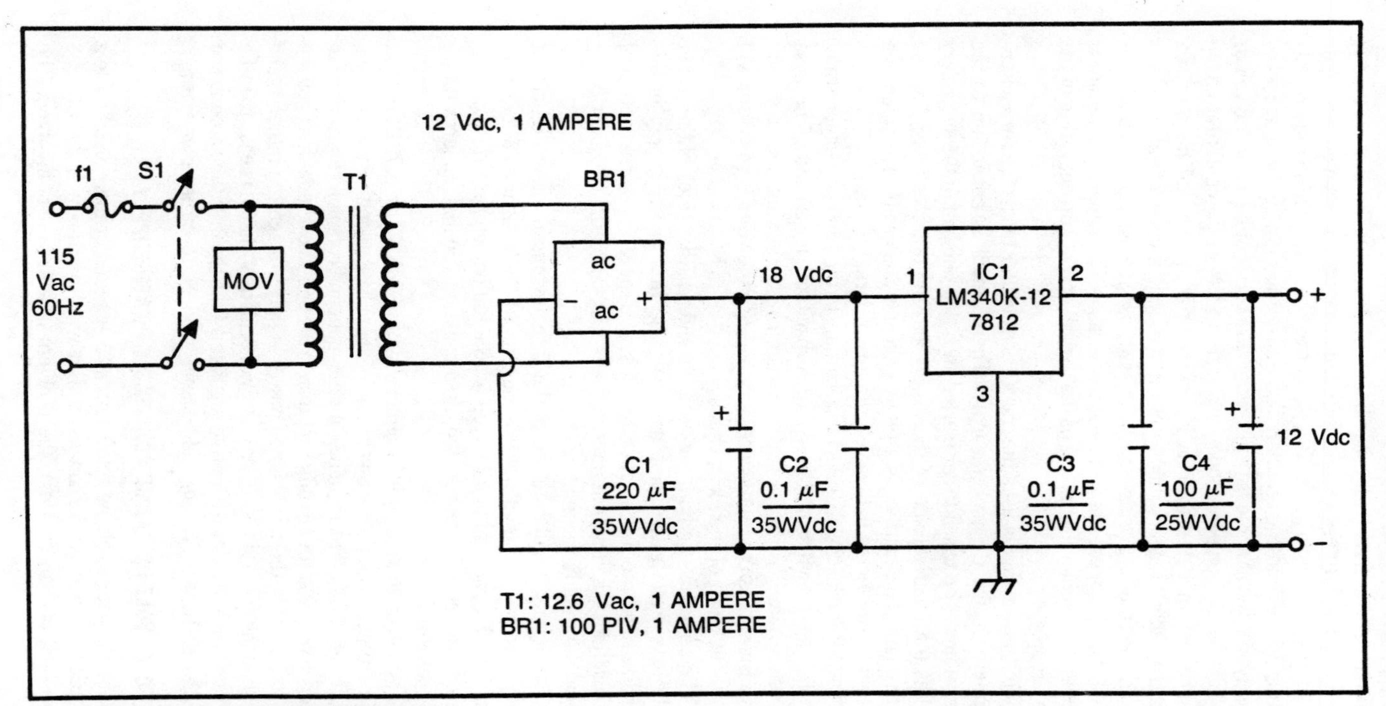

Fig. B-3. A 12-volt, 1-ampere power supply.

amplifier circuits (and with other linear IC devices). But that method is wasteful of transformers and rectifiers and therefore it is not well regarded.

The circuit shown in Fig. B-4 is a better solution that will require only one transformer and one rectifier. The transformer is a 25.6 volt ac *center-tapped* type rated at not less than 2-amperes. The popular Triad 2.8 volt or the Radio Shack 3-ampere models are preferred. Note the center tap on the secondary of this transformer. No center tap is required on previous circuits so some readers might miss this essential connection!

The rectifier is a bridge stack that will pass at least 2 amperes without harm. *Note*: 3-amperes is a standard size, as is 1.5 amperes. The latter, however, will require de-rating of the overall output current rating of the power supply.

This power supply uses the transformer center tap as the zero potential reference for the power supply. Therefore, it is connected to the common line. The transformer is used such that one-half of the secondary supplies the positive side of the supply and the other half supplies the negative half. The rectifier is used in a manner that can be described as a pair of interconnected half-wave bridge rectifiers.

The filter capacitor is selected according to the 2000 μF/ampere rule. Note that purists will want to see more capacitance for C1 and C5 because the rectifiers are half wave (thereby requiring somewhat higher capacitance). But this isn't strictly necessary because the voltage regulator will smooth out much of the extra ripple.

The capacitors on both the negative and positive sides of the power supply have exactly the same use as in the first power supply in this appendix. Read the first section (5-volts, 1-ampere) for a description of their function. Like the first project, the output capacitors (C4 and C8) are optional, but highly recommended.

The voltage regulators are of the three-terminal, integrated-circuit variety. The positive regulator is either an LM-340K-12 or a 7812 device. Again, the "K" package is preferred for the full one-ampere rating. If the "T" package devices are selected, then count on 750 milliamperes rather than 1 ampere.

The negative regulator is either an LM-320K-12 or a 7912 device. These are negative polarity versions of the LM-340 and 78×× devices, respectively. *Note*: The terminals for the input and common connections to the negative regulator are different than in the positive regulator. If you are used to inputting the unregulated power supply voltage to pin no. 1, and grounding the case (pin no. 3) on positive regulators, then it is easy to make the mistake when using a negative regulator. I did the first time around and the LM-320-12 went *pooofff* and became a silicon-to-carbon converter!

1.25 TO 25 VOLT DC, 5-AMP ADJUSTABLE POWER SUPPLY

The design of voltage regulators at 5 amperes or more used to be a little tricky, especially for amateurs. But with the advent of the LM-338 device (and certain cousins), the problem is a little less involved. The

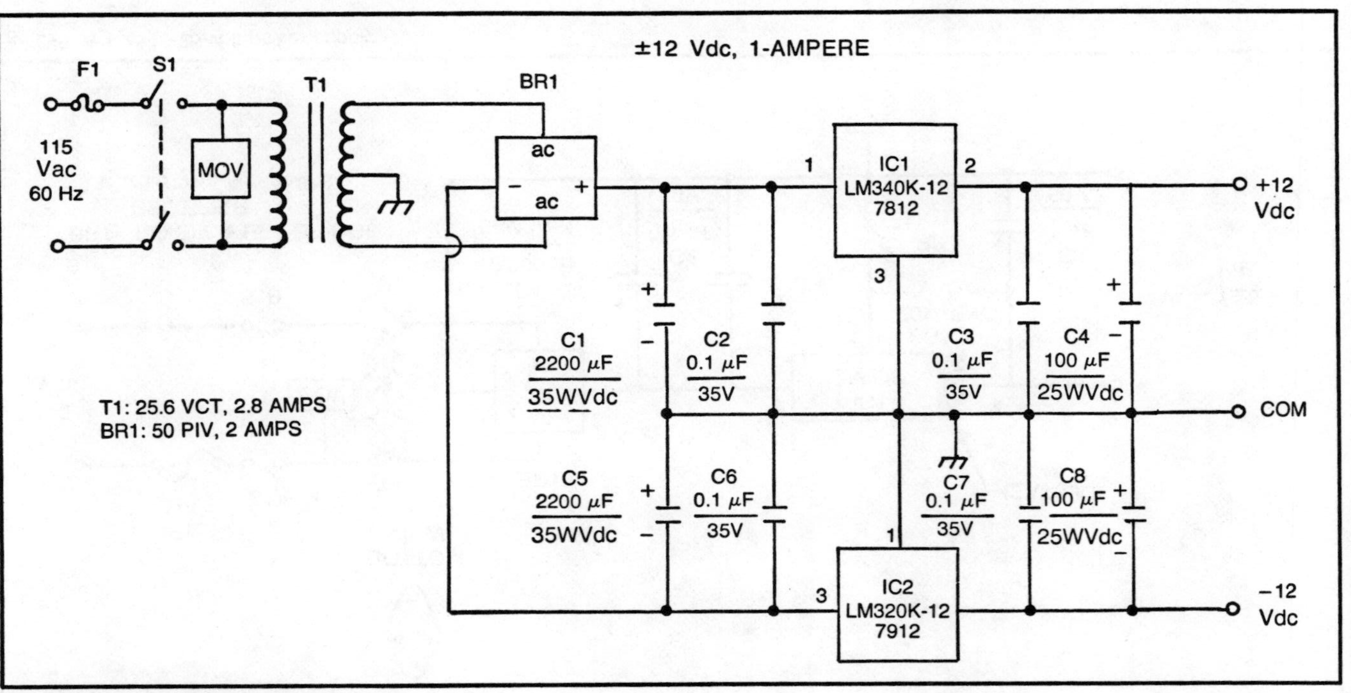

Fig. B-4. A dual-polarity power supply.

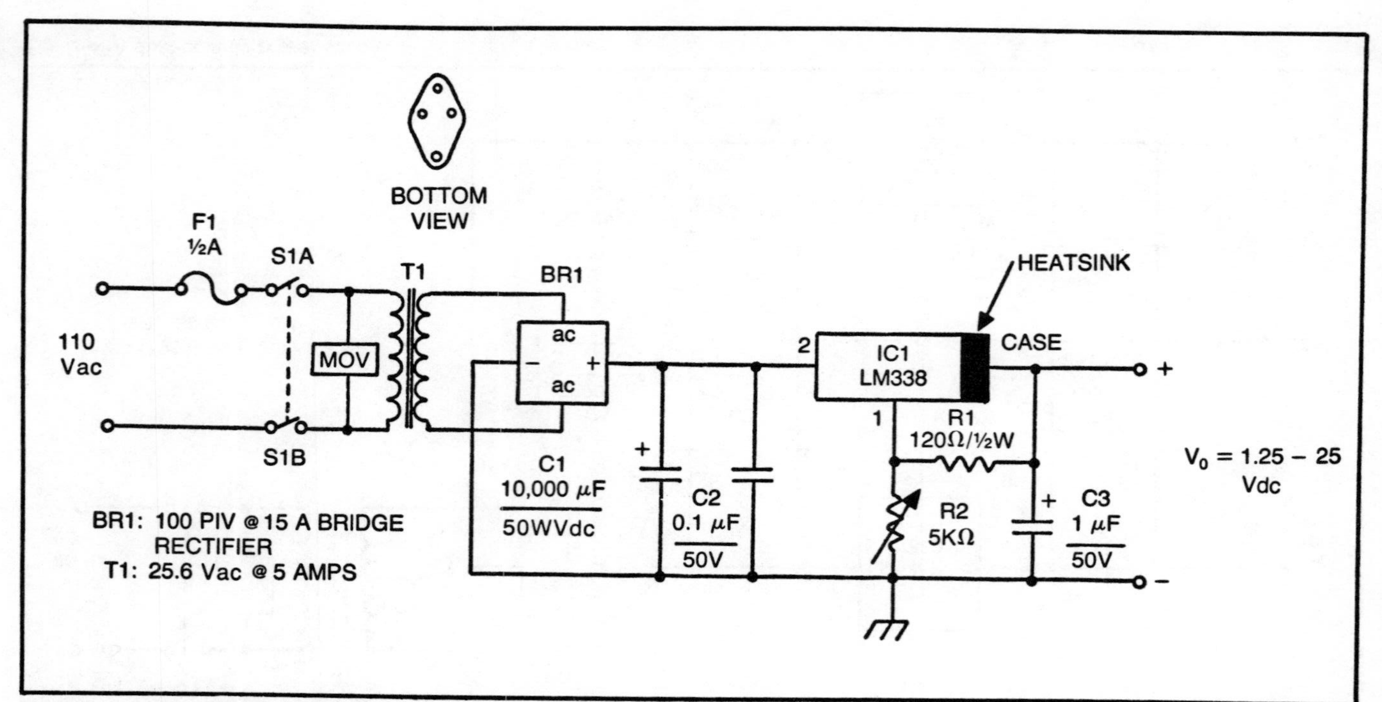

Fig. B-5. A 1.25-to-25-volt power supply.

LM-338K is a T0-3 packaged, three-terminal IC voltage regulator that will pass up to 5 amperes of dc current (heatsink is recommended).

The pin-outs of this regulator are a little different than other three-terminal regulators. The output terminal, for example, is the case (pin no. 3). This means that we must insulate the heatsink from ground. Also, the unregulated input power is applied to pin no. 2 and the adjustment resistor is applied to pin no. 1. This might well be a little confusing to one who is used to the LM-340, LM-309K, and 78×× devices.

The output voltage from this regulator is set by potentiometer R2 and will be equal to:

$$V_{out} = \frac{R2}{R1} + 1 \times 1.25 \text{ Vdc}$$

The value of R1 is set to 120 ohms while that of R2 is set by the user according to the desired output voltage. If you want control over the output voltage from the front panel of the power supply, then make R2 a panel-mounted potentiometer and supply it with a knob. If, on the other hand, the intent is to set the voltage to some level and then forget it, make the potentiometer a "trimmer" type and mount it at some convenient point.

The transformer used in this project (Fig. B-5) is a 25.6 volt ac 5-ampere version such as offered by Radio Shack and others. No centertap is needed.

The bridge rectifier requires a rating of at least 5 amperes, but I recommend a 25-ampere bridge mounted to either the chassis or a heatsink. This arrangement will permit cooler, hence more reliable, operation of the supply.

Appendix C

Some Burr-Brown Devices and Applications

BURR-BROWN®

OPA27/OPA37

Ultra-Low Noise Precision OPERATIONAL AMPLIFIERS

FEATURES

- EXTREMELY LOW NOISE
  - $3nV/\sqrt{Hz}$ at 1k Hz
  - 80nV, p-p from 0.1 Hz to 10 Hz
- LOW OFFSET VOLTAGE
  - $10\mu V$
  - $0.2\mu V/°C$
- HIGH SPEED
  - OPA27, $2.8V/\mu sec$
  - OPA37, $17V/\mu sec$
- EXCELLENT CMRR
  - 126 dB over ±11V Input
- HIGH GAIN
  - 1800V/mV (125 dB)
- FITS OP-07, OP-05, 725, AD510, AD517 SOCKETS

APPLICATIONS

- TRANSDUCER AMPLIFIER
- LOW NOISE INSTRUMENTATION AMPLIFIER
- DATA ACQUISITION PREAMPLIFIER
- PHONO AND TAPE PREAMPLIFIER
- FAST D/A CONVERTER OUTPUT
- WIDE BANDWIDTH INSTRUMENTATION AMPLIFIERS
- PRECISION COMPARATOR

DESCRIPTION

Low noise integrated processing, a unique circuit design, and advanced wafer level trimming techniques are combined in the OPA27/37 to produce an extremely-high performance "instrumentation grade" operational amplifier.

The OPA27/37 provide superior performance in three areas - low noise, excellent dc performance, and high speed (OPA37 is stable in gains > 5).

Noise is typically only $3nV/\sqrt{Hz}$ at 1k Hz with an exceptionally low 1/f corner frequency of 2.7 Hz. Peak-to-peak noise is just 80nV in a 0.1 Hz to 10 Hz bandwidth.

Offset voltage is typically just $10\mu V$ and drift is only $0.2\mu V/°C$. 125 dB open-loop gain is matched with 125 dB common-mode rejection ratio. Power consumption is only 3mA.

The same basic op amp comes in two frequency compensation versions. The OPA37 is lightly compensated and provides $17V/\mu sec$ slew rate and 63M Hz gain-bandwidth product. The OPA27 is more heavily compensated for better frequency stability in low gain applications. It has a $2.8V/\mu sec$ slew rate and an 8M Hz unity gain frequency.

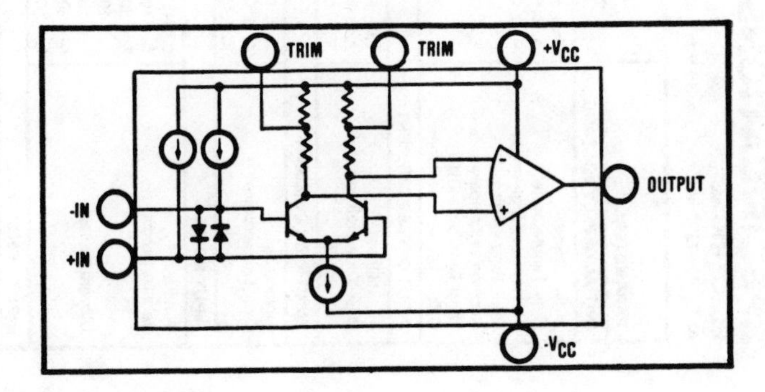

SPECIFICATIONS

ELECTRICAL

At T_A = +25°C and $\pm V_{CC}$ = 15 Vdc unless otherwise noted.

PARAMETERS	CONDITIONS	OPA27/37A, OPA27/37E			OPA27/37B, OPA27/37F			OPA27/37C, OPA27/37G			UNITS
		MIN	TYP	MAX	MIN	TYP	MAX	MIN	TYP	MAX	
INITIAL OFFSET VOLTAGE											
Initial Offset(1)	T_A = +25°C		10	25		20	60		30	100	μV
Over Temperature	A, B, C -55°C ≤ T_A ≤ +125°C		30	60		50	200		70	300	μV
Average vs Temperature	A, B, C -55°C ≤ T_A ≤ +125°C(2)		0.2	0.6		0.3	1.3		0.4	1.8	μV/°C
Over Temperature	E, F, G -25°C ≤ T_A ≤ +85°C		20	50		40	140		55	22	μV
Average vs Temperature	E, F, G -25°C ≤ T_A ≤ +85°C(2)		0.2	0.6		0.3	1.3		0.4	1.8	μV/°C
Long Term Stability(3)			0.2	1.0		0.3	1.5		0.4	2.0	μV/mo
Offset Adjustment Range			±4			•			•		mV
INPUT OFFSET CURRENT											
Initial Offset	T_A = +25°C		7	35		9	50		12	75	nA
Over Temperature	A, B, C -55°C ≤ T_A ≤ +125°C		15	50		22	85		30	135	nA
	E, F, G -25°C ≤ T_A ≤ +85°C		10	50		14	85		20	135	nA
INPUT BIAS CURRENT											
Initial Bias	T_A = +25°C		±10	±40		±12	±55		±15	±80	nA
Over Temperature	A, B, C -55°C ≤ T_A ≤ +125°C		±20	±60		±28	±95		±35	±150	nA
	E, F, G -25°C ≤ T_A ≤ +85°C		±14	±60		±18	±95		±25	±150	nA
INPUT NOISE											
Voltage	0.1 Hz to 10 Hz(4)(5)		0.08	0.18		•	•		0.09	0.25	μV, p-p
Voltage Density	f_o = 10 Hz(4)		3.5	5.5		•	•		3.8	8.0	nV $\sqrt{Hz}$
	f_o = 30 Hz(4)		3.1	4.5		•	•		3.3	5.6	nV $\sqrt{Hz}$
	f_o = 1000 Hz(4)		3.0	3.8		•	•		3.2	4.5	nV $\sqrt{Hz}$
Current Density	f_o = 10 Hz(4)(6)		1.7	4.0		•	•		•		pA $\sqrt{Hz}$
	f_o = 30 Hz(4)(6)		1.0	2.3		•	•		•		pA $\sqrt{Hz}$
	f_o = 1000 Hz(4)(6)		0.4	0.6		•	•		•	•	pA $\sqrt{Hz}$
INPUT RESISTANCE											
Differential(7)		1.5	6		1.2	5		0.8	4		MΩ
Common-Mode			3			2.5			2		GΩ

INPUT VOLTAGE RANGE											
Initial Input Voltage	$T_A = +25°C$	±11.0	±12.3		•	•		•	•		V
Over Temperature	A, B, C $-55°C \leq T_A \leq +125°C$	±10.3	±11.5		•	•		•	•		V
	E, F, G $-25°C \leq T_A \leq +85°C$	±10.5	±11.8		•	•		•	•		V
COMMON-MODE REJECTION RATIO											
Initial Rejection Ratio	$V_{CM} = \pm 11V$	114	126		106	123		100	120		dB
Over Temperature	A, B, C $-55°C \leq T_A \leq +125°C$	108	122		100	119		94	116		dB
Over Temperature	E, F, G $-25°C \leq T_A \leq +85°C$	110	124		102	121		96	118		dB
POWER SUPPLY REJECTION RATIO											
Initial Rejection Ratio	$\pm V_{CC} = 4V$ to 18V	100	120		•	•		94	118		dB
Over Temperature	A, B, C $-55°C \leq T_A \leq +125°C$ ($\pm V_{CC} = 4.5V$ to 18V)	96	116		94	114		86	110		dB
Over Temperature	E, F, G $-25°C \leq T_A \leq +85°C$ ($\pm V_{CC} = 4.5V$ to 18V)	97	118		96	116		90	114		dB
LARGE SIGNAL VOLTAGE GAIN(7)(8)											
Initial Voltage Gain	$R_L \geq 2k\Omega$, $V_O = \pm 10V$	1000	1800		•	•		700	1500		V/mV
	$R_L \geq 1k\Omega$, $V_O = \pm 10V$	800	1500		•	•			•		V/mV
	$R_L \geq 600\Omega$, $V_O = \pm 1V$, $V_{CC} = \pm 4V$	250	700		•	•		200	500		V/mV
Over Temperature	A, B, C $-55°C \leq T_A \leq +125°C$ ($R_L \geq 2k\Omega$, $V_O = \pm 10V$)	600	1200		500	1000		300	800		V/mV
Over Temperature	E, F, G $-25°C \leq T_A \leq +85°C$ ($R_L \geq 2k\Omega$, $V_O = \pm 10V$)	750	1500		700	1300		450	1000		V/mV
RATED OUTPUT											
Initial Voltage Swing	$R_L \geq 2k\Omega$	±12.0	±13.8		•	•		±11.5	±13.5		V
	$R_L \geq 600\Omega$	±10.0	±11.5		•	•		•	•		V
Over Temperature	A, B, C $-55°C \leq T_A \leq +125°C$ ($R_L \geq 2k\Omega$)	±11.5	±13.5		±11.0	±13.2		±10.5	±13.0		V
Over Temperature	E, F, G $-25°C \leq T_A \leq +85°C$ ($R_L \geq 2k\Omega$)	±11.7	±13.6		±11.4	±13.5		±11.0	±13.3		V
Output Resistance	Open Loop		70			•			•		Ω
DYNAMIC RESPONSE											
Slew Rate	OPA27	1.7	2.8		•	•		•	•		V/μsec
	OPA37	11	17		•	•		•	•		V/μsec
Gain-Bandwidth Product	OPA27	5	8		•	•		•	•		MHz
	OPA37		40			•			•		MHz

ELECTRICAL (CONT)

PARAMETERS	CONDITIONS	OPA27/37A, OPA27/37E			OPA27/37B, OPA27/37F			OPA27/37C, OPA27/37G			UNITS
		MIN	TYP	MAX	MIN	TYP	MAX	MIN	TYP	MAX	
POWER SUPPLY											
Rated Voltage			±15			*			*		Vdc
Voltage Range		±4		±22	*		*	*		*	Vdc
Current, Quiescent			±3	±4.7		*	*		±3.3	±5.7	mA
Power Comsumption			90	140		*	*		100	170	mW
TEMPERATURE RANGE											
Specification A, B, C		-55		+125	*		*	*		*	°C
Specification E, F, G		-25		+85	*		*	*		*	°C
Operating A, B, C		-55		+125	*		*	*		*	°C
Operating E, F, G		-25		+85	*		*	*		*	°C
Storage		-65		+150	*		*	*		*	°C

*Specification same as OPA27/37A and OPA27/37E.

NOTES:

1. Input Offset Voltage measurements are performed by automated test equipment approximately 0.5 seconds after application of power. A/E grades guaranteed fully warmed up.
2. The TCV_{OS} performance is within the specifications unnulled or when nulled with $R_P = 8k\Omega$ to $20k\Omega$.
3. Long Term Input Offset Voltage Stability refers to average trend line of V_{OS} vs Time over extended periods after the first 30 days of operation. Excluding the initial hour of operation, changes in V_{OS} during the first 30 days are typically 2.5μV (refer to Typical Performance Curves).
4. Parameter is not 100% tested; 90% of units meet this specification.
5. See Figures 1 and 2.
6. See Figure 1 for current noise measurement.
7. Parameter is guaranteed by design and is not tested.
8. Closed-loop gain ≥ 5 is required for stability in the OPA37. OPA27 is stable at unity gain.

ABSOLUTE MAXIMUM RATINGS

Supply Voltage .... ±22V
Internal Power Dissipation(1) 500mW
Input Voltage(2) .... ±22V
Output Short Circuit Duration .... Indefinite
Differential Input Voltage(3) .... ±0.7V
Differential Input Current(3) .... ±25mA
Storage Temperature Range .... -65°C to +150°C
Operating Temperature Range
  A, B, C .... -65°C to +150°C
  E, F, G .... -25°C to +85°C
Lead Temperature Range

NOTES:

1. Maximum Package Power Dissipation vs ambient temperature.

Package Type	Maximum Ambient Temperature for Rating	Derate Above Maximum Ambient Temperature
TO-99 (J)	80°C	7.1mW/°C
8-Pin Heremetic Dip (Z)	75°C	6.7mW/°C

2. For supply voltages less than ±22V, the absolute maximum input voltage is equal to the supply voltage.
3. The inputs are protected by back-to-back diodes. Current limiting resistors are not used in order to achieve low noise. If differential input

ORDERING INFORMATION

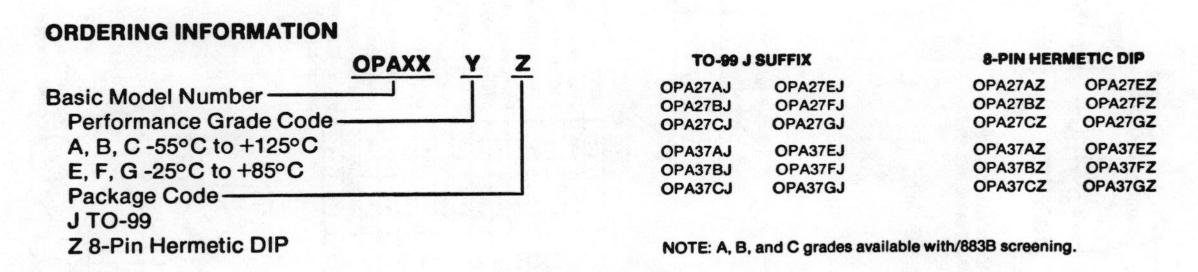

TO-99 J SUFFIX		8-PIN HERMETIC DIP	
OPA27AJ	OPA27EJ	OPA27AZ	OPA27EZ
OPA27BJ	OPA27FJ	OPA27BZ	OPA27FZ
OPA27CJ	OPA27GJ	OPA27CZ	OPA27GZ
OPA37AJ	OPA37EJ	OPA37AZ	OPA37EZ
OPA37BJ	OPA37FJ	OPA37BZ	OPA37FZ
OPA37CJ	OPA37GJ	OPA37CZ	OPA37GZ

NOTE: A, B, and C grades available with/883B screening.

PRICES

PRICES	OPA27 or OPA37	A	E	B	F	C	G
1 - 24	"J" Package TO-99	$75.00	$23.25	$33.75	$15.00	$19.50	$10.35
25 - 99		60.00	18.60	27.00	12.00	15.60	8.30
100 - 999		50.00	15.50	22.50	10.00	13.00	6.90
1 - 24	"Z" Package 8-Pin Mini DIP	$63.75	$19.80	$28.75	$12.00	$16.60	$ 8.25
25 - 99		51.00	15.85	23.00	9.60	13.30	6.60
100 - 999		42.50	13.20	19.15	8.00	11.05	5.50

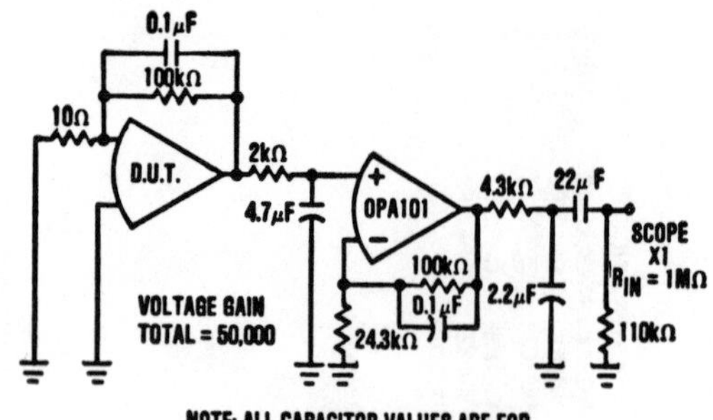

FIGURE 1. 0.1 Hz to 10 Hz Noise Test Circuit.

MECHANICAL

TO-99 PACKAGE
("J" SUFFIX)

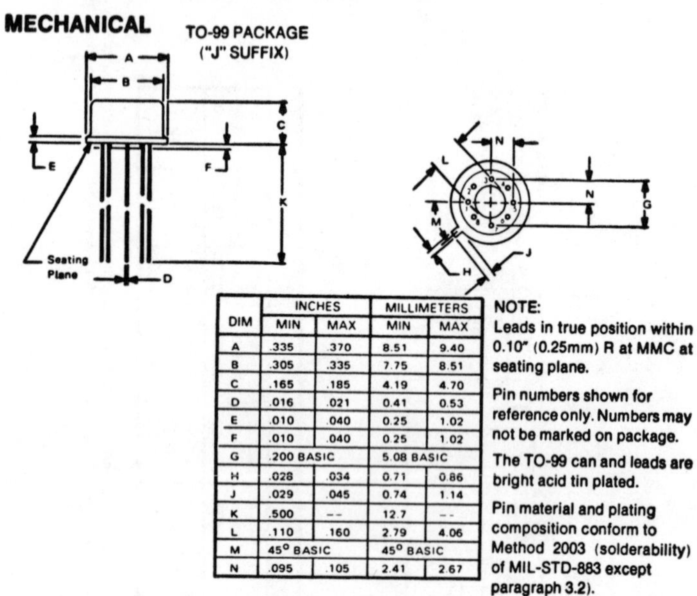

DIM	INCHES		MILLIMETERS	
	MIN	MAX	MIN	MAX
A	.335	.370	8.51	9.40
B	.305	.335	7.75	8.51
C	.165	.185	4.19	4.70
D	.016	.021	0.41	0.53
E	.010	.040	0.25	1.02
F	.010	.040	0.25	1.02
G	.200 BASIC		5.08 BASIC	
H	.028	.034	0.71	0.86
J	.029	.045	0.74	1.14
K	.500	--	12.7	--
L	.110	.160	2.79	4.06
M	45° BASIC		45° BASIC	
N	.095	.105	2.41	2.67

NOTE:
Leads in true position within 0.10" (0.25mm) R at MMC at seating plane.

Pin numbers shown for reference only. Numbers may not be marked on package.

The TO-99 can and leads are bright acid tin plated.

Pin material and plating composition conform to Method 2003 (solderability) of MIL-STD-883 except paragraph 3.2).

PIN CONFIGURATION

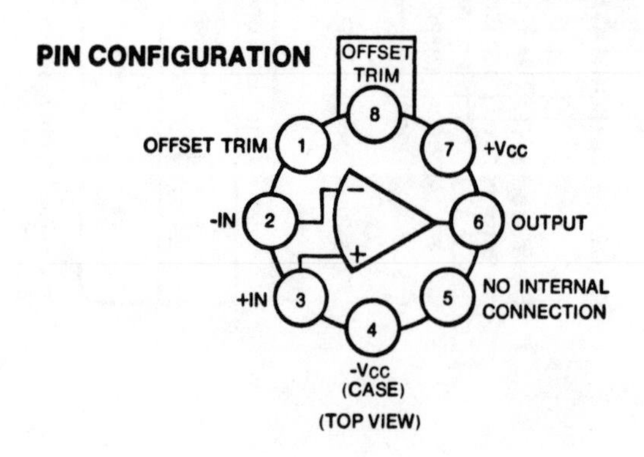

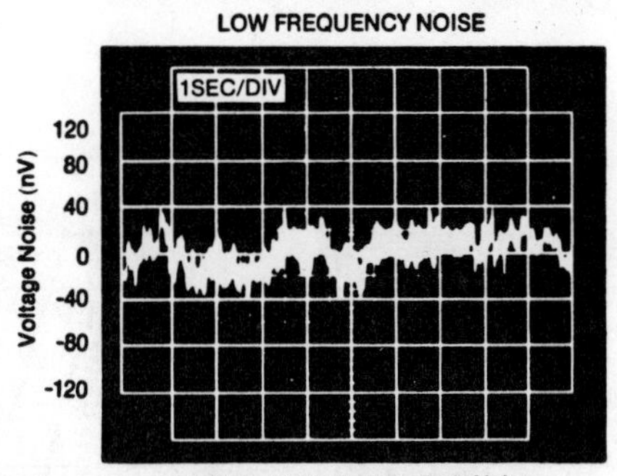

0.1 Hz to 10 Hz Peak-to-Peak Noise

FIGURE 2. Low Frequency Noise.

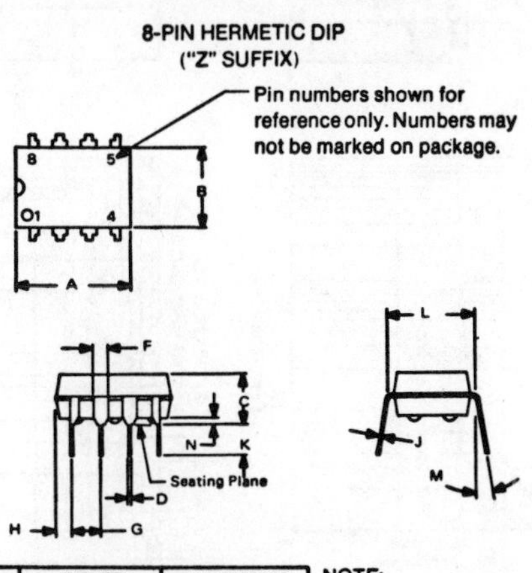

DIM	INCHES MIN	INCHES MAX	MILLIMETERS MIN	MILLIMETERS MAX
A	.370	.400	9.40	10.16
B	.230	.290	5.84	7.37
C	.120	.200	3.05	5.08
D	.015	.023	0.38	0.58
F	.030	.070	0.76	1.78
G	.100 BASIC		2.54 BASIC	
H	.030	.050	0.76	1.27
J	.008	.015	0.20	0.38
K	.070	.135	1.78	3.43
L	.300 BASIC		7.62 BASIC	
M	--	10°	--	10°
N	.010	.030	0.25	0.76

NOTE:
Leads in true position within 0.10" (0.25mm) R at MMC at seating plane.

Pin material and plating composition conform to Method 2003 (solderability) of MIL-STD-883 except paragraph 3.2).

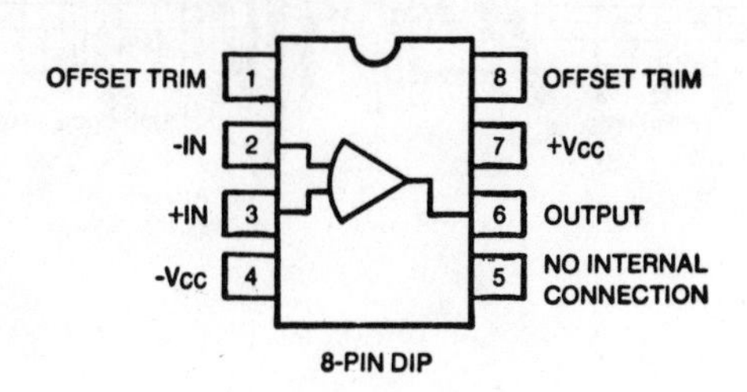

8-PIN DIP

TYPICAL PERFORMANCE CURVES

($T_A = +25°C$, $\pm V_{CC} = 15V$ dc unless otherwise noted)

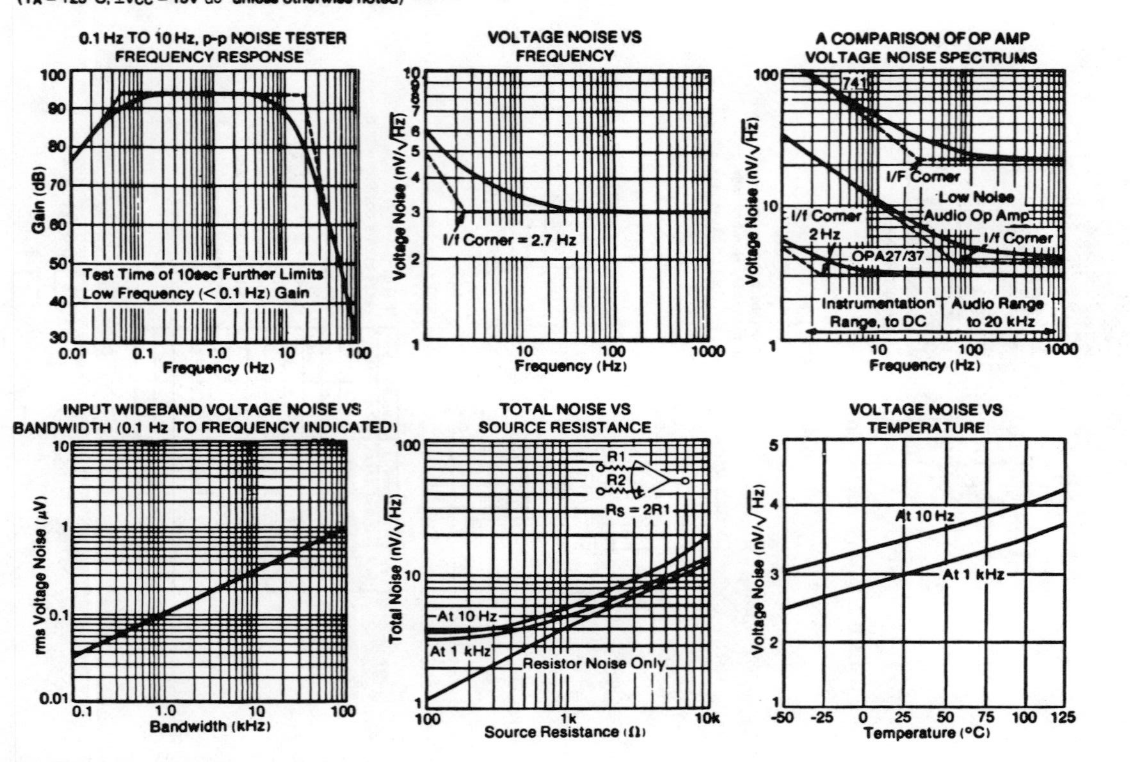

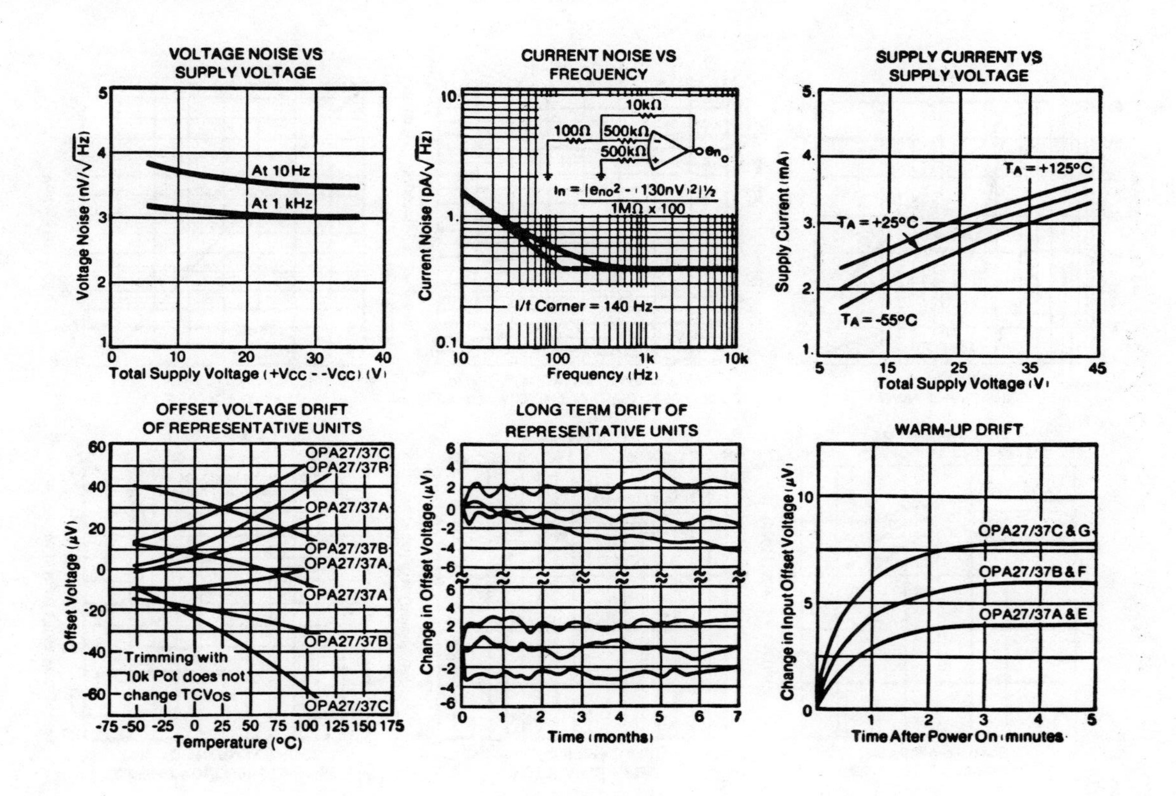

VOLTAGE NOISE VS SUPPLY VOLTAGE
Voltage Noise (nV/√Hz)
At 10 Hz
At 1 kHz
Total Supply Voltage (+Vcc - -Vcc) (V)
CURRENT NOISE VS FREQUENCY
Current Noise (pA/√Hz)
100Ω
10kΩ
500kΩ
500kΩ
e_{no}
In = [e_{no}^2 - (130nV)^2]½ / 1MΩ x 100
1/f Corner = 140 Hz
Frequency (Hz)
SUPPLY CURRENT VS SUPPLY VOLTAGE
Supply Current (mA)
T_A = +125°C
T_A = +25°C
T_A = -55°C
Total Supply Voltage (V)
OFFSET VOLTAGE DRIFT OF REPRESENTATIVE UNITS
Offset Voltage (μV)
OPA27/37C
OPA27/37B
OPA27/37A
OPA27/37B
OPA27/37A
OPA27/37A
OPA27/37B
OPA27/37C
Trimming with 10k Pot does not change TCVos
Temperature (°C)
LONG TERM DRIFT OF REPRESENTATIVE UNITS
Change in Offset Voltage (μV)
Time (months)
WARM-UP DRIFT
Change in Input Offset Voltage (μV)
OPA27/37C & G
OPA27/37B & F
OPA27/37A & E
Time After Power On (minutes)

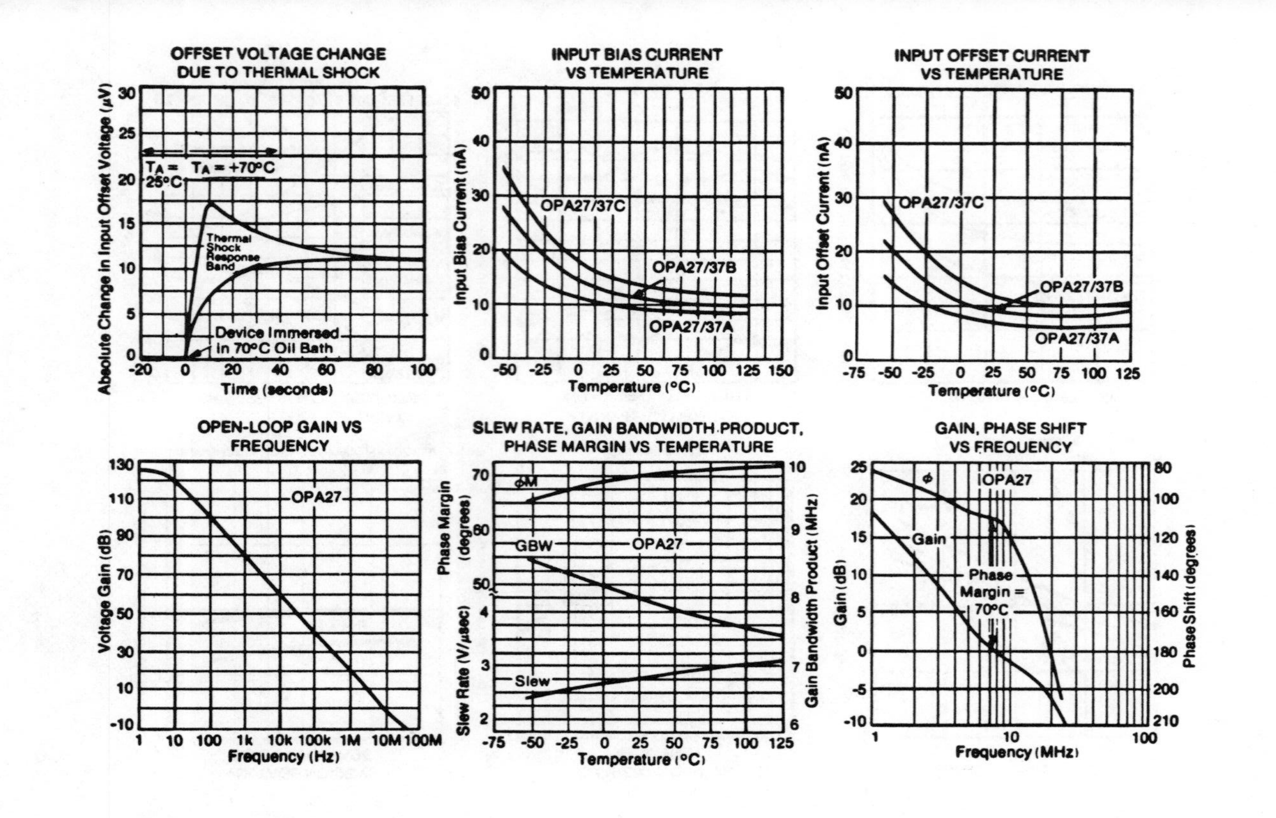

OFFSET VOLTAGE CHANGE DUE TO THERMAL SHOCK
Absolute Change in Input Offset Voltage (μV)
30
25
20
15
10
5
0
-20
0
20
40
60
80
100
Time (seconds)
T_A = 25°C
T_A = +70°C
Thermal Shock Response Band
Device Immersed in 70°C Oil Bath
INPUT BIAS CURRENT VS TEMPERATURE
Input Bias Current (nA)
50
40
30
20
10
0
-50
-25
0
25
50
75
100
125
150
Temperature (°C)
OPA27/37C
OPA27/37B
OPA27/37A
INPUT OFFSET CURRENT VS TEMPERATURE
Input Offset Current (nA)
50
40
30
20
10
0
-75
-50
-25
0
25
50
75
100
125
Temperature (°C)
OPA27/37C
OPA27/37B
OPA27/37A
OPEN-LOOP GAIN VS FREQUENCY
Voltage Gain (dB)
130
110
90
70
50
30
10
-10
1
10
100
1k
10k
100k
1M
10M
100M
Frequency (Hz)
OPA27
SLEW RATE, GAIN BANDWIDTH PRODUCT, PHASE MARGIN VS TEMPERATURE
Phase Margin (degrees)
70
60
50
Slew Rate (V/μsec)
4
3
2
Gain Bandwidth Product (MHz)
10
9
8
7
6
-75
-50
-25
0
25
50
75
100
125
Temperature (°C)
ϕM
GBW
OPA27
Slew
GAIN, PHASE SHIFT VS FREQUENCY
Gain (dB)
25
20
15
10
5
0
-5
-10
Phase Shift (degrees)
80
100
120
140
160
180
200
210
1
10
100
Frequency (MHz)
ϕ
OPA27
Gain
Phase Margin = 70°C

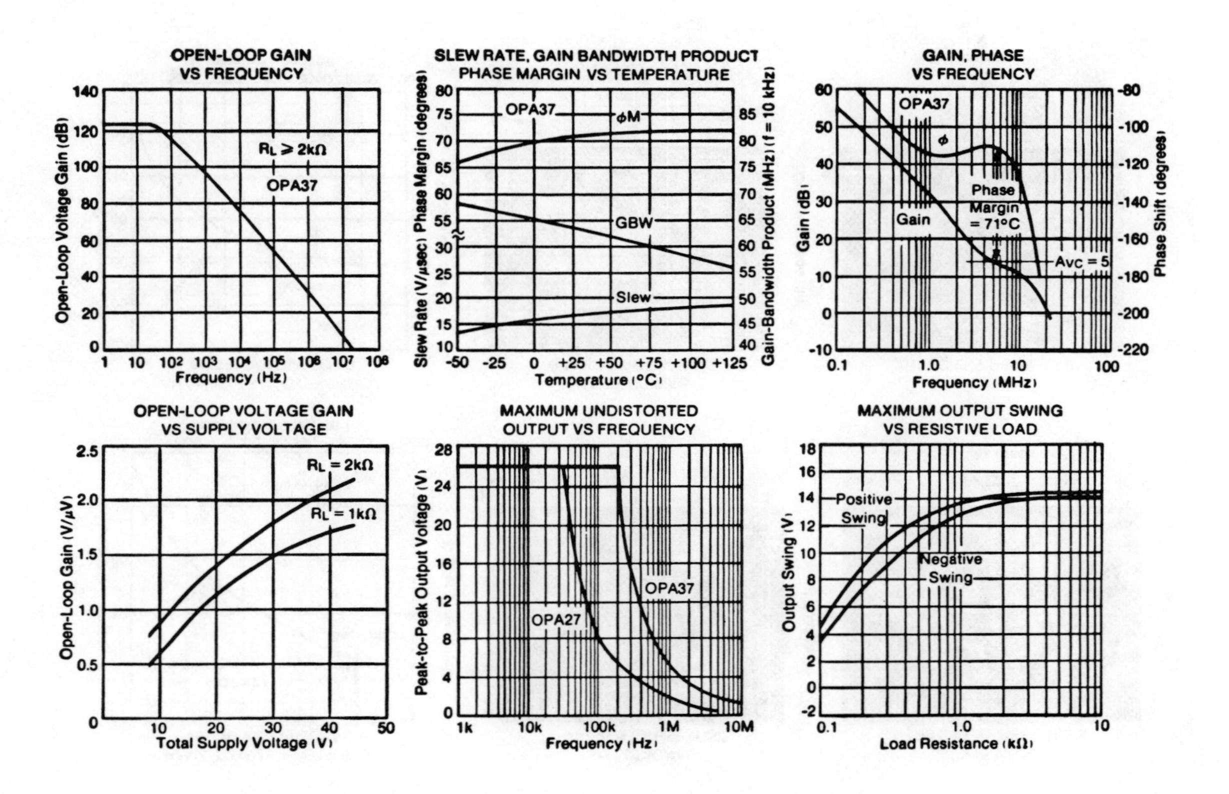
OPEN-LOOP GAIN
VS FREQUENCY
Open-Loop Voltage Gain (dB)
$R_L \geq 2k\Omega$
OPA37
Frequency (Hz)
SLEW RATE, GAIN BANDWIDTH PRODUCT
PHASE MARGIN VS TEMPERATURE
Slew Rate (V/µsec) Phase Margin (degrees)
Gain-Bandwidth Product (MHz) (f = 10 kHz)
OPA37
φM
GBW
Slew
Temperature (°C)
GAIN, PHASE
VS FREQUENCY
Gain (dB)
Phase Shift (degrees)
OPA37
φ
Phase
Margin
= 71°C
Gain
A_{VC} = 5
Frequency (MHz)
OPEN-LOOP VOLTAGE GAIN
VS SUPPLY VOLTAGE
Open-Loop Gain (V/µV)
$R_L = 2k\Omega$
$R_L = 1k\Omega$
Total Supply Voltage (V)
MAXIMUM UNDISTORTED
OUTPUT VS FREQUENCY
Peak-to-Peak Output Voltage (V)
OPA27
OPA37
Frequency (Hz)
MAXIMUM OUTPUT SWING
VS RESISTIVE LOAD
Output Swing (V)
Positive
Swing
Negative
Swing
Load Resistance (kΩ)

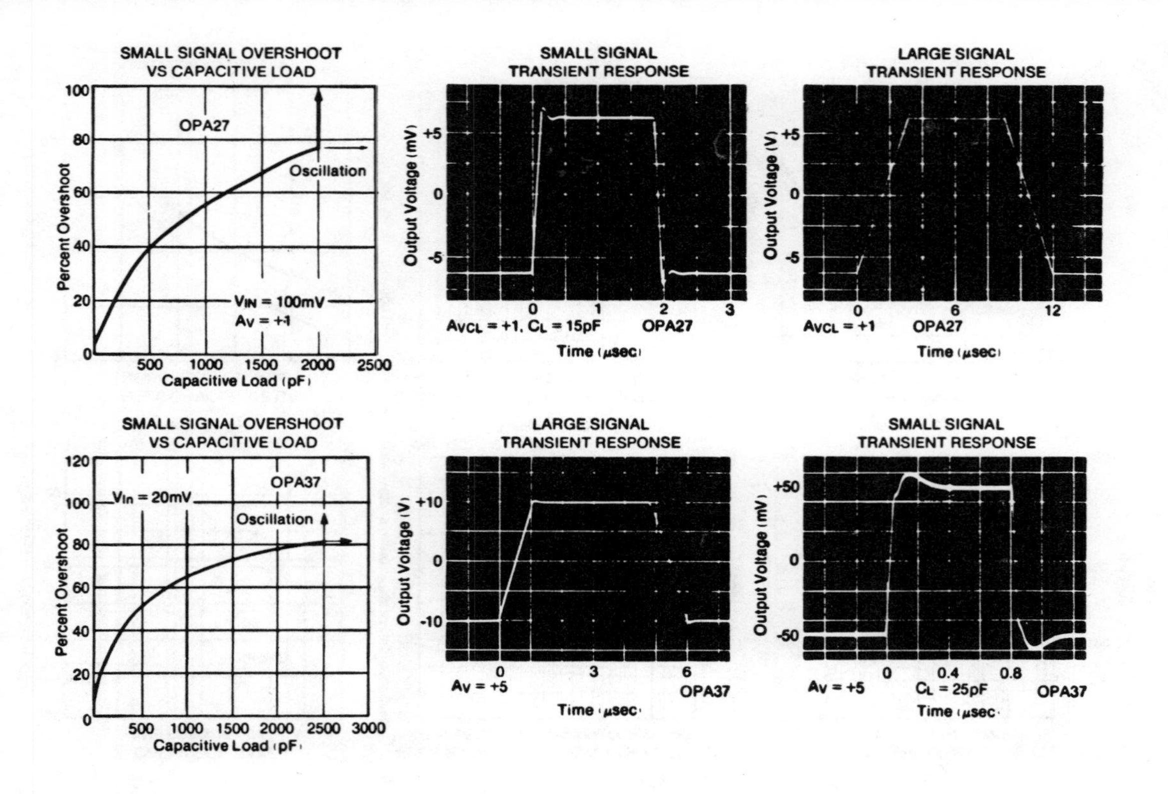

SMALL SIGNAL OVERSHOOT
VS CAPACITIVE LOAD
Percent Overshoot
OPA27
Oscillation
VIN = 100mV
AV = +1
Capacitive Load (pF)
SMALL SIGNAL
TRANSIENT RESPONSE
Output Voltage (mV)
AVCL = +1, CL = 15pF
OPA27
Time (μsec)
LARGE SIGNAL
TRANSIENT RESPONSE
Output Voltage (V)
AVCL = +1
OPA27
Time (μsec)
SMALL SIGNAL OVERSHOOT
VS CAPACITIVE LOAD
Percent Overshoot
OPA37
VIn = 20mV
Oscillation
Capacitive Load (pF)
LARGE SIGNAL
TRANSIENT RESPONSE
Output Voltage (V)
AV = +5
OPA37
Time (μsec)
SMALL SIGNAL
TRANSIENT RESPONSE
Output Voltage (mV)
AV = +5
CL = 25pF
OPA37
Time (μsec)

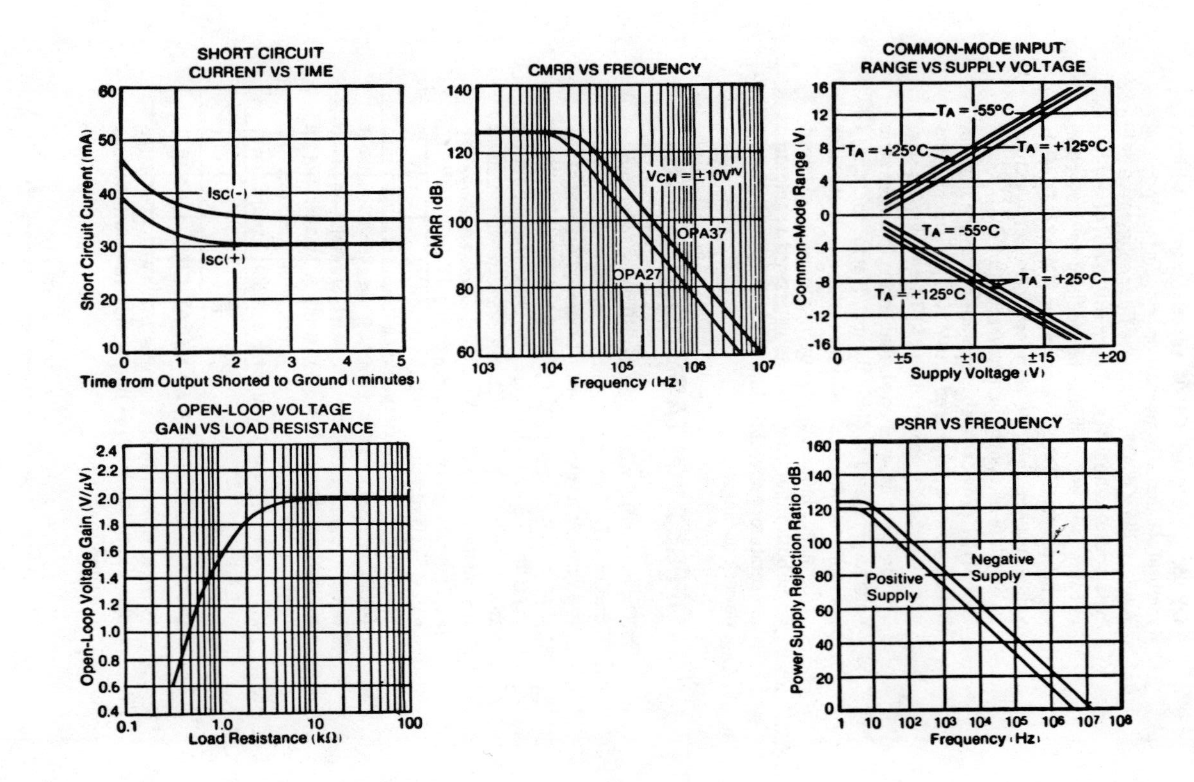
SHORT CIRCUIT CURRENT VS TIME
Short Circuit Current (mA)
Time from Output Shorted to Ground (minutes)
Isc(-)
Isc(+)
CMRR VS FREQUENCY
CMRR (dB)
Frequency (Hz)
VCM = ±10V
OPA37
OPA27
COMMON-MODE INPUT RANGE VS SUPPLY VOLTAGE
Common-Mode Range (V)
Supply Voltage (V)
TA = -55°C
TA = +25°C
TA = +125°C
OPEN-LOOP VOLTAGE GAIN VS LOAD RESISTANCE
Open-Loop Voltage Gain (V/μV)
Load Resistance (kΩ)
PSRR VS FREQUENCY
Power Supply Rejection Ratio (dB)
Frequency (Hz)
Positive Supply
Negative Supply

APPLICATION INFORMATION

OPA27/37 Series units may be inserted directly into 725, OP-06, OP-07 and OP-05 sockets with or without removal of external compensation or nulling components. Additionally, OPA27/37 may be fitted to unnulled 741-type sockets; however, if conventional 741 nulling circuitry is in use, it should be modified or removed to enable proper OPA27/37 operation. OPA27/37 offset voltage may be nulled to zero (or other desired setting) through use of a potentiometer (see Figure 3).

OPA27/37 provides stable operation with load capacitances up to 2000pF and ±10V swings; larger capacitances should be decoupled with 50Ω decoupling resistor.

The designer is cautioned that stray thermoelectric voltages generated by dissimilar metals at the contacts to the input terminals can prevent realization of the drift performance indicated. Best operation will be obtained when both input contacts are maintained at the same temperature, preferable close to the temperature of the device's package.

OFFSET VOLTAGE ADJUSTMENT

The input offset voltage and its drift with temperature of the OPA27/37 are permanently trimmed at wafer testing to a very-low level. However, if further adjustment of V_{OS} is necessary, nulling with a 10kΩ potentiometer will not degrade TCV_{OS} (see Figure 4). Other potentiometer values from 1kΩ to 1MΩ can be used with a slight degradation (0.1 to 0.2μV/°C) of TCV_{OS}. Trimming to a value other than zero creates a drift of (V_{OS}/300) μV/°C, e.g., if V_{OS} is adjusted to 100μV, the change in TCV_{OS} will be 0.33μV/°C. The offset voltage adjustment range with a 10kΩ potentiometer is ±4mV. If smaller adjustment range is required, the sensitivity and/or resolution of the nulling can be increased by using a smaller pot in conjunction with fixed resistors. For example, the network in Figure 3 will have a ±280μV adjustment range.

UNITY GAIN BUFFER APPLICATIONS - OPA27.

When $R_f \leqslant 100\Omega$ and the input is driven with a fast, large signal pulse (> 1V), the output waveform will look as shown in Figure 4.

1 4.7kΩ 1kΩ POT 4.7kΩ 8

FIGURE 3. Higher Resolution Nulling Circuit.

During the fast feedthrough-like portion of the output, the input protection diodes effectively short the output to the input and a current, limited only by the output short circuit protection, will be drawn by the signal generator. This results in the waveform shown in Figure 5. With $R_f \geq 500\Omega$, the output is capable of handling the current requirements ($I_L \leq 20mA$ at 10V) and the amplifier stays in its active mode and a smooth transition will occur.

As with all operational amplifiers when $R_f \geq 2k\Omega$, a pole will be created with R_f and the amplifier's input capacitance (8pF), creating additional phase shift and reducing the phase margin. A small capacitor (20pF to 50pF) in parallel with R_f will eliminate this problem.

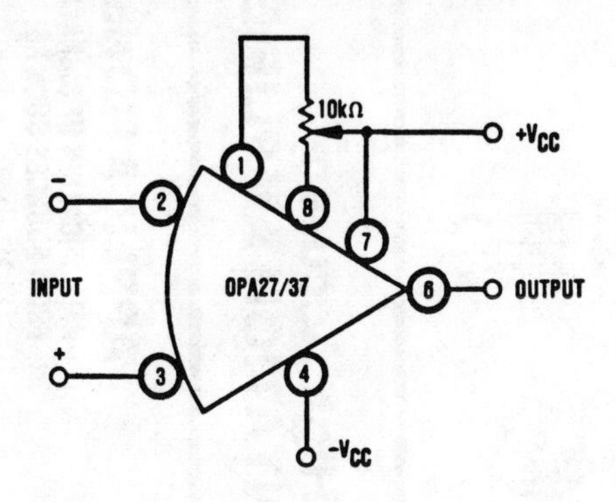

FIGURE 4. Offset Nulling Circuit.

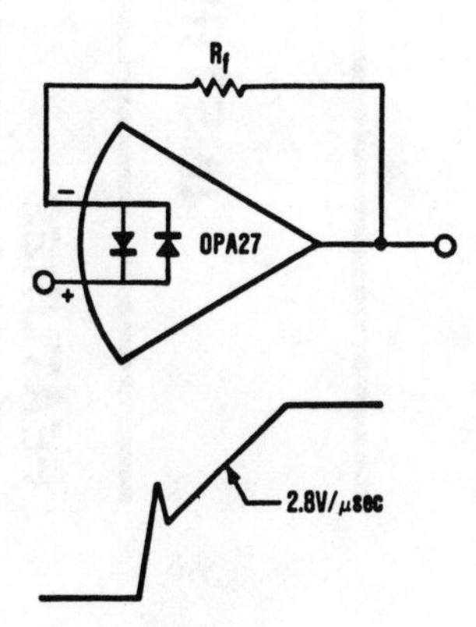

FIGURE 5. Pulsed Operation.

BURR-BROWN®

INA101

Very-High Accuracy INSTRUMENTATION AMPLIFIER

FEATURES

- ULTRA-LOW VOLTAGE DRIFT - 0.25μV/°C
- LOW OFFSET VOLTAGE - 25μV
- LOW NONLINEARITY - 0.002%
- LOW NOISE - 13nV/$\sqrt{Hz}$ at f_0 = 10 kHz
- HIGH CMR - 106 dB at 60 Hz
- HIGH INPUT IMPEDANCE - $10^{10}\Omega$
- LOW COST

APPLICATIONS

- AMPLIFICATION OF SIGNALS FROM SOURCES SUCH AS:
  - Strain Gages
  - Thermocouples
  - RTDs
- REMOTE TRANSDUCERS
- LOW LEVEL SIGNALS
- MEDICAL INSTRUMENTATION

DESCRIPTION

The INA101 is a high accuracy, multistage, integrated-circuit instrumentation amplifier designed for signal conditioning requirements where very-high performance is desired. All circuits, including the interconnected thin-film resistors, are integrated on a single monolithic substrate.

A multiamplifier design is used to provide the highest performance and maximum versatility with monolithic construction for low cost. The input stage uses Burr-Brown's ultra-low drift, low noise technology to provide exceptional input characteristics.

Gain accuracy is achieved with precision nichrome resistors. This provides high initial accuracy, low TCR (temperature coefficient of resistance) and TCR matching, with outstanding stability as a function of time.

State-of-the-art wafer-level laser-trimming techniques are used for minimizing offset voltage and offset voltage drift versus temperature. This advanced technique also maximizes common-mode rejection and gain accuracy.

The INA101 introduces premium instrumentation amplifier performance and with the lower cost makes it ideal for even higher volume applications.

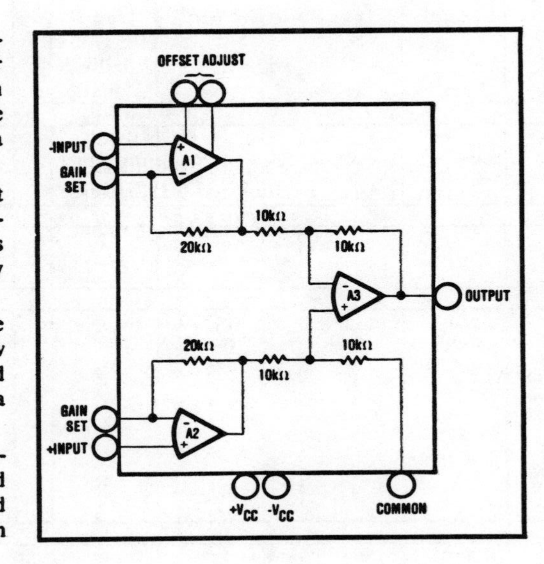

SPECIFICATIONS

ELECTRICAL

At +25°C with ±15 Vdc power supply and in circuit of Figure 2 unless otherwise noted.

MODEL	INA101AM			INA101BM, INA101SM			INA101CM			UNITS
	MIN	TYP	MAX	MIN	TYP	MAX	MIN	TYP	MAX	
GAIN										
Range of Gain	1		1000	•		•	•		•	V/V
Gain Equation		$G = 1 + (40k/R_G)$			•			•		V/V
Error From Equation, dc (1)		±(0.04±0.000016G - 0.02/G)	±(0.1±0.0003G - 0.05/G)		•	•		•	•	% of FS
Gain Temp. Coefficient(2)										
G = 1		2	5		•	•		•	•	ppm/°C
G = 10		20	100		•	•		•	•	ppm/°C
G = 100		22	110		•	•		•	•	ppm/°C
G = 1000		22	110		•	•		•	•	ppm/°C
Nonlinearity, dc		$\pm(0.002 + 10^{-5}G)$	$\pm(0.005 + 2 \times 10^{-5}G)$		$\pm(0.001 + 10^{-5}G)$	$\pm(0.002 + 10^{-5}G)$		$\pm(0.001 + 10^{-5}G)$	$\pm(0.002 + 10^{-5}G)$	% of p-p FS
RATED OUTPUT										
Voltage	±10	±12.5		•	•		•	•		V
Current	±5	±12.5		•	•		•	•		mA
Output Impedance		0.01			•			•		Ω
INPUT OFFSET VOLTAGE										
Initial Offset at +25°C(3)		±25 ±200/G	±50 ±400/G		±10 ±100/G	±25 ±200/G		±10 ±100/G	±25 ±200/G	μV
vs. Temperature			±2 ±20/G			±0.75 ±10/G			±0.25 ±10/G	μV/°C
vs. Supply		±(1 + 20/G)			•			•		μV/V
vs. Time		±(1 + 20/G)			•			•		μV/mo
INPUT BIAS CURRENT										
Initial Bias Current (each input)		±15	±30		±10	±30		±5	±20	nA
vs. Temperature		±0.2			•			•		nA/°C
vs Supply		±0.1			•			•		nA/V
Initial Offset Current		±15	±30		±10	±30		±5	±20	nA
vs. Temperature		±0.5			•			•		nA/°C
INPUT IMPEDANCE										
Differential		$10^{10} \parallel 3$			•			•		Ω ǁ pF
Common-mode		$10^{10} \parallel 3$			•			•		Ω ǁ pF

INPUT VOLTAGE RANGE										
Range, Linear Response	±10			•	•		•	•		V
CMR with 1kΩ Source Imbal.										
DC to 60 Hz, G = 1	80	90		•	•		•	•		dB
DC to 60 Hz, G = 10	96	106		•	•		•	•		dB
DC to 60 Hz, G = 100 to 1000	106	110		•	•		•	•		dB
INPUT NOISE										
Input Voltage Noise										
f_B = 0.01 Hz to 10 Hz			0.8			•			•	μV, p-p
Density, G = 1000										
f_o = 10 Hz			18			•			•	$nV/\sqrt{Hz}$
f_o = 100 Hz			15			•			•	$nV/\sqrt{Hz}$
f_o = 1 k Hz			13			•			•	$nV/\sqrt{Hz}$
Input Current Noise										
f_B = 0.01 Hz to 10 Hz			50			•			•	pA, p-p
Density										
f_o = 10 Hz			0.8			•			•	$pA/\sqrt{Hz}$
f_o = 100 Hz			0.46			•			•	$pA/\sqrt{Hz}$
f_o = 1 k Hz			0.35			•			•	$pA/\sqrt{Hz}$
DYNAMIC RESPONSE										
Small Signal, ±3 dB Flatness										
G = 1		300			•			•		kHz
G = 10		140			•			•		kHz
G = 100		25			•			•		kHz
G = 1000		2.5			•			•		kHz
Small Signal, ±1% Flatness										
G = 1		20			•			•		kHz
G = 10		10			•			•		kHz
G = 100		1			•			•		kHz
G = 1000		200			•			•		Hz
Full Power, G = 1 - 100		6.4			•			•		kHz
Slew Rate, G = 1 - 100	0.2	0.4		•	•		•	•		V/μsec
Settling Time (0.1%)										
G = 1		30	40		•	•		•	•	μsec
G = 100		40	55		•	•		•	•	μsec
G = 1000		35	470		•	•		•	•	μsec
Settling Time (0.01%)										
G = 1		30	45		•	•		•	•	μsec
G = 100		50	70		•	•		•	•	μsec
G = 1000		500	650		•	•		•	•	μsec

SPECIFICATIONS

ELECTRICAL

At +25°C with ±15 Vdc power supply and in circuit of Figure 2 unless otherwise noted.

MODEL	INA101AM			INA101BM, INA101SM			INA101CM			UNITS
	MIN	TYP	MAX	MIN	TYP	MAX	MIN	TYP	MAX	
GAIN										
Range of Gain	1		1000	•		•	•		•	V/V
Gain Equation		$G = 1 + (40k/R_G)$			•			•		V/V
Error From Equation, dc(1)		±(0.04±0.000016G - 0.02/G)	±(0.1±0.0003G - 0.05/G)		•	•		•	•	% of FS
Gain Temp. Coefficient(2)										
G = 1		2	5		•	•		•	•	ppm/°C
G = 10		20	100		•	•		•	•	ppm/°C
G = 100		22	110		•	•		•	•	ppm/°C
G = 1000		22	110		•	•		•	•	ppm/°C
Nonlinearity, dc		$\pm(0.002 + 10^{-5}G)$	$\pm(0.005 + 2 \times 10^{-5}G)$		$\pm(0.001 + 10^{-5}G)$	$\pm(0.002 + 10^{-5}G)$		$\pm(0.001 + 10^{-5}G)$	$\pm(0.002 + 10^{-5}G)$	% of p-p FS
RATED OUTPUT										
Voltage	±10	±12.5		•	•		•	•		V
Current	±5	±12.5		•	•		•	•		mA
Output Impedance		0.01			•			•		Ω
INPUT OFFSET VOLTAGE										
Initial Offset at +25°C(3)		±25 ±200/G	±50 ±400/G		±10 ±100/G	±25 ±200/G		±10 ±100/G	±25 ±200/G	μV
vs. Temperature			±2 ±20/G			±0.75 ±10/G			±0.25 ±10/G	μV/°C
vs. Supply		± 1 + 20/G			•			•		μV/V
vs. Time		± 1 + 20/G			•			•		μV/mo
INPUT BIAS CURRENT										
Initial Bias Current each input		±15	±30		±10	±30		±5	±20	nA
vs. Temperature		±0.2			•			•		nA/°C
vs Supply		±0.1			•			•		nA/V
Initial Offset Current		±15	±30		±10	±30		±5	±20	nA
vs. Temperature		±0.5			•			•		nA/°C
INPUT IMPEDANCE										
Differential		$10^{10} \parallel 3$			•			•		Ω ‖ pF
Common-mode		$10^{10} \parallel 3$			•			•		Ω ‖ pF

INPUT VOLTAGE RANGE										
Range, Linear Response	±10			•	•		•	•		V
CMR with 1kΩ Source Imbal										
dc to 60 Hz, G = 1	80	90		•	•		•	•		dB
dc to 60 Hz, G = 10	96	106		•	•		•	•		dB
dc to 60 Hz, G = 100 to 1000	106	110		•	•		•	•		dB
INPUT NOISE										
Input Voltage Noise										
f_B = 0.01 Hz to 10 Hz		0.8			•			•		μV p-p
Density, G = 1000										
f_o = 10 Hz		18			•			•		nV/√Hz
f_o = 100 Hz		15			•			•		nV/√Hz
f_o = 1k Hz		13			•			•		nV/√Hz
Input Current Noise										
f_B = 0.01 Hz to 10 Hz		50			•			•		pA, p-p
Density										
f_o = 10 Hz		0.8			•			•		pA/√Hz
f_o = 100 Hz		0.46			•			•		pA/√Hz
f_o = 1k Hz		0.35			•			•		pA/√Hz
DYNAMIC RESPONSE										
Small Signal, ±3 dB Flatness										
G = 1		300			•			•		kHz
G = 10		140			•			•		kHz
G = 100		25			•			•		kHz
G = 1000		2.5			•			•		kHz
Small Signal, ±1% Flatness										
G = 1		20			•			•		kHz
G = 10		10			•			•		kHz
G = 100		1			•			•		kHz
G = 1000		200			•			•		Hz
Full Power, G = 1 - 100		6.4			•			•		kHz
Slew Rate, G = 1 - 100	0.2	0.4		•	•		•	•		V/μsec
Settling Time (0.1%)										
G = 1		30	40		•	•		•	•	μsec
G = 100		40	55		•	•		•	•	μsec
G = 1000		35	470		•	•		•	•	μsec
Settling Time (0.01%)										
G = 1		30	45		•	•		•	•	μsec
G = 100		50	70		•	•		•	•	μsec
G = 1000		500	650		•	•		•	•	μsec

ELECTRICAL (CONT)

MODEL	INA101AM			INA101BM, INA101SM			INA101CM			UNITS
	MIN	TYP	MAX	MIN	TYP	MAX	MIN	TYP	MAX	
POWER SUPPLY										
Rated Voltage		±15			*			*		V
Voltage Range	±5		±20	*		*	*		*	V
Current, Quiescent		±6.7	±8.5		*	*		*	*	mA
TEMPERATURE RANGE										
Specification(4)	-25		+85	*		*	*		*	°C
Operation	-55		+125	*		*	*		*	°C
Storage	-65		+150	*		*	*		*	°C
PRICES										
1 - 24		$13.20			$16.00	$19.50		$18.40		$
25 - 99		11.20			13.80	16.20		15.50		$
100's		9.90			12.00	14.40		13.80		$

*Specifications same as for INA101AM.

NOTES:

1. Typically the tolerance of R_G will be the major source of gain error. 2. Not including the TCR of R_G.
3. Adjustable to zero at any one gain. 4. -55°C to +125°C for INA101SM.

The information in this publication has been carefully checked and is believed to be reliable; however, no responsibility is assumed for possible inaccuracies or omissions. Prices and specifications are subject to change without notice. No patent rights are granted to any of the circuits described herein.

CONNECTION DIAGRAM

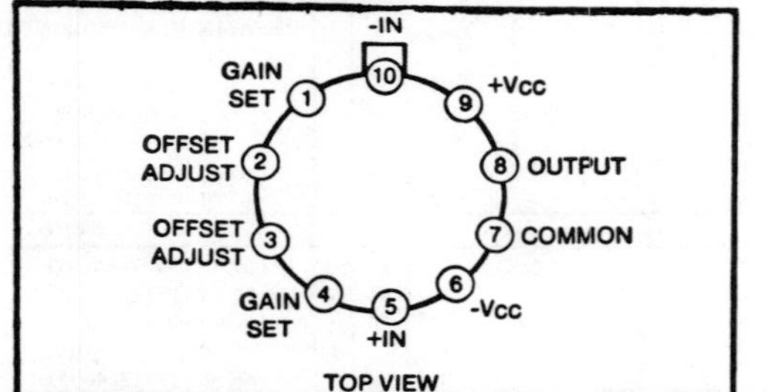

ABSOLUTE MAXIMUM RATINGS

Supply	±20V
Internal Power Dissipation	600mW
Input Voltage Range	±Vcc
Operating Temperature Range	-55°C to +125°C
Storage Temperature Range	-65°C to +150°C
Lead Temperature (soldering 10 seconds)	+300°C
Output Short-circuit Duration	Continuous to ground

MECHANICAL

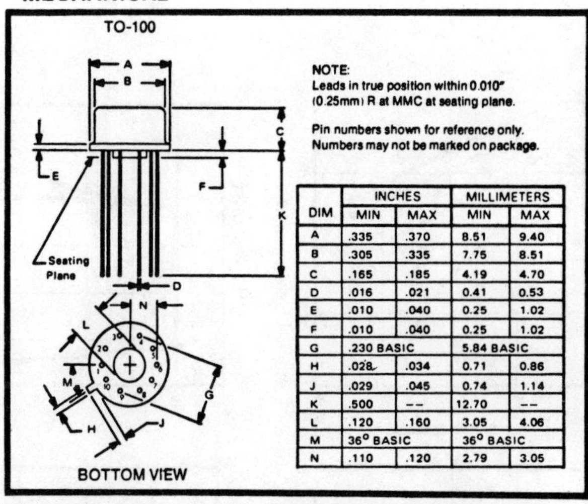

DIM	INCHES		MILLIMETERS	
	MIN	MAX	MIN	MAX
A	.335	.370	8.51	9.40
B	.305	.335	7.75	8.51
C	.165	.185	4.19	4.70
D	.016	.021	0.41	0.53
E	.010	.040	0.25	1.02
F	.010	.040	0.25	1.02
G	.230 BASIC		5.84 BASIC	
H	.028	.034	0.71	0.86
J	.029	.045	0.74	1.14
K	.500	--	12.70	--
L	.120	.160	3.05	4.06
M	36° BASIC		36° BASIC	
N	.110	.120	2.79	3.05

TYPICAL PERFORMANCE CURVES

At +25°C and in circuit of Figure 2 unless otherwise noted.

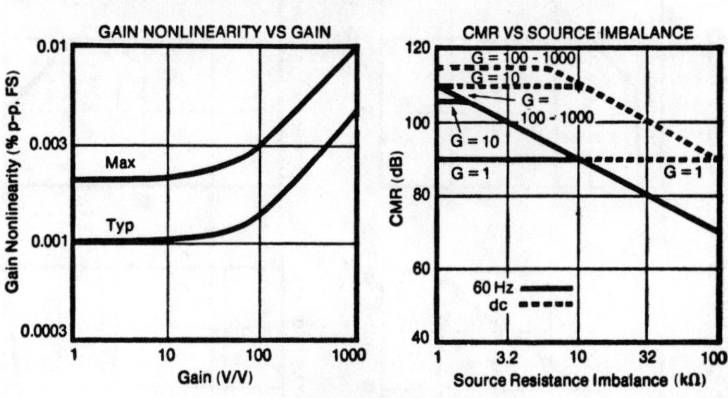

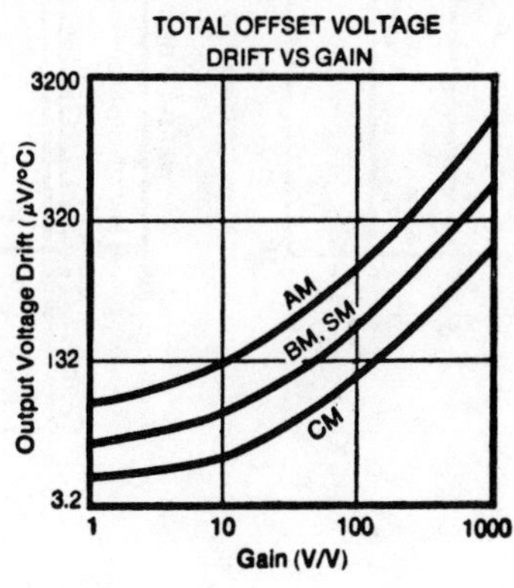

TYPICAL PERFORMANCE CURVES (CONT)

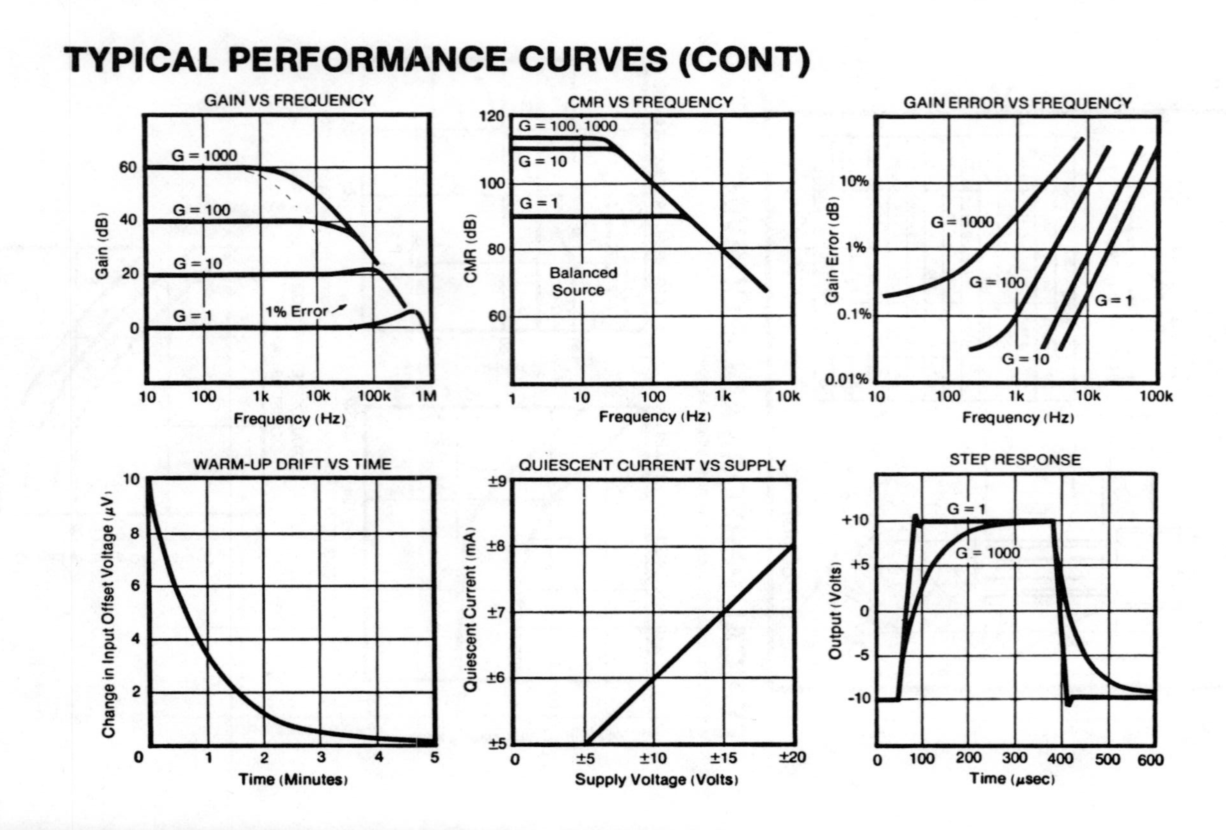

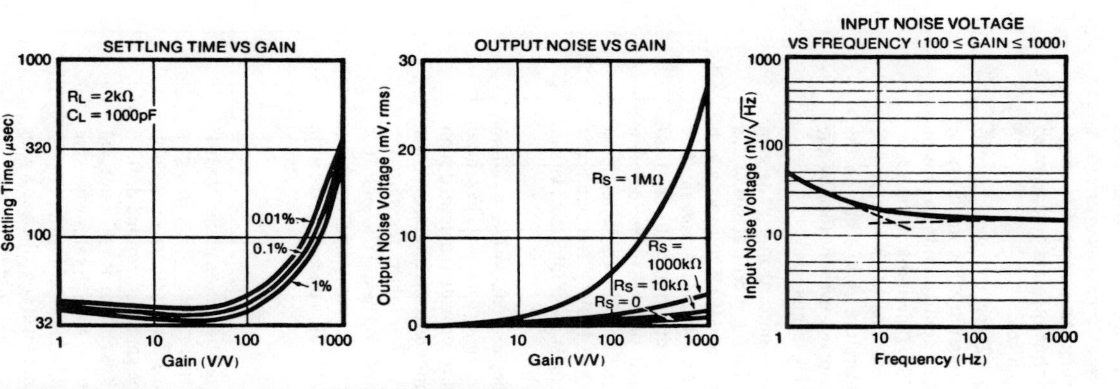

DISCUSSION OF PERFORMANCE

INSTRUMENTATION AMPLIFIERS

Instrumentation amplifiers are differential input closed-loop gain blocks whose committed circuit accurately amplifies the voltage applied to their inputs. They respond only to the difference between the two input signals and exhibit extremely-high input impedance, both differentially and common-mode. Feedback networks are packaged within the amplifier module. Only one external gain setting resistor must be added. An operational amplifier, on the other hand, is an open-loop, uncommitted device that requires external networks to close the loop. While op amps can be used to achieve the same basic function as instrumentation amplifiers, it is very difficult to reach the same level of performance. Using op amps often leads to design trade-offs when it is necessary to amplify low level signals in the presence of common-mode voltages while maintaining high input impedances. Figure 1 shows a simplified model of an instrumentation amplifier that eliminates most of the problems.

THE INA101

A simplified schematic of the INA101 is shown on the first page of this data sheet. It is a three-amplifier device which provides all the desirable characteristics of a premium performance instrumentation amplifier. In addition, it has features not normally found on integrated circuit instrumentation amplifiers.

The input section (A1 and A2) incorporates high performance, low drift amplifier circuitry. The amplifiers are connected in the noninverting configuration to provide the high input impedance ($10^{10}\Omega$) desirable in the instrumentation amplifier function. The offset voltage and offset voltage versus temperature is low due to the monolithic design and improved even further by the state-of-the-art laser-trimming techniques.

The output section (A3) is connected in a unity-gain difference amplifier configuration. A critical part of this stage is the matching of the four $10k\Omega$ resistors which provide the difference function. These resistors must be initially well matched and the matching must be maintained over temperature and time in order to retain excellent common-mode rejection. (The 106dB minimum at 60 Hz for gains greater than 100V/V is a significant improvement compared to most other integrated circuit instrumentation amplifiers.)

All of the internal resistors are compatible thin-film nichrome formed with the integrated circuit. The critical resistors are laser-trimmed to provide the desired high gain accuracy and common-mode rejection. Nichrome ensures long-term stability of trimmed resistors and simultaneous achievement of excellent TCR and TCR tracking. This provides gain accuracy and common-mode rejection when the INA101 is operated over wide temperature ranges.

USING THE INA101

Figure 2 shows the simplest configuration of the INA101. The gain is set by the external resistor, R_G with a gain equation of $G = 1 + (40K/R_G)$. The reference and TCR of R_G contribute directly to the gain accuracy and drift.

For gains greater than unity, resistor R_G is connected externally between pins 1 and 4. At high gains where the value of R_G becomes small, additional resistance (i.e., relays, sockets) in the R_G circuit will contribute to a gain error. Care should be taken to minimize this effect.

The optional offset null capability is shown in Figure 2. The adjustment affects only the input stage component of the offset voltage. Thus, the null condition will be disturbed when the gain is changed. Also, the input drift will be affected by approximately $0.31\mu V/^{\circ}C$ per $100\mu V$

of input offset voltage that is trimmed. Therefore, care should be taken when considering use of the control for removal of other sources of offset. Output offsetting can be accomplished in Figure 3 by applying a voltage to the Common (pin 7) through a buffer amplifier. This limits the resistance in series with pin 7 to minimize CMR error. Resistance above 0.1Ω will cause the common-mode rejection to fall below 106 dB. Be certain to keep this resistance low.

BASIC CIRCUIT CONNECTION

The basic circuit connection for the INA101 is shown in Figure 2. The output voltage is a function of the differential input voltage times the gain.

OPTIONAL OFFSET ADJUSTMENT PROCEDURE

It is frequently desirable to null the input component of offset (Figure 2) and occasionally that of the output (Figure 3). The quality of the potentiometer will affect the results, therefore, choose one with good temperature and mechanical-resistance stability. The procedure is as follows:

1. Set $E_1 = E_2 = 0V$ (be sure a good ground return path exists to the input).
2. Set the gain to the desired value by choosing R_G.
3. Adjust to 100kΩ potentiometer in Figure 2 until the output reads 0V ±1mV or desired setting. Note that the offset will change when the gain is changed. If the output component of offset is to be removed or if it is desired to establish an intentional offset, adjust the 100kΩ potentiometer in Figure 3 until the output reads 0V ±1mV or desired setting. Note that the offset will not change with gain, but be sure to use a stable external amplifier with good dc characteristics. The

range of adjustment is ±15mV as shown. For larger ranges change the ratio of R_1 to R_2.

TYPICAL APPLICATIONS

Many applications of instrumentation amplifiers involve the amplification of low level differential signals from bridges and transducers such as strain gages, thermocouples, and RTD's. Some of the important parameters include common-mode rejection (differential cancellation of common-mode offset and noise, see Figure 1), input impedance, offset voltage and drift, gain accuracy, linearity, and noise. The INA101 accomplishes all of these with high precision.

Figures 4 through 9 show some typical applications circuits.

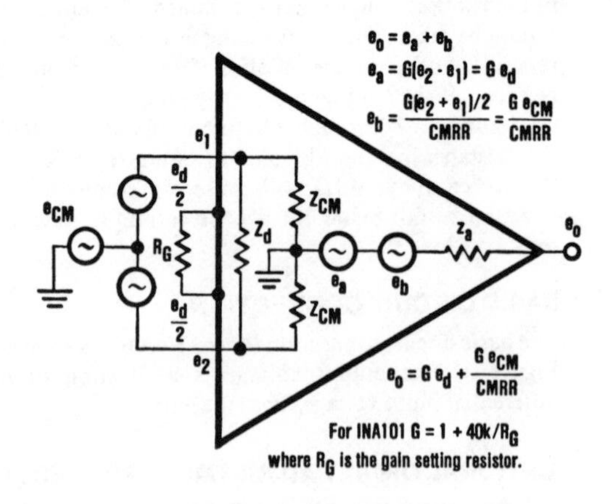

FIGURE 1. Model of an Instrumentation Amplifier.

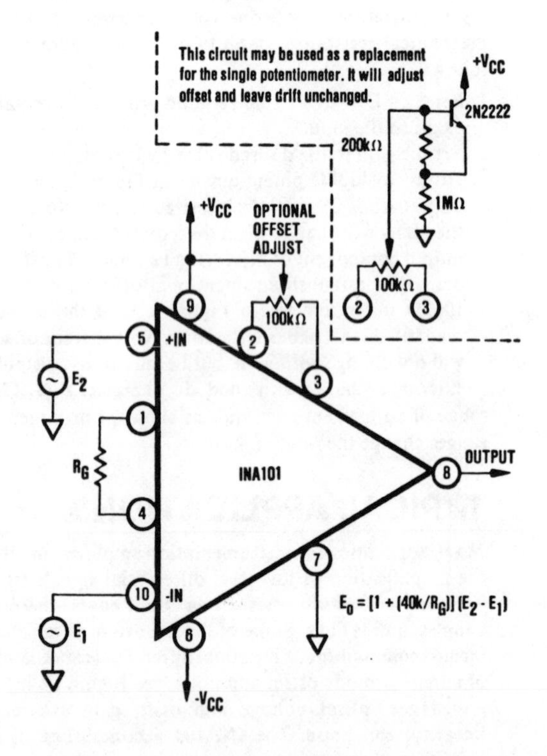

FIGURE 2. Basic Circuit Connection for the INA101 Including Optional Input Offset Null Potentiometer.

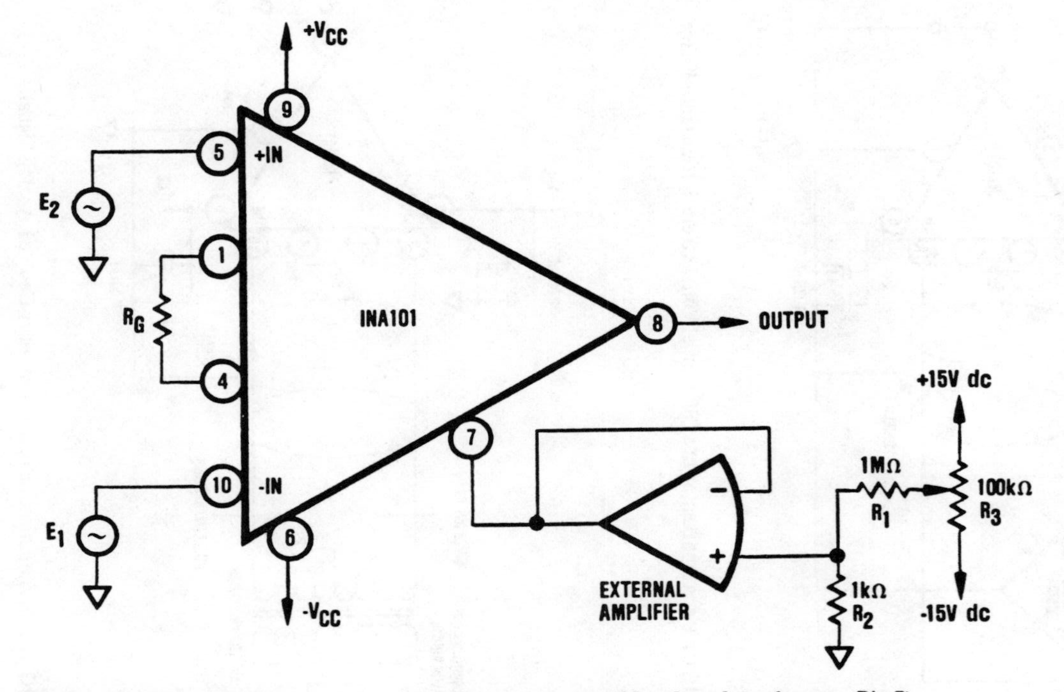

FIGURE 3. Optional Output Offset Nulling or Offsetting Using External Amplifier (Low Impedance to Pin 7).

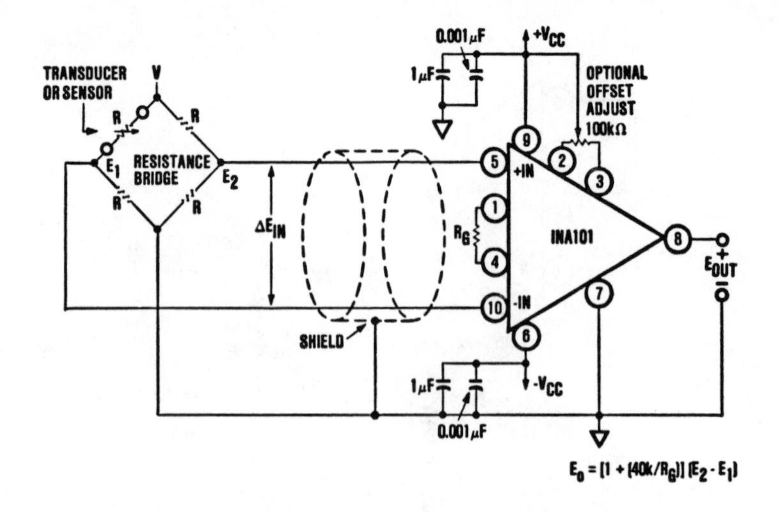

FIGURE 4. Amplification of a Differential Voltage from a Resistance Bridge.

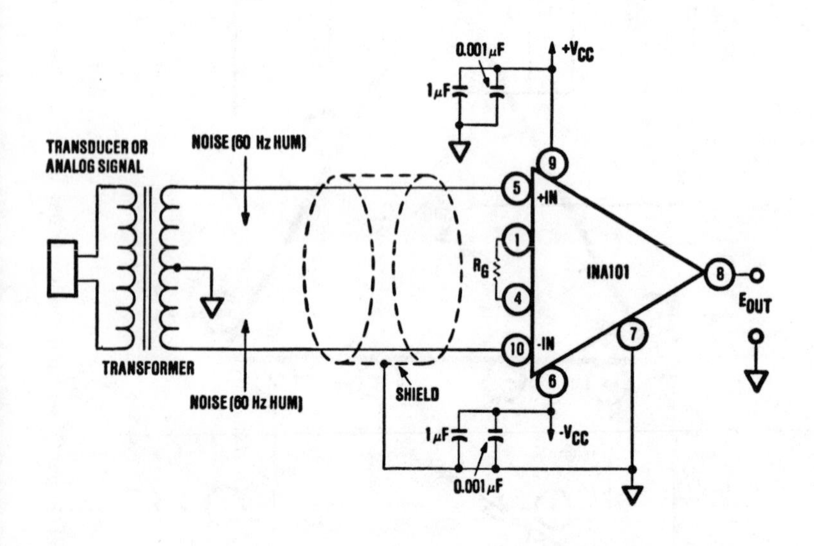

FIGURE 5. Amplification of a Transformer Coupled Analog Signal.

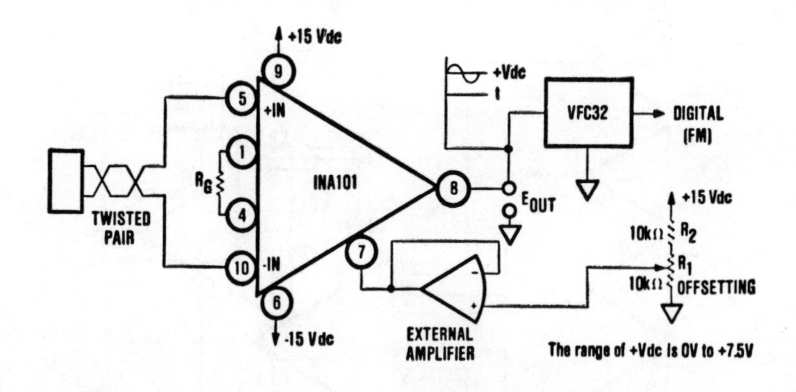
+15 Vdc
9
5
+IN
1
R_G
4
10
-IN
6
-15 Vdc
TWISTED
PAIR
INA101
8
E_{OUT}
7
EXTERNAL
AMPLIFIER
+Vdc
t
VFC32
DIGITAL
(FM)
+15 Vdc
10kΩ R_2
R_1
10kΩ OFFSETTING
The range of +Vdc is 0V to +7.5V

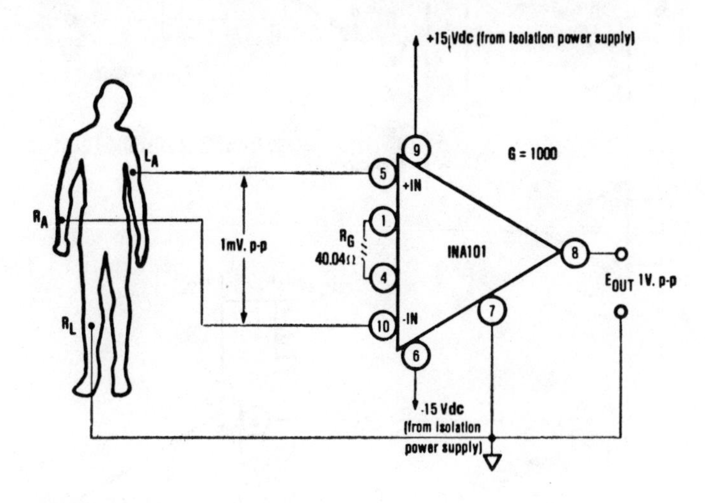
+15 Vdc (from isolation power supply)
G = 1000
L_A
R_A
R_L
1mV, p-p
9
5
+IN
1
R_G
40.04Ω
4
10
-IN
INA101
8
E_{OUT} 1V, p-p
7
6
-15 Vdc
(from isolation
power supply)

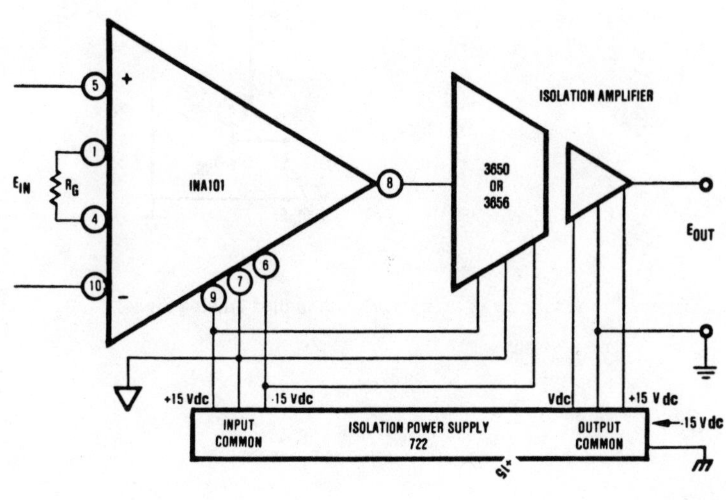
ISOLATION AMPLIFIER
5
+
1
E_{IN}
R_G
4
10
−
INA101
8
3650
OR
3656
E_{OUT}
9
7
6
+15 Vdc
-15 Vdc
Vdc
+15 V dc
INPUT
COMMON
ISOLATION POWER SUPPLY
722
OUTPUT
COMMON
-15 Vdc
+15

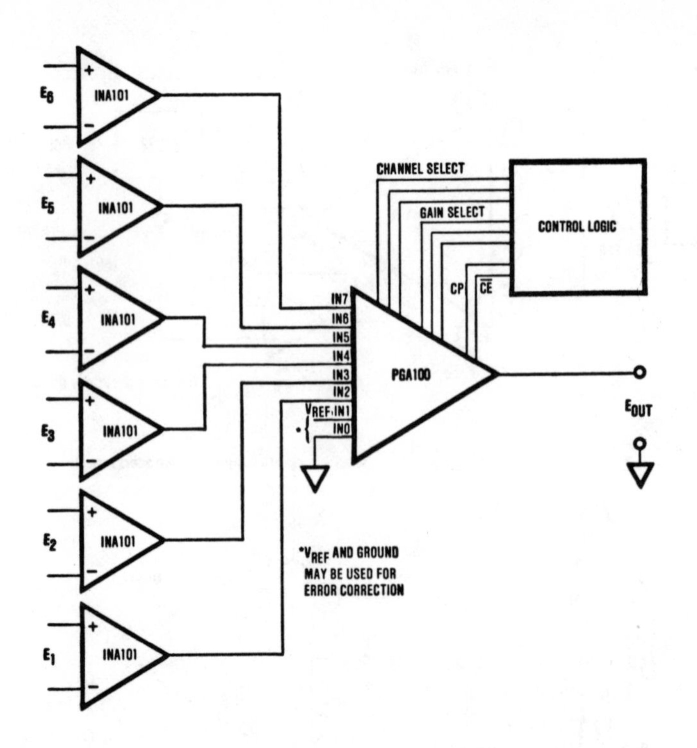
E6
INA101
E5
INA101
E4
INA101
E3
INA101
E2
INA101
E1
INA101
CHANNEL SELECT
GAIN SELECT
CONTROL LOGIC
CP
CE
IN7
IN6
IN5
IN4
IN3
IN2
VREF IN1
IN0
PGA100
EOUT
*VREF AND GROUND
MAY BE USED FOR
ERROR CORRECTION

Appendix D

Typical Specification Sheet

Figures D-1 and D-2 show two sides of a typical operational amplifier specification sheet. The general description provides a ready reference for the intended use of the device. Certain data that does not fit into the "standard" list of specifications is often mentioned here. Application data may also be given.

Some spec sheets will include a schematic of the internal components of the device, as shown in Fig. D-1. This information is not necessary in the usual applications, but it provides the designer with insight into the device.

Generally, absolute maximum ratings occupy a prominent position on the data sheet, but as mentioned in the text, these ratings must be observed with caution.

In addition to containing the electrical characteristics of the device, most spec sheets include data pertaining to how the device is packaged. Usually, several different packaging arrangements are available.

SCHEMATIC

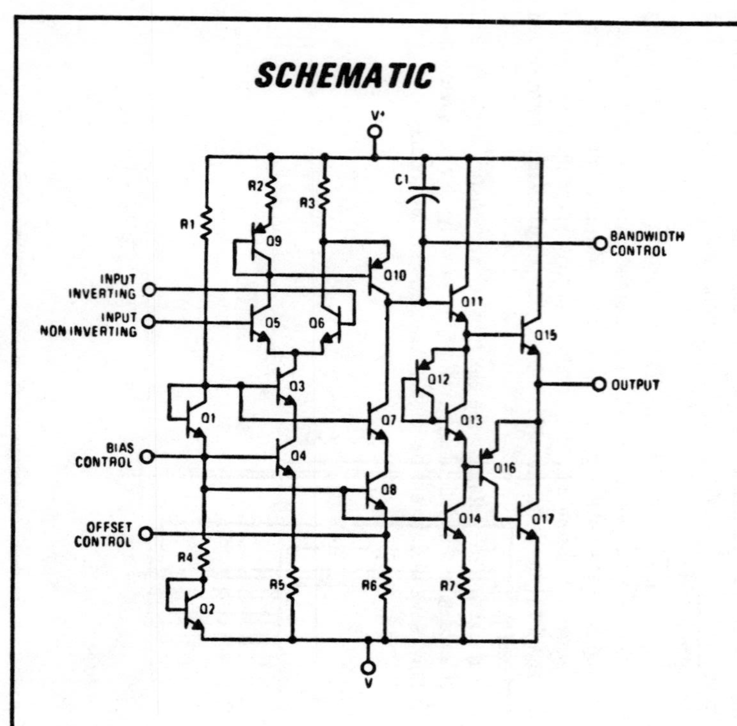

GENERAL DESCRIPTION

The integrated circuit covered by this data sheet forms a part of Harris' family of linear circuits intended for use as universal building blocks for analog circuitry. This Low Noise Operational Amplifier provides the 6 dB per octave high frequency roll-off required for unconditional stability in operational feedback connections without the use of external compensation networks.

Simple resistive trim adjustment for zeroing input offset voltage is provided on the TO-86 package. The circuit is comprised of vertical npn and pnp transistors in separate dielectrically isolated islands using advanced isolation techniques. These advanced production processes give the designer access to high performance integrated circuits without the technical compromises necessary with conventional junction isolation and lateral pnp fabrication methods.

The circuit is designed to meet or exceed the mechanical and environmental requirements of MIL-STD-883.

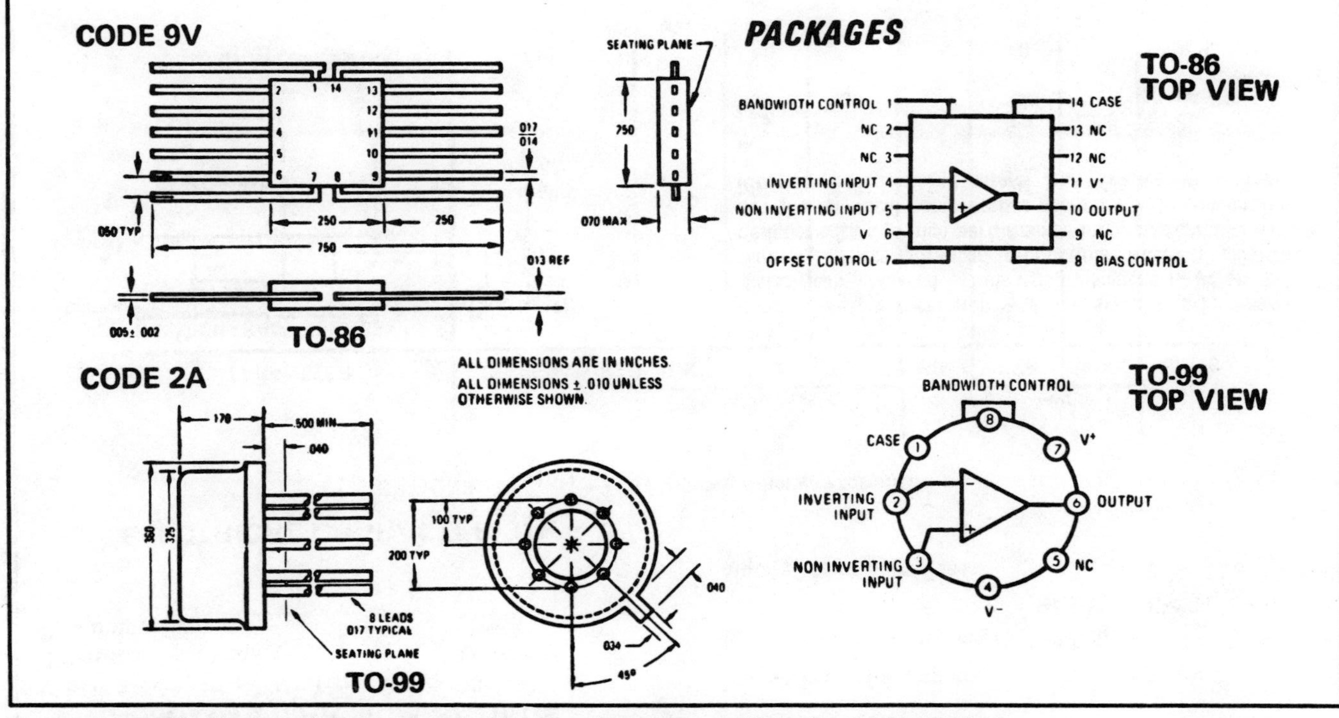

Fig. D-1. Front side of a typical op-amp specification/data sheet (courtesy Harris Semiconductor Co.).

ABSOLUTE MAXIMUM RATINGS

Voltage Between V^+ and V^- Terminals	50.0V
Differential Input Voltage	±7.0V
Peak Output Current	±50mA
Internal Power Dissipation	300mW
Operating Temperature Range – HA-909	$-55^oC \leq T_A \leq +125^oC$
Operating Temperature Range – HA-911	$0^oC \leq T_A \leq +75^oC$
Storage Temperature Range	$-65^oC \leq T_A \leq +150^oC$

ELECTRICAL CHARACTERISTICS

TEST CONDITIONS: $V_{Supply} = \pm 15.0V$ unless otherwise specified.

PARAMETER	TEMPERATURE	HA-909 −55°C to +125°C			HA-911 0°C to +75°C			UNITS
		MIN.	TYP.	MAX.	MIN.	TYP.	MAX.	
INPUT CHARACTERISTICS								
Offset Voltage	+25°C		2.0	5.0		2.0	6.0	mV
	Full			6.0			7.5	mV
Equivalent Input Noise (Note 9)			1.0	5.0		1.0		μV
Bias Current	+25°C		87	300		200	500	nA
	Full			750		300	750	nA
Offset Current	+25°C		25	150		100	300	nA
	Full		50	300		150	450	nA
Offset Current Average Drift	Full		1.0			1.0		nA/°C

Input Resistance	+25°C	200	600		100	250		KΩ
	Full	100	300					KΩ
Common Mode Range	Full		±12.0		±12.0			V
TRANSFER CHARACTERISTICS								
Large Signal Voltage Gain (Note 1)	+25°C	25K	45K		20K	45K		V/V
	Full	25K	45K		15K	45K		V/V
Common Mode Rejection Ratio (Note 2)	Full	80	96		74	90		dB
Unity Gain Bandwidth (Note 3)	+25°C		7			7		MHz
OUTPUT CHARACTERISTICS								
Output Voltage Swing (Note 1)	Full	±12.0			±11.0			V
Output Current (Note 4)	+25°C	±20			±15			mA
Output Resistance	+25°C		150			500		Ohms
TRANSIENT RESPONSE								
Rise Time (Notes 1, 5, 6 & 8)	+25°C		40	75		40	75	ns
Overshoot (Notes 1, 5, 6 & 8)	+25°C		15	40		15	40	%
Slew Rate (Notes 1, 4, 5 & 8)	+25°C	+3.5	+5.0			+5.0		V/μs
	Full	−1.2	−2.0			−2.0		
POWER SUPPLY CHARACTERISTICS								
Supply Current	+25°C		1.8	2.5		1.8	2.5	mA
Power Supply Rejection Ratio (Note 7)	Full	80	92		74	90		dB

Fig. D-2. Reverse side of typical op-amp specification/data sheet (courtesy Harris Semiconductor Co.).

Index